# MAKERS OF MATHEMATICS

*by* ALFRED HOOPER

# MAKERS OF
# Mathematics

*by*

ALFRED HOOPER

 VINTAGE BOOKS

A DIVISION OF RANDOM HOUSE

*New York*

VINTAGE BOOKS
are published by ALFRED A. KNOPF, INC.
and RANDOM HOUSE, INC.

# CONTENTS

# Foreword

Many hundreds of books have been written about the history of mathematics and the people to whom the development of this great branch of human knowledge is due, while untold thousands of weighty tomes offer us the results of their labors.

Nevertheless, it seems to me there is need for a modest little volume that offers the story of those who laid the foundations of modern mathematics and which, at the same time, explains as simply as possible the outstanding landmarks and details of the various mathematical concepts and processes developed by them, concepts and processes which are, in the main, based on surprisingly familiar, everyday ideas.

Since this story gradually develops during some eight millennia, side by side with the development of thinking man, we shall, from time to time, take our eye off the mathematical road on which we shall be traveling together, in order to get our bearings in the wider story of mankind.

For many generations, mathematics "The Queen of the Sciences" was a much-maligned lady. It was tacitly understood that she reserved her favors exclusively for the select few who had the good fortune to be endowed with a peculiar mental kink that enabled them to penetrate the esoteric halls in which this most attractive lady resided (for such was the description of her dwelling place sedulously spread abroad by the fortunate few who were lucky enough to have found the key).

During the past few years, however, a great deal of this myth has been exploded. There is little in mathematics—at least until you are well into the differential calculus—that cannot be grasped and enjoyed by anyone of normal intelligence who knows how to add, subtract, multiply and divide simple numbers.

I have assumed that some of my readers will have no greater mathematical background than this. Therefore, those who have penetrated further into the subject must please forgive certain explanations which to them will be unnecessary.

It is hoped that students and teachers may find some value and inspiration in the historical background that has been woven into the story of mathematics and mathematicians, and that such inspiration will be handed on by them to others, and especially to those of school age.

It is high time that the dry-as-dust notion so often associated with mathematics was swept away and the student introduced to the fascination not only of the story of mathematics and mathematicians, but also of the actual mathematical processes themselves.

I must express my gratitude and indebtedness to all those who knowingly or unknowingly have assisted me in writing this book: to the many librarians whose apparently inexhaustible patience and cheerful help still arouses my surprise and admiration after five years residence in the United States; to Professor D. E. Richmond for reading the manuscript and offering many helpful suggestions; to my editor, Saxe Commins, for doing his arduous job in such a way that working with him becomes a real pleasure; to Mrs. David E. Smith for her kindness in permitting me to make use of certain illustrations and material in Dr. D. E. Smith's *History of Mathematics;* to the authors and publishers who have been good enough to permit me to make use of certain illustrations and material in their books; to the countless unmentioned books to which I am unconsciously indebted for the background of the history of mathematics. Such of these books as seem to me most likely to interest the general reader or to be of value to the student of mathematics are mentioned in the bibliography on page 387.

A. H.

# MAKERS OF MATHEMATICS

# CHAPTER I

# The Birth of Numbers

As children, we accepted without question most of the things we were taught; familiarity, later, made us take them for granted, and most of us have taken them for granted ever since. This is true of many mathematical concepts. Consequently, few of us realize the surprising simplicity of the ideas from which most of them sprang. The object of this book is to point out this simplicity, and by tracing the development of one idea from another, to remove some of the mystery that the average man so often associates with mathematics.

To be on the safe side, the author has assumed that many of his readers will have no real working knowledge of geometry, algebra, trigonometry, analytic geometry and the calculus. He is convinced that by following the story of the development of these branches of mathematics from the simple ideas from which they arose, any person of normal intelligence can understand the basic thought-processes that lie behind them, and realize, possibly for the first time, that behind numbers and symbols lies a story of absorbing human interest.

Let us commence at the very beginning and think of some of the concepts we met when we made our first acquaintance with mathematics by learning to count in the way our elders counted.

Before we learned how much quicker and easier it is to "work in our heads," many of us made use of our ten fingers when we had to count or add numbers. Perhaps we imagined—

if we thought about it at all—that it was just a lucky chance that the number of our fingers seemed to fit in so nicely with the numbers with which we had to deal. How many of us realize that it was not chance at all, but that the vast edifice of modern mathematics is based on a number-scale—some deny it is the best possible number-scale—which arose from the fact that Nature decreed that man should have ten fingers?

When primitive man, by learning to count up to ten, proved that he was in some strange way different from all the rest of animal creation, he invented only ten number-sounds. The reason was that he counted in the way a small child counts to-day, one by one, making use of his fingers. Since those primeval days, only five other basic number-sounds have been invented. The needs and possessions of primitive man were few: he required no large numbers. When he wished to express a number greater than ten he simply combined certain of the ten sounds connected with his fingers. Thus, if he wished to express "one more than ten" he said "one-ten," (compare the Latin *un-decim*), hence our word "eleven," which is simply a modern form of the Teutonic *ein-lifon*, "one over." Similarly, "twelve" is a modern form of *twe-lif*, "two-over," and to the Romans was simply *duo-decim* "two ten." Our "twenty" is *twe-tig*, "two-tens," "thirty" is *thri-tig*, "three tens," and so on. The only basic number-sounds in addition to the ten primary ones are "hundred," "thousand," "million," "billion" (a thousand millions in America, a million millions in England), "trillion" (a million millions in America, a million-million millions in England).

Just because primitive man invented the same number of number-sounds as he had fingers, our number-scale today is a *decimal* one, that is, a scale based on *ten*, and consisting of endless repetitions of the first ten basic number-sounds.

Had men been given twelve fingers instead of ten, we should doubtless have a *duo-decimal* number-scale today, one based

The holder of this ticket agrees with the CBC that, in consideration for the CBC permitting him to view the broadcast performance, he releases the CBC and its employees from liability for injury or damage to his person, and for loss, injury, or damage to his personal belongings, whether or not such loss, injury, or damage was caused by the negligence of either the CBC or its employees. The CBC reserves the right to revoke this ticket at any time.

CHILDREN UNDER 16 MUST BE ACCOMPANIED BY AN ADULT. NO VERY YOUNG CHILDREN, PLEASE.

No 112

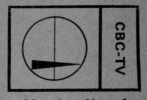

CBC-TV

**Monday, Nov. 1**

## NIGHTCAP

CBC Studio 4, 1140 Yonge Street
Doors open : 10.15–10.30 p.m.
Performance : 10.45–11.45 p.m.

See conditions on reverse side
If unable to use this ticket please pass it on to a friend

**Canadian Broadcasting Corporation**

on twelve, consisting of endless repetitions of twelve basic number-sounds. Assuming that the sounds "eleven" and "twelve" had been chosen for the two extra fingers, we should now say "one-twelve" instead of thirteen (three-ten); "two-twelve" instead of fourteen; "eight-twelve" instead of twenty, and so on. Instead of twenty-four we should have a word something like "twe-twelves" (two-twelves), and twenty-five would then be "twe-twelves-one," and so on. A duodecimal system like this would hold certain distinct advantages over a decimal system such as ours, since twelve can be divided exactly by two, three, four and six, whereas ten can only be exactly divided by two and five. However, it is now too late to do anything about it. Nature gave man ten fingers, and our mathematical system is irrevocably tied to a *decimal* number-scale in consequence.

We must not imagine that primitive man ever conceived of a number-scale. To him a number was not an abstract concept, as it is to us. It had merely a descriptive or adjectival use, as "four fish," "nine men." The concept of a number-scale consisting of "things" called numbers, commencing with zero and with no upper limit, grew slowly in men's minds.

Some early races, including the highly civilized Mayas in South America, based their number system on twenty instead of ten. Possibly this was because those who first built up such a system made use of their toes as well as their fingers when counting.

Long before the invention of writing, primitive man had devised a method of recording numbers. We have seen that he counted on his fingers. Now, a finger can easily be represented by a single cut or stroke. It was natural, therefore, that our remote ancestors should have made such marks on the walls of their caves or on pieces of stone when they wished to keep a record or tally of a number of objects. Each mark or cut would stand for one object. It would not be possible to see at a glance the total number represented by a collection of these strokes; the only way to find their total would be to count them one by one. Many ancient cave dwellings show such markings, the earliest attempts made by men to represent spoken numbers by written symbols. Such number-writings go back before even those far-off days when men made the tremendous discovery that the seeds of certain kinds of grass were good to eat, and forthwith started agriculture. This simple yet clumsy method of recording numbers continued for many thousands of years, and even today it is still encountered among some backward tribes.

As civilization developed, many different ways of writing numbers were invented. Long before the Babylonians had conquered the Jews, as recorded in the Old Testament, they had invented a system of number-symbols which were wedge-shaped, ⌄ ⌃, since they were made by pressing a rod with a pointed end into a clay tablet. The Latin word for a wedge was *cuneus*. So these wedge-shaped characters are known as "cuneiform" writing. The clay tablet on which they were written would afterwards be baked in the sun or in a kiln, so that it hardened into a kind of brick.

Early in the sixteenth century the Spaniards found their way from the West Indies to the mainland of America. They were amazed to discover more than sixty ruined cities in the district we call Yucatan, now part of Mexico. There were ruined temples, palaces and great underground reservoirs, lined with blocks of stone. They had been built by the Maya people, who had developed a civilization of which the inhabitants of Europe had known nothing. This was the race we mentioned as using a number-scale which had twenty basic number-sounds instead of ten. Carved on some of their monuments have been found twenty number-symbols, made up chiefly of dots and dashes. They even had a symbol for zero, which suggests that they must have had some kind of abacus, or counting frame, for, as we shall see, the work done by the symbol 0 is to indicate that there are no counters or beads on that particular wire or line of the counting frame.

Both the Hebrews and the Greeks used the letters of their alphabets to represent numbers, the Greek system being based on that of the Hebrews. Just to give an idea of how the Greek system worked we will choose four Greek number-symbols that can easily be recognized by every reader, since they are very much like our letters a, b, i and k.

α (alpha) always stood for *one;*

β (beta) always stood for *two;*

ι (iota) always stood for *ten;*

κ (kappa) always stood for *twenty.*

Now, while ιβ ("ten and two") would represent 12, these symbols could not be interchanged as our modern symbols for 12 can be interchanged to form 21. To represent 21, the symbols κα would have to be employed. In other words, the Greeks, despite all their brilliant intellectual achievements, never hit on the beautiful simplicity of employing only ten number-symbols and thinking of them as representing counters on a counting frame, thereby bringing in the concept of one and the same number-symbol representing entirely different values, according to its *position* with regard to other number-symbols written alongside.

Not having hit on this simple idea of *positional values*, the Greeks had to use all twenty-four letters of their alphabet, and three other symbols in addition to these, even to represent small numbers. It is easy to be wise after the event, but now that we have our simple *positional* concept which requires only ten symbols to represent any number, no matter how large, one cannot help marveling that the great Greek mathematicians whose genius produced the wonderful "Golden Age of Greek Mathematics," which we shall discuss later, should not have devised a less complicated and cumbersome method of writing numbers. Of course, it just never occurred to them that any simpler system of writing numbers was possible. Before we criticize the Greeks for putting up with a clumsy system like this, let us remember that we are still putting up with incredibly clumsy and complicated medieval weights and measures, even though we have a beautiful time- and labor-saving metric system merely waiting to be adopted.

The Roman system, known as Roman numerals, contained the germ of the idea of *positional* value, but only to a very limited extent. Nobody knows for certain how these Roman numerals arose. It is thought that they were probably based on the cave-man's finger writing. This view has the support of Dr. Mommsen, who was one of the greatest authorities on Roman times and it is further supported by the fact that the Latin word for "finger" was *digitus*, which word was also used by the Romans to describe in a general way any one of their number-symbols, just as we use the word "digit" today.

The Romans originally wrote the numbers *one* to *four* as

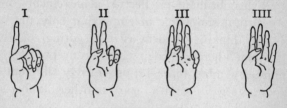

FIG. 1

The symbol for *five* was a V-shaped mark which may well have represented the gap between thumb and fingers, thus:

FIG. 2

It was in connection with this symbol that the germ of the all-important idea of *positional value* arose. To avoid the clumsy IIII for *four*, it became customary to put the symbol I on the *left* of the symbol V. This same idea was applied to other symbols, it being understood that whenever a symbol was written *on the left* of a symbol of higher value, the number represented was equal to the *difference* between the two symbols.

On the other hand, whenever a symbol was written on the *right* of a symbol of higher value, the number represented was understood to be equal to the *sum* of these two symbols. Undoubtedly this concept arose from the primitive way of indicating the numbers six, seven, eight, and, originally, nine, using the fingers of both hands, thus:

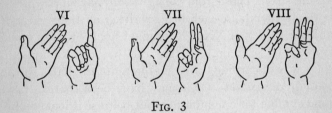

VI          VII          VIII

Fig. 3

*Nine* was originally written VIIII, but this was later simplified by writing the symbol I on the *left* of the symbol for *ten*. This symbol was X, which may have been suggested by crossed hands, or crossed thumbs, or may have stood for strokes made across ten of the strokes which represented one each. Such a method enables anyone to see more rapidly the number of strokes he has made. Thus:

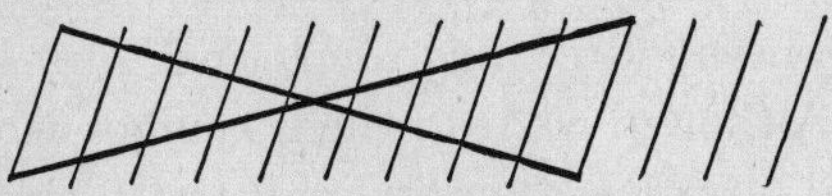

Fig. 4

represents "thirteen," which the Romans wrote as XIII.
Since X stood for *ten*, IX came to stand for *nine*, the difference between the values represented by X and I. Thus the
first ten Roman numerals came to be, and still are

I   II   III   IV   V   VI   VII   VIII   IX   X.

We have seen that the primitive number-scale, on which
the whole great edifice of modern mathematics is based, consists only of endless repetitions of the ten primary number-
sounds. This concept is clearly reflected in the way in which
Roman numerals were built up, the numbers *eleven* to *twenty*
being represented by placing one or other of the primary ten
symbols to the right of the symbol for ten, thus: XI, XII, XIII,
XIV, and so on. Those from *twenty* to *thirty* again repeated the
ten primary symbols, each being written on the right of the
symbol for *twenty*, or XX. The original symbol for *one hundred*
was probably [. It may be that this was the Roman stone-
mason's way of carving C, the first letter of the Latin word for
one hundred (*centum*). Or it may have been that [ was the
original symbol for one hundred, but because it looked like C,
this symbol came in time to be written as such. As was said
before, nobody knows for certain how these symbols arose.
Since C stands for one hundred, CXXVIII, for instance,
stands for the sum of C, XX, and VIII, namely, for *one hundred twenty-eight*, while CCXXXIX stands for the sum of CC,
XXX and I-less-than- X, namely, for *two hundred thirty-nine*.
An X written on the left of a C stood for the difference between C and X, so *ninety* was written as XC.
Instead of the clumsy XXXXX for *fifty*, the lower half of the
[ symbol for one-hundred was used, since fifty is one-half of
one hundred. Although we read the L symbol as if it were the
letter L, it had no connection originally with this letter, since
the Latin word for *fifty* does not contain an L. This seems to

point to the probability that [ and not C was the original symbol for one hundred.

Since L stands for *fifty*, an X written on the *left* of L stands for the difference between L and X, namely, *forty*, while an X written on the *right* of an L stands for the sum of L and X, namely, sixty.

The symbol for *one thousand* was originally the Greek letter *phi,* which was written Φ. In course of time, this symbol became simplified into (I), which in turn came to be written as M, possibly because the Latin word for a thousand was *mille*.

The symbol for *five hundred*, or half of a thousand, was originally I). Notice that this is simply the right-hand portion of the (I) symbol for a thousand. In time, this I) symbol came to be written as D.

In a book by Suetonius, printed in 1715, the title page bears the date

$$\text{(I) I) CCXV.}$$

The first symbol represents the Greek Φ; the next is the symbol representing 500, or half Φ; the CCXV, of course, stands for 215.

The symbols we have discussed include all those commonly used today for dates on monuments, public buildings, and the like, and for chapter and page numbers in books, even though a much better system of writing numbers has been in use for nearly a millennium.

For thousands of years no real development was possible in the simple number-reckoning known to the Greeks as *logistic* ("calculation") and now called "arithmetic." The reason was that it was hopelessly fettered by clumsy and complicated systems of writing numbers. It was not until the fifteenth century that simple modern processes, such as those of multiplication and division, became possible, thanks to the invention of a simple method of writing numbers.

Before we discuss our present simple method, we must

digress and take a look at the way in which calculations were made in ancient times, since our present method of writing numbers was invented to fit in with such calculations.

When nowadays we wish to make some computation that we cannot do "in our heads," we simply take pencil and paper and set about it. It is hard to realize the difficulties, both mental and physical, that had to be overcome during the thousands of years that elapsed before a simple method of indicating numbers was invented, and before writing materials became cheap and plentiful.

First, let us deal with the physical difficulty of obtaining material on which to write—though it must be remembered that it was almost impossible for the average man to make even simple calculations in writing as long as number-reckoning was fettered by clumsy systems of writing numbers. Some kind of counting-frame was almost essential under such circumstances.

Few of us realize that, even a hundred years ago, paper was expensive, since the manufacture of paper from wood pulp by machinery had not then been invented and it was made, by hand, from linen rags. Even this linen paper was not made in Europe until the fourteenth century, though the Chinese knew how to make it at least a thousand years before that date.

Before the introduction of linen paper into Europe in the fourteenth century and the development of printing in the following hundred years, books of all kinds were so scarce and precious that they were available only to the rich and to members of communities who treasured them in their libraries. Some of them were in the form we know today, consisting of bound sheets of hand-written papyrus or parchment; others were in the form of rolls of such materials, both of which were very expensive and scarce.

Papyrus was a kind of writing material made originally in Egypt from a reed called *papu* by the Egyptians. We read in the Old Testament about an "ark of bulrushes" made for the baby Moses. These "bulrushes" were probably papu reeds. They grew in shallow water by the edge of the River Nile. The stem of the reed was cut into thin strips, which were laid side by side on a board so as to form a sheet of the required width. Another layer of these strips was then placed on top, and the two layers were soaked in water. It is thought that there was a natural gum in the plant, for when the layers were pressed out and dried in the sun, they stuck together. The surface was then polished with a smooth shell or a piece of ivory. When several of these sheets of *papyrus* were finished, they were joined together into a long strip. A rod was then fastened to one end of the strip, and at last it was ready for a writer, or scribe. Having written his book, an author would have to employ a large number of copyists who would laboriously—and often with many accidental departures from the original—copy the work by hand. Each book would then be rolled up, put in a little box, and carefully guarded in some library. All this shows how costly and scarce books written on papyrus must have been.

The oldest known mathematical book in the world was written on papyrus by an Egyptian scribe named Ahmes, or Ahmose, more than thirty-five centuries ago. It is now in the British Museum and has been translated into English by Professor T. E. Peet, who renders the title as "Rules for Enquiring into Nature, and for Knowing All That Exists." Ahmes was not the author of the book, his papyrus being a copy of a book written in the reign of King Amenemhat III, about 2200 B.C., or some four thousand years ago. Ahmes adds a note: "Behold, this roll was written under the King of Upper and Lower Egypt, Aauserre. It was the scribe Ahmose who wrote this copy."

This Ahmes Papyrus, as it is called, shows that even four thousand years ago the Egyptians were inventing ways of dealing with fractions, while they knew how to work problems that we should nowadays work by algebraic equations. They had also discovered that the circumference of a circle can always be divided a fixed but indeterminable (as we shall see) number of times by its own diameter.

Parchment was even more costly and scarce than papyrus. It was, and still is, made from the skins of animals, usually sheep or lambs. A still more expensive form of parchment is vellum, which is made from the skins of calves.

Parchment was so costly and valuable, and consequently so scarce, that the custom arose during the Middle Ages of washing the ink off an old manuscript and using the parchment again for a new book. Such manuscripts are known as *palimpsests* (*palin*, "again," *psao*, "rub smooth"). Fortunately, in course of time, the original writing on many palimpsests shows again, to some extent. Some valuable knowledge of the ancient world has come to us by making out the original writing under the second—or even third—handwriting on an old parchment. In the British Museum is a theological book of the ninth or tenth century, written over a sixth-century book on Latin grammar which in turn had been written over a history written in the fifth century. Another book in the same collection is a work of the ninth century which is written partly on parchment taken from a sixth-century copy of Homer's *Iliad*, partly on a copy of the Gospel of St. Luke, also written in the sixth century, and partly on a fragment of the *Elements* of Euclid, written in the seventh century.

Enough has been said to make it clear that it would have been impossible to take a sheet of parchment or papyrus in the way we take a sheet of paper today for jotting down some calculation, even if such calculation had been possible under a complicated and cumbersome system of writing numbers.

A pupil in a Roman school two thousand years ago was taught to write on a tablet made of wood, one side of which had been coated with wax. Instead of a pen or pencil he used a stylus, or pointed stick, the blunt end of which was used for smoothing out the wax preparatory to using it again. A pupil might possibly have written on his tablet the *results* of his calculations, but the actual calculations would have been made on a counting frame called an *abacus*, which will shortly be described. Sometimes two or more tablets would be joined together by leather hinges (Figure 5). These tablets had raised edges to prevent the words that were written on the wax from being rubbed out by friction.

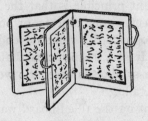

Fig. 5

[Reproduced, by permission of Ginn and Company, from *Latin for Today*.]

It is thought that our present form of book originated from these hinged Roman tablets.

Before and during the time of the Roman Empire, very simple calculations, such as the counting of votes, were often made on a tray covered with sand. Marks were made in the sand with a pointed stick. Afterwards, the sand would be smoothed out by hand. Euclid and other mathematicians used such sand-trays for drawing geometrical figures. Practically all the geometry learned in school today was first worked out by figures drawn on such sand-trays more than twenty-two centuries ago. The Greek word for a flat board or tray was *abax*, and the sand-tray used for making calculations was called an *abacus*.

The word abacus was later employed for many different kinds of counting frames used in ancient Egypt, India, Greece, the Roman Empire, and many other lands. The abacus is still used in China and Japan and in parts of Russia. Sometimes an abacus was simply a board with lines drawn on it. Pebbles, beads or counters were placed on the lines. The Latin for a pebble was *calculus*, hence our word "calculate." Each counter that was placed on one particular line stood for one object; each counter placed on another line represented ten of those objects; each counter on a third line represented one hundred such objects, and so on.

The all-important principle is that the same counter may stand for one object, or ten objects, or one hundred objects, or one thousand objects, its value depending on the line on which it is placed. It is on this principle that our present system of written number-symbols is based. So we must consider the abacus in some detail.

An improvement on the ruled board was a board in which grooves were cut. Counters were then placed in these grooves.

In the later years of the Roman Empire, rods or wires were often used instead of grooves. Beads or counters would then have holes bored in them so that they could be slipped on to the wires.

Should the reader wish to introduce a child to arithmetic in an interesting way that will make clear the reason for our present methods of working addition and subtraction, he will find it helpful to make him a model abacus, and teach him to play about with it. Take a piece of wood about 8 inches by 2 inches and about $\frac{1}{2}$ inch thick. Drive four long nails through the wood, so that their points stick out as in Figure 6.

Cut out about thirty small pieces of cardboard, to serve as counters, and bore a hole in each piece. If it is desired to teach him Roman numerals at the same time, let him pretend he is a Roman merchant living about A.D. 200. Being a Roman, he must mark his abacus with the Roman numerals I, X, C and

M, as shown in Figure 6. He must also pretend that the only numbers he knows are Roman numerals.

Two of his ships have just docked at Ostia, the port of Rome, carrying blocks of Egyptian granite ordered for a new building in Rome. One of his captains reports that his ship carries

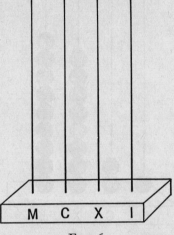

FIG. 6

M CC LXXX IX blocks, the other captain says that his ship has brought M XXX VIII blocks. He wishes to know how many blocks of granite have arrived in the two ships. This is what he must do:

He takes his abacus and sets out counters on it to represent M CC LXXX IX, as shown in Figure 7.

He now turns to his other number, M XXX VIII. Starting with the eight units (VIII), he commences to add eight counters to the units' wire. He finds, however, that with the addition of the first of these eight counters the total number of counters on this wire becomes ten. So he takes off all these ten counters from the units' wire and instead of them places one counter on the X (tens') wire. *This counter looks like all the others, but when it is on the X wire it represents ten times as great a number as it would on the units' wire.* After this operation, the units' wire is empty. He can now slip the remaining seven of the VIII unit counters on to it.

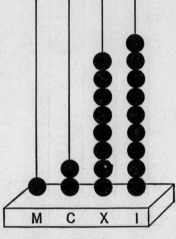

FIG. 7

He then turns to the three tens (**XXX**) in the number M **XXX** VIII. The X wire, he notices, now contains nine counters, including the one just added to it. As he starts to add three counters to this wire, to represent the three tens, or XXX to be added, he finds that the addition of the first of them makes the number of counters on this wire up to ten. So he takes off all those counters and instead of them places a single counter on the C wire. *Again, this counter looks like all the others, but when it is placed on the C wire it at once assumes a value that is ten times as great as that of a counter on the X wire, and one hundred times as great as that of a counter on the units' wire.* The two remaining X counters can now be placed on the empty X wire.

As there are no hundreds in the number M XXX VIII he now passes to the thousands. Here he finds only one M, so he merely adds one counter to the M wire. His abacus will now look like this:

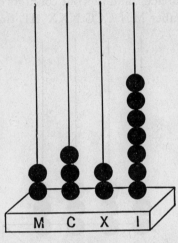

The Roman merchant could now take his wax tablet and write down MM CCC XX VII, *an exact "picture" of the final appearance of the abacus.*

This is the way a Roman worked addition. He did just what we do in our heads when we add, only we have a much simpler way of indicating the numbers. As we shall see, our present method of writing numbers was developed expressely to indicate counters on the abacus.

Subtraction too was worked on an abacus by a method which was exactly similar to the one we use today, only we do the work in our heads, thanks to the simplicity of our number symbols.

Once more let your child pretend he is a Roman merchant, this time one who deals in olive oil. When he last took stock, he had **MM CCC XXX III** amphorae, or jars, of olive oil in his storeroom. Now he takes stock again, and finds there are only **M CCCC X VII** amphorae there. He wants to know how many he has sold.

He takes his abacus, and sets out counters on it to represent the original number **MM CCC XXX III**, thus:

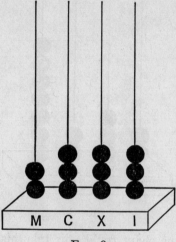

FIG. 9

He will now have to *remove* counters representing the **M CCCC X VII** amphorae that remain in his storeroom. Then the counters remaining on his abacus will stand for the number of amphorae he has sold.

Starting as before with the units, he at once runs into the problem of how to take seven (VII) counters off a wire that holds only three (III) counters. To get over this difficulty, he takes one counter off the X wire and instead of it puts *ten counters* on the units' wire, which will then have thirteen counters on it. He can now take seven (VII) counters off the units' wire, and only six counters will remain on it.

Turning to the X wire, he finds he now has only two counters

left on it. However, he can take away the solitary X in the
number M CCCC **X** VII, leaving only one counter on the X
wire.

The C wire has not had any of its three counters disturbed,
but he cannot take away four C counters (representing the
CCCC in the number he is subtracting) until he has taken one
M counter from the M wire and put *ten C counters* on the C
wire to make up for it. This C wire now has thirteen counters
on it, and he is able to take away his four C counters (CCCC),
leaving nine of them on the C wire.

The M wire has only one counter left on it: this he takes off,
since the number he is subtracting contains one M.

His abacus will now look like this:

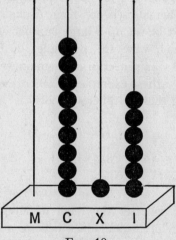

Fig. 10

It tells him that he has sold nine hundred sixteen amphorae
of oil. A Roman would have written this number on his tablet
either as CM X VI or as DCCCC X VI.

We now know how a Roman used his abacus in making the
simple calculations that came his way. How does it happen

that we can do such calculations so easily today, without using an abacus? Partly because we can jot down numbers on any old scrap of paper, but chiefly because we use only ten number symbols, which are given a *positional value* that enables them to give us a mental "picture" of counters on an abacus.

How, when and where did we get those symbols? To find out, we shall have to take a look, first at India as it was twenty-one hundred years ago, then at a great Arab empire that formed a connecting bridge for commerce and ideas between Asia and Europe a thousand years ago.

Some two hundred years before Christ, a powerful king named Asoka ruled over most of India. He was converted to the religion called Buddhism and spent his life in spreading that religion throughout his kingdom. What interests us as students of mathematics is not King Asoka's religious belief, but the fact that he set up a large number of stone columns, carved into which were the principles of Buddhism. Only thirty of King Asoka's inscriptions remain, but on them have been found the earliest examples of our present-day number-symbols. Among these number-symbols are

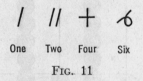

| One | Two | Four | Six |

FIG. 11

A century or so after the reign of King Asoka, certain records were cut in the walls of a cave in a hill called Nana Ghat, near the city of Poona, in Bombay. These carvings include certain Hindu number-symbols, among them being

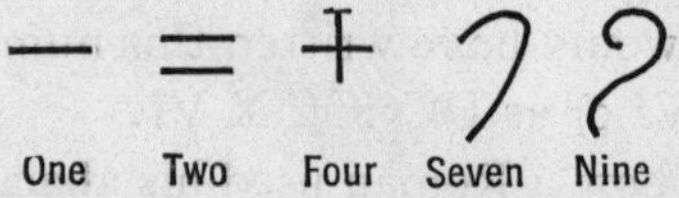

$$- \quad = \quad + \quad 7 \quad ?$$

One  Two  Four  Seven  Nine

FIG. 12

About four hundred years after King Asoka, that is, about A.D. 200, someone carved inscriptions in caves at Nasik, a Bombay town held sacred by the Hindus. Among these inscriptions are certain number-symbols, of which the following are of interest to us:

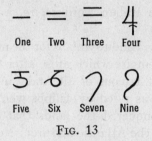

One    Two    Three    Four

Five    Six    Seven    Nine

Fig. 13

If these number-symbols are studied it will be realized that our present-day number-symbols are Hindu characters. It is important to notice that no symbol for zero occurs in any of these early Hindu number systems we have been discussing. Further, they contain symbols (which we have not shown) for numbers like twenty, forty, and so on. So it is clear that they could not originally have been used with a *positional value* in the way we use them today for representing the appearance of counters on an abacus. However, the idea of positional value must certainly have been introduced into India before the ninth century, since an Arab mathematician named al-Khowarizmi, the librarian of the caliph al-Mamun, wrote a book on the subject about the year A.D. 825. By that time a symbol for zero had been invented in India; it is found on inscriptions carved in A.D. 876 and it was certainly used in India before that date. Why was the invention of this symbol for zero so important? Because its use enabled the nine Hindu symbols 1, 2, 3, 4, 5, 6, 7, 8 and 9 to suffice for the representation of any number, no matter how great. *The work of a zero is to keep the other nine symbols in their proper abacus places*, by indicating that there are no counters on this or that wire of the counting frame. Our word "zero" comes from the Arabic *sifr*, which was a translation of a Hindu word *sunya*, meaning "void" or "empty." *Sifr* has also passed into the English language, as an alternative to "zero," in the word "cipher." "Zero" is itself a contraction of the Italian word *zepiro*, a rendering of the Arabic *sifr*.

Let us leave these Hindu symbols for the moment and take a glance at a great empire which arose after the death of Mohammed, the most famous of all Arabs. After his death in A.D. 632, Arabia was ruled by caliphs who, during the next hundred years, conquered the lands that stretch from the border of India to the Atlantic and from North Africa to the Pyrenees.

In A.D. 711, the Arabs, or Moors as they are often called, invaded Spain from North Africa. After the fall of the Roman Empire, Spain had been ruled by the descendants of the barbarian Visigoths who had seized it from the Romans. The Arabs had only intended to make a plundering raid, but so divided were the Gothic rulers of Spain that the intended plundering raid developed into a conquest which was to last for a longer period than that which has elapsed since the landing of the Pilgrim Fathers to the present day.

We have much for which to thank the Moors. They introduced new ideas about medicine and medical knowledge; they taught improved methods of working in metal and leather; they built waterworks, sluices and canals in Spain; in all, they brought the wisdom of India and the East to a Europe which had sunk back into ignorance and savage ways.

The Arabs were familiar with the work of the great Greek mathematicians who had built up the "Golden age of Greek mathematics" before the fragile and wonderful civilization of ancient Greece was absorbed by the intensely practical and utilitarian Romans; *they also introduced into Spain the new and revolutionary method of writing numbers that they had learned from the Hindus,* a method that was to pave the way for our modern world of science and engineering and aeronautics.

The earliest example of a European manuscript that contained the then new-fangled Hindu-Arabic number-symbols is one that was written in Spain in A.D. 976. Figure 14 shows how they were then written.

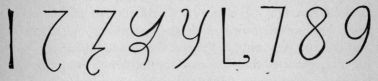

FIG. 14

Reproduced, by permission of Ginn and Company, from Smith's *History of Mathematics*

It will be seen that no symbol for zero is included in this group. This symbol, however, was already used by the Arabs, for it is met with in earlier Arabic documents.

The numerals 2 and 3 as shown in this figure were undoubtedly developed from the = and ≡ symbols of the Hindus. If the = symbol is written rapidly, starting at the left of the top line and not lifting one's pen from the paper, our modern 2 will emerge. Similarly, our modern 3 was developed from the ≡ symbol. In the Spanish manuscript of A.D. 976, this symbol has been beautified by the scribe into the 3 shown in Figure 14. Our modern 4 and 5 have departed from their corresponding symbols in this figure. Until the development of printing did away with handwritten books, many variations in these two symbols were made by individual writers. It is interesting to notice how similar our modern 4 and 5 are to the Hindu symbols for these numbers found at Nasik (Figure 13). Yet the modern 4 and 5 are found in documents only after the introduction of printing, and the Nasik inscriptions were then unknown in Europe.

Centuries after the Arabs had introduced the new number-symbols into Europe many people still clung to the old familiar Roman numerals and would have nothing to do with the new system, which they associated with traders and heathens. By the thirteenth century, however, the new system of writing numbers had become established in various parts of Europe. It was not until then that any real development in the number-reckoning we now call elementary arithmetic could take place. Even our present simple methods of working multiplication and division were only developed slowly and laboriously during the centuries that followed the introduction of the new symbols into Europe. Many different methods were tried—developments, in many cases, of Hindu, Arab and Persian ideas—before our present simple procedures were finally established in the sixteenth and seventeenth centuries.

It is a remarkable fact that so many thousands of years should have passed before men thought of a really simple way of indicating numbers. It all seems so clear to us, after the event, that it is difficult for us to realize the long years of struggle and effort that lie behind our present simple system of numbering and our easy arithmetical processes. As, however, we follow the development of mathematical ideas through the ages, we shall see again and again that concepts and processes that appear abstruse and difficult to one generation become clear and matter-of-fact to a later generation, thanks, in many cases, to some inspiration leading to the development of a new mathematical concept.

Having traced the development of simple number-reckoning, we must go back once more to primitive times and discover how another, and immensely important branch of mathematics arose, for it was to become the foundation on which all modern mathematics is ultimately based.

# CHAPTER II

# The Birth of Geometry and the Golden Age of Greek Mathematics

Man's essential material needs are those of every animal. He must satisfy his appetites and secure protection from the elements. Unlike the rest of the animal creation, however, man was given the ability to make use of natural objects such as wood, stone and metal, and to take advantage of laws and forces, infinitely more powerful than himself, that are beyond his complete understanding even today.

Fundamentally, the material development of mankind is the story of the slow and often painful steps by which men have striven to secure food, shelter and security for themselves. Today, so far has man advanced along this road, that he can control natural forces so immense that his power for good or evil numbs the imagination. Today, man need have little fear of non-survival, so far as the violence of the elements or of creatures many times his own strength are concerned. His only cause for fear lies in himself.

Unlike the animals around him, primitive man began to look for ways of improving his chances of survival, by making use of objects and forces outside himself. By doing this, he made life easier for himself, if more complicated and possibly no happier.

He learned how to make cutting instruments, not only for hunting and fighting, but also for working in wood and stone. This meant he was no longer tied to living in a cave on a moun-

27

tain; he could now build himself a home wherever food and water were most easily obtainable.

He found methods of shaping and baking pots and pans; not only could he cook his food more easily, he could store it away when times were good as an insurance against times of dearth.

His wife took a thin pointed splinter of bone, made a hole in the blunt end, threaded it with a piece of gut or hair, and therewith, to her great delight and satisfaction, not only started the art of dressmaking, but also made life less hazardous and more comfortable.

After a time, his wife would doubtless become dissatisfied with a rough-and-ready hut and would stimulate her man to set about improving it. As he worked on it, he found that he made a better job, and therefore saved trouble and labor in the long run, if he was careful to cut the beams and logs so that their ends were—as we should say—at right angles to the edges. So in time he fastened two straight pieces of wood together at what he judged to be the desired angle, and thus made the first carpenter's square.

He found it desirable to build his house on level ground. But perhaps there was no such ground where he wished to live. So he made himself a level. He fastened three pieces of wood together so that they formed what we should call an isosceles triangle with base extended in each direction, and he cut a

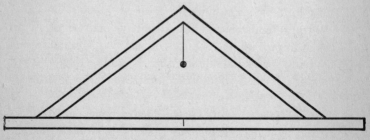

FIG. 15

notch at the mid-point of the base. He then fastened a cord at the vertex, or top of his triangle, and tied a weight at the other end of the cord, as shown in Figure 15.

When he was digging into a hillside to make a level foundation, he would take his leveling instrument from time to time, and rest its base on the surface. When he found that the weighted cord lay directly over the notch at the mid-point of the base, he knew that the ground-level was what he wanted. Of course, he could not explain *why* his instrument acted the way it did. The point is, he had found out how to apply one of the forces of nature to his needs. In order that this force of nature might serve his purpose, he knew that a certain number of pieces of wood of certain lengths must be put together in a certain way; a weight must be suspended from a certain point; a notch cut in a certain position. When this was done, and only when this was done, some power greater than his own came to his aid. Without in the least knowing that he was doing so, he was employing mathematical laws in order to harness the mysterious force of gravitation to work for him. Here we have a very simple illustration of what science has been doing ever since.

The kind of leveling instrument we have described has been found among carvings in ancient Egyptian tombs, while pictures of it are carved on some Roman surveyors' tombs.

Since this leveling instrument was used as late as Roman times and since it was known to the ancient Egyptians, it is certain that no more elaborate leveling instrument was used in laying out the foundations and erecting the enormous Egyptian pyramids and temples.

As civilization slowly advanced, men invented more and more of these simple instruments as their practical need arose. In doing this, they were unconsciously laying the foundations of mathematics and physical science.

To mark out the foundations of his buildings properly, a man needed some method for getting lines of considerable

length absolutely at right angles to each other. Anyone who
has tried to mark out the foundations of even a garage, or to
mark out a tennis court with the aid of just a carpenter's
square and a long measuring tape, will know how difficult it is
to get absolute accuracy with such instruments. The amateur
surveyor cannot do better than use a home-made instrument
discovered by the ancient Egyptians and also used in India,
China and Babylonia centuries before the Christian era. The
Egyptians made use of it at least 2500 years before the birth
of Christ. It was simply a rope with two knots tied in it.

Picture a scene in ancient Egypt thousands of years ago. An
Egyptian surveyor or *harpedonapta* is walking toward the site
chosen for Pharaoh's next great palace. Following him are
three slaves, one of them carrying a rope that is divided into
three sections by two knots.

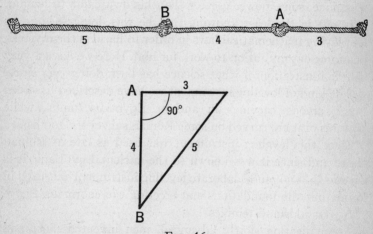

Fig. 16

The surveyor marks out one line of the foundations of the
building and stations a slave at one end of this line. This slave
holds the rope at the point we have marked A. A second slave
gathers both ends of the rope and walks along the line marked

out by the surveyor until the shorter end in his hands is stretched taut. Still holding both ends of the rope, he puts his hands down on the line. The third slave now takes hold of the rope at the point marked B in our figure, and walks away from the line until the whole rope is tightly stretched. As if by magic the rope takes the shape of a right triangle with the right angle at the point where the first slave is stationed.

The title *harpedonapta*, or surveyor, simply meant "rope-stretcher," indicating the great use made of this simple instrument in ancient times. No better home-made instrument exists for the amateur who wants to mark out a foundation for a building. The longer the cord or rope, the more accurate will be the resulting angle at A. All that matters is that the knots must be tied so that the segments of the rope are in the proportion 3:4:5, that is, they may be 6 ft., 8 ft., 10 ft., or 9 ft., 12 ft., 15 ft., or 12 ft., 16 ft., 20 ft., and so on.

It was with primitive tools such as these that the ancient Egyptians not only marked out the foundations of their great buildings, but also achieved the astonishing feat of erecting their pyramids, for instance, in such a way that each triangular face met at exactly the same point far up in the air and exactly above the center of the base—an amazing feat in view of the instruments at their disposal.

They were not interested in the *reason why*, for instance, their level or their knotted rope worked the way it did. They did not know there was an explanation, based on mathematics, for all these things that appeared to be mysteries to them.

In the course of many centuries, the Egyptian priests acquired a great fund of this practical, empirically discovered knowledge, that is, knowledge based merely on experiment and testing, and not on logical reasoning. It was left to the Greeks to discover the *reasons* that lay behind such knowledge.

Life in Egypt centered around the river Nile; in fact, Egypt has been called "the gift of the Nile." The Nile, in turn, may be called the mother of geometry, and, indeed, of mathematics.

For countless centuries the Nile overflowed its banks year by year, and the flood waters washed down the dark, fertile mud of the Abyssinian mountains toward the delta, or triangular shaped mouth into which the Nile divides before it pours its waters into the Mediterranean Sea. The very name "Egypt" is a Coptic word meaning "black earth," a reference to this fertile mud brought down by the Nile. The new deposits of mud covered up landmarks year after year and therefore compelled the Egyptians to mark out their landholdings over and over again. This "earth measurement" taught them a great deal about what we call geometrical figures, in a simple, practical form.

Thousands of years after the Egyptians had commenced to use their "earth measurement," a merchant from Miletus, the richest Greek city of those days, visited Egypt and became interested in the wealth of practical knowledge of geometrical matters that had been gathered together in the course of centuries by the scholarly priests of Egypt. Let us take a glance at this Greek merchant. He may be regarded as the father of our mathematics.

In the district we now call Asia Minor, there is a river that was once known as the Meander. Because it twists and turns a great deal in its course, it has given us our word "meandering" to describe the course of any stream or path that twists and turns. Today, the river flows into the sea through a desolate marsh. But twenty-five centuries ago Miletus, the most prosperous of all Greek cities of its time, stood on this site.

In 640 B.C. a boy named Thales was born in Miletus. His parents were descendants of the original Greek settlers in this city. From his earliest days he showed great energy and ability. He became a merchant, and was presumably successful, as he was able to retire and devote himself to politics and other matters at an early age. It is said that he once made a "corner" by buying up all the olive-presses around Miletus, but having shown that such an action was possible, he was apparently satisfied, for he sold his olive oil at a reasonable price.

Early in life he acquired a reputation for political wisdom, and was chosen as one of the "Seven Wise Men" of Greece.

His fame, however, does not rest on his trading ability nor on his political sagacity, but on his intellectual achievements. If trade and politics had been his only activities, his name would have perished as completely as the material splendor of his city has faded away. We have seen that during his trading days he had visited Egypt and had become interested in the "earth measurement" of the Egyptians. Having retired from business, he devoted his leisure time to the study of astronomy and mathematics. He still called his mathematics "earth measurement," but being a Greek, he used the word *geometry*. He had the insatiable thirst for knowledge that characterized so many Greeks of his and succeeding centuries, and that was to blossom forth into some of the greatest intellectual achievements of the human race.

During his travels, he had also become interested in Babylonian astronomy, for he introduced this science into Greece. On one occasion, he astonished his fellow Greeks by predicting an eclipse of the sun in 585 B.C. They were still more astonished when the eclipse actually took place, on May 28th, 585 B.C. The Greek historian Herodotus tells us that it occurred during a battle, and that it stopped the fighting and led to a lasting peace. Thales probably obtained his information about this eclipse from Babylonian sources; the Babylonians were deeply interested in astronomy centuries before Thales. Thanks to the lead given by him, however, certain Greek mathematicians whom we shall meet in the course of this book discovered facts about the universe whose truth was not generally recognized until modern times.

It is not, however, for his astronomical work that we re- member Thales today, but for his contribution to the science of mathematics. He wished to satisfy his curiosity by finding an explanation for the geometric facts discovered empirically by the Egyptians. This led him to take the first steps which were to lead to what is now known as the deductive science of geo- metry. By this is meant a system of logical reasoning which uses geometry as a medium by means of which a great struc- ture of intellectual thought can be built up. It is this kind of reasoning that has led to the development of most of our mathematical concepts.

It is not easy to describe in simple terms just what is meant by deductive reasoning, but the non-mathematical reader may be able to get a rough idea of what it is from the following two pages.

Deduction is a form of pure reasoning. The thinker starts with certain first principles, and argues from them until he reaches some conclusion. During this process he uses only facts that are agreed first principles or have themselves been proved from such first principles. This form of reasoning was known in ancient times as *a priori* reasoning, or reasoning "from that which comes first." Figure 17 may help to make this clearer.

In practice, a preliminary stage precedes the actual de- ductive proof of a geometric proposition. The first stage, which is usually worked mentally, is known as the "analysis," or "loosening," for this is the exact meaning of the Greek word *analusis* (*analysis*). When a chemist analyzes a substance, he breaks it up into the elements of which it is composed. When a mathematician analyzes a problem, he is making a pre- liminary examination and "loosening" or breaking up the conclusion he wishes to reach into some agreed mathematical fact or facts, then proceeding by logical steps until he reaches the particular fact from which he hopes to draw that desired conclusion.

He then retraces his steps and *puts together* the arguments he used in his analysis, in reverse order. This process of "putting together" is known as *synthesis*, a Greek work that means "putting together." "Synthetic" rubber is artificial rubber made by *putting together* various substances.

## "A Priori" reasoning  ["from that which comes first"]

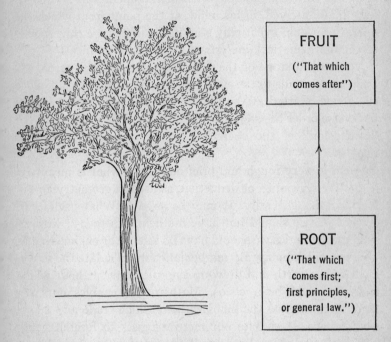

FRUIT

("That which comes after")

ROOT

("That which comes first; first principles, or general law.")

Fig. 17

During the victorious advance of the Russian armies in World War II, Russian engineers waded across a river by night and laid under-water foundations for a bridge, *starting from a suitable landing-place on the enemy-held bank of the river* and working their way backward toward their own side of the river. Afterwards, it was a comparatively easy matter for the

Russians to throw a bridge across the river *from their own bank,* using step by step the foundations that had been laid in reverse order to that followed during the actual attack.

The first stage in the above military operation was the development of a plan in the mind of a Russian general. He thought out the line of attack *from* his objective (the point that was to mark the *conclusion* of the operation, he hoped) and finally arrived, in his mind, at the point from which the operation would eventually start. This first stage corresponds to the mathematical *analysis* of a geometric problem.

The second stage of the operation, namely, the actual attack, corresponds to the synthesis of the mathematician, since the attack started at the "jumping-off-point," then followed in reverse order the steps laid down in the first stage, until the "conclusion" of the operation, on the enemy's bank, was reached.

Such, in very rough and brief outline, is what is meant by deductive reasoning, or deduction, as used in geometry and in mathematics generally. It may be asked, "What use is it?" Without it we should not have mathematics today; without such mathematics we should have no science or engineering as we know them today. By mathematics we calculate the movement of the earth and draw up the calendars, without which our life would be a chaos. Mathematics enables our cartographers to draw the maps without which trade and travel would cease. It enables our meteorologists to foretell wind, rain, frost and tides. It makes it possible for the navigator to find his way over pathless seas and trackless deserts. Without its aid, scientists and engineers would be powerless, and our present-day civilization would come to an end. Our architects, builders, electricians, radio workers, radiographers and countless others would find themselves out of employment. Our machinery, telephones, telegraphs, radios, X-rays, moving pictures, electric lighting and heating, together with countless forms of modern equipment might as well be thrown on the scrap heap.

And the foundation of all this mathematics is deductive reasoning. So we can be grateful that the retired business man Thales made wise use of his leisure time.

Unlike many later Greek mathematicians, Thales liked to apply his knowledge of geometry in practical ways. He seems to have astonished the Egyptians by being able to calculate the height of one of their pyramids by measuring the length of its shadow. According to the writer Pliny, he did this at the hour of the day when a man's shadow is the same length as himself. It seems highly doubtful, however, whether this would have impressed the Egyptians, for as early as 1500 B.C. they had sundials and so were thoroughly familiar with questions connected with shadows, even though they knew nothing of similar triangles, as such. A more probable version of the story is given by Plutarch, who states that the problem did not depend on the hour of the day but required a knowledge of the properties of similar triangles.

Thales also applied his knowledge of geometry to calculate the distance of a ship from the shore. Doubtless he made many other practical applications of the subject, but we have no information on this point. Although we have no record of any book or document written by him, the name of Thales will always rank high among mathematicians for the pioneer work he performed.

Some thirty-six years before the death of Thales, another great mathematician was born only a few miles from Thales' birthplace.

Off the coast of Asia Minor is the mountainous little island of Samos, about one-seventh the size of Long Island. At that time Samos was inhabited by descendants of Greek settlers who had gone there about 1000 B.C.

About the year 580 B.C. (nobody knows the exact date) a

Greek boy was born in Samos whose name is found in every text book on geometry today. That name is Pythagoras. Little is known of his early life except that he studied under Thales and probably visited Egypt on his master's advice in order to study the "earth measurement" of the Egyptian priests. When he was about fifty years old he left Samos and went to live in a town called Crotona, in Southern Italy.

We do not know the reasons that led Pythagoras to leave Samos, but once at Crotona he quickly gathered together a kind of brotherhood and school of mathematical philosophy. Many of the beliefs held by the Pythagoreans strike us as far-fetched and fanciful, but nevertheless mathematics owes much to the work done by the followers of Pythagoras, who continued to function long after his death. The members of his school exercised a great influence throughout the Greek world. They appear to have practiced communism, not in the literal sense, and certainly not in the modern political sense, but strictly among themselves. Not only did they share their worldly goods among each other, but also all their mathematical and philosophical discoveries. They were at first bound by an oath not to reveal the secrets and teaching of their brotherhood. At first, these teachings are believed to have been treasured orally among the members of the society, but as time passed they were put into writing, and one of these Pythagorean documents exercised a great influence on Plato.

Either Pythagoras or one of his followers discovered the harmonic progression in the musical scale, connecting the length of a string and the pitch of its vibrating note. It may have been this discovery that led them to believe that "number" forms the element from which all things have developed, and that everything in creation can be expressed in numbers.

They invented the terms "odd" and "even" numbers: "odd" numbers were male, "even" numbers female. Being an exclusively male society they of course laid down the obvious fact that odd numbers were divine, even numbers earthly.

Doubtless, their "even-number" womenfolk were in complete agreement, at any rate, with their discovery that odd numbers were the lucky ones, even numbers the unlucky ones! These superstitions lasted even to Shakespeare's day. In *The Merry Wives of Windsor* Falstaff says:

"This is the third time; I hope good luck lies in odd numbers. . . . They say there is divinity in odd numbers, either in nativity, chance, or death."

The Pythagoreans made no practical use of the geometry they studied. They were interested only in the abstract side of mathematics. They continued, and greatly extended, the work done by Thales in building up the lower foundations of geometry as we know it, finding logical proofs, by deductive reasoning, about geometric facts. The statement and proof of such a fact was called a *proposition*, and the name of Pythagoras is always linked with a proposition, or theorem, which states that the area of a square drawn on the longest side of a right triangle is always equal to the sum of the areas of squares drawn on the other two sides. It is doubtful whether the Pythagoreans could prove that this holds good in the case of *any* right triangle. Pythagoras, it is true, is said to have sacrificed an ox in celebration of the discovery of this theorem, but the truth of this story seems unlikely, since the Pythagoreans would allow no blood to be shed in this way. What is more probable is that they knew of two *special cases* of this theorem. If the sides of a right triangle are in the proportion 3:4:5; or if a right triangle has its two shorter sides equal, the truth of the theorem is self-evident if, in each case, a simple construction is made. Even though the reader may know nothing about deductive reasoning, he can see for himself that the large square in Figure 18 is equal to the sum of the two smaller squares.

This theorem explains the mysterious behavior of the Egyptians' knotted rope.

Figure 19 shows the other special case: the shaded part is the right triangle with its two shorter sides equal to each other. If the diagonals of the largest square in this figure are drawn, it will be seen that the four right triangles into which that square is divided will exactly fit the two smaller squares.

When we come to the story of algebra we shall see how this theorem led to a very perplexing and disturbing problem for

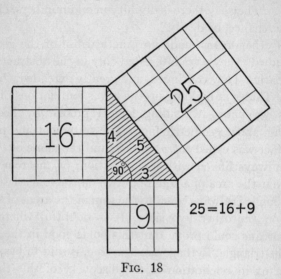

$$25 = 16 + 9$$

FIG. 18

those who held the Pythagorean view that everything could be expressed in some way by numbers. They were to find that they could not express the exact length of the diagonal of a square by any number on the number-scale.

Many mathematical terms can be traced to the Pythagoreans. The very word "mathematics" was probably first used by them. The Greek word *mathema* simply meant "science." If the Pythagoreans were constructing a figure that was to be equal in area to a given figure of different shape they called it a case of *parabole*, "lying side by side," "equal," if the base of the final figure fitted the original base; of *ellipsis* "left short," if it fell short of that base; of *hyperbole* "exceeding," if it exceeded that base. Hundreds of years later, a great Greek geometer named Apollonius followed their lead and chose the names *parabola*, *ellipse* and *hyperbola* to describe sections of a cone, in whose construction a certain line equalled, fell short of, or exceeded another line.

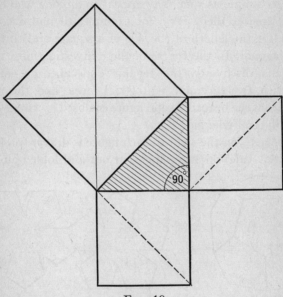

FIG. 19

The Pythagoreans were the first to discover that the earth is a sphere. This they did by observing the shadow cast by the earth on the moon. Although this fact became an accepted commonplace to later Greek mathematicians, it was not until the time of the great navigations of the fifteenth and sixteenth centuries that the average man was convinced that the earth was not flat.

The most important researches made by the Pythagoreans in other fields were (1) those connected with the theory of

numbers, which we shall deal with later in the book; (2) the
search for an answer to the questions "Can any two lengths
each be divided into parts, all of which are equal to each
other?"; "Can any flat surface be completely filled by repetitions of the same figure?"; "Can any volume be filled by repetitions of the same solid figure?" The answers to these questions
are not as simple as they may appear to anyone who has not
tried to answer them. Try, for example, to find a common
measure for the length of the side of a square and the length
of its diagonal! In the course of these investigations, the Pythagoreans discovered the regular dodecahedron, or solid
figure with twelve equal pentagonal faces, and the regular
icosahedron, the beautiful solid figure enclosed by twenty equal
and equilateral triangles.

If the "net" on the right of each figure is drawn (preferably
on a larger scale) on stiff paper, cut out and folded along the

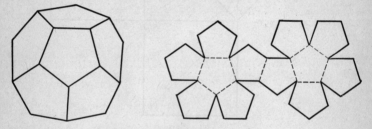

The dodeca-hedron ("12-faced" solid)

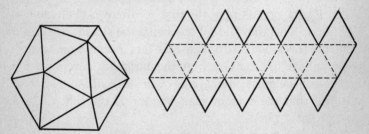

The icosa-hedron ("20-faced" solid)

Fig. 20

dotted lines, the reader can make the solid figures suggested in the perspective drawings on the left. Join the faces with Scotch tape.

There are only five of these regular solids; the other three were discovered by the Egyptians. They are the cube, the tetrahedron, or solid enclosed by four equal and equilateral triangles, and the octahedron, or solid enclosed by eight such triangles.

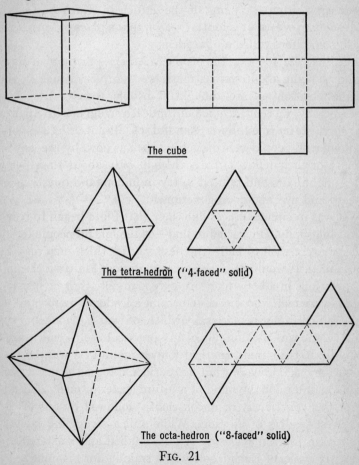

The cube

The tetra-hedron ("4-faced" solid)

The octa-hedron ("8-faced" solid)

Fig. 21

Our story of geometry now passes to the year 400 B.C. About a mile outside the city of Athens there was then a pleasant garden, surrounded by a wall and containing walks, groves and fountains. It was believed to have belonged to a person called Akademos, and it was called Akademia after him. Here, for nearly fifty years, a great philosopher, who owned a small estate near by, used to teach his philosophy. The philosopher was Plato. His school of philosophy became known as the Academy, from the name of the garden in which he taught for so many years. It is for this reason that a place of learning is still sometimes called an "academy."

In the year 400 B.C., the people of Athens—or those of them who thought about serious matters—were very much in the same position as are thoughtful people today. Athens, a democracy, was engaged in a life or death struggle with Sparta, a slave-state ruled by a handful of all-powerful despots. Thoughtful people were distressed, then as now, by the way so many of their fellow citizens thought only about their petty personal affairs and refused to try to understand questions of peace and war and good government.

It was in circumstances like these that Plato began to teach his philosophy. He wished to find—as thoughtful people today desperately wish to find—the best way in which men may be governed. It would be out of place to discuss Plato's ideas and suggestions in a book like this, except to note that he insisted that every man who wished to become a leader of men ought to be trained in mathematics, by which, of course, he meant geometry. He was not thinking of any practical use to which they could put their mathematical knowledge; all he wanted was that they should have what he considered to be the finest possible training for the mind of a future leader of men. This advice was consciously or unconsciously followed by one of the greatest leaders of all time. While still a struggling lawyer, Abraham Lincoln *at the age of forty* studied and mastered the first six books of Euclid, solely as a training for his mind.

Plato's attractive views on the way in which mathematics ought to be taught to young people seem very modern. Amusement and pleasure, said Plato, ought to be combined with instruction, in order to make the subject interesting. There should be games of various kinds, such as a game played with different kinds of coins mixed together. There should also be problems connected with boxing and wrestling matches. These things, said Plato, make a pupil useful to himself and more wide awake.

In the rules he laid down for his grown-up followers, Plato was very strict. "Let no man destitute of geometry enter my doors" was the inscription over the entrance to his school. He insisted, even more strongly than had the Pythagoreans, that geometric facts must be proved by rigorous logical reasoning. In order to avoid constructions that involved the puzzling problem of infinity he insisted on the hard-and-fast rule, probably made before his time, that only a ruler and compasses might be used for geometric constructions. In consequence, people puzzled their heads vainly for hundreds of years, trying to trisect an angle, that is, divide any angle (not merely a right angle, which can easily be trisected) into three equal parts, using only ruler and compasses. They also tried in vain to draw a square equal in area to a given circle, and to draw a line equal to the edge of a cube that would be double the volume of a given cube. They did not know that none of these three constructions can be done if only a ruler and compasses are allowed to be used. The long, unsuccessful search for their solution was not all wasted time, for it led to the development of very important mathematical processes and concepts.

The book that helped to train the mind of Abraham Lincoln was written some three hundred years before the Christian era. In 300 B.C. we meet a man whose name has been more widely known than that of any other mathematician who has ever lived. He was far from being the world's greatest mathematician, but he wrote the world's best-selling mathematical textbook of all time, although he, the author, never knew this. It was a book on geometry that was to be used for more than two thousand years all over Europe, and, toward the end of that long period, in America. Until about fifty years ago, school geometries had his name, Euclid, as their only title.

We do not know when or where Euclid was born; we know remarkably little about his life, except that he taught mathematics in the royal school at Alexandria in Egypt that had been founded by King Ptolemy, the illegitimate son and successor of Alexander the Great, the founder of Alexandria. But we do know that by patient scholarly labor he collected all the geometrical facts known in his day, arranged the various theorems in proper order, improved their proofs where necessary, and added theorems he himself had thought out.

His was the master mind that was able to collect all the muddled, confused pieces of a vast mathematical jig-saw puzzle and put them together in such a way that a clear and beautiful picture suddenly emerged from what had been a welter of odds and ends of mathematical knowledge. This was the reason why his textbook proved to be the world's best-seller.

His masterpiece consisted of thirteen "books," each written on a separate roll of parchment. The whole work was called the *Elements*. For twenty centuries the first six books were the student's usual introduction to geometry.

All the proofs Euclid included were, of course, based on certain agreed first principles. So long as these first principles are agreed upon, Euclid's conclusions hold good. If, however, some of the first principles he used in his arguments are *not* agreed upon, some of his conclusions no longer hold good. Some of the higher branches of mathematics today make use of geometries that are based on first principles different from those chosen by Euclid, such as the geometries of Lobachevsky and Riemann. These two mathematicians lived during the first half of the nineteenth century. The systems of Euclid, Lobachevsky and Riemann are all equally logical, and each applies to its own special field of inquiry. So far as terrestrial calculations are concerned, Euclid's geometry is unchallenged.

It is interesting to trace the way in which the *Elements* became known to the Europe of the Middle Ages. Strange to say, this knowledge did not come directly from any Greek manuscript, but from the Arabic.

Some time between 750 and 800, an Arab caliph secured a copy of Euclid's *Elements*, in the original Greek. It came from Constantinople, which had not fallen to barbarians when the rest of the Roman Empire disintegrated. Several Arabic translations were made from it, one of them while Harun al-Rashid, the caliph of the *Arabian Nights Tales*, ruled the Arab empire.

In 1120, an Englishman, Athelhard, or Adelard of Bath, made a Latin translation from an Arabic version. Several other Latin translations were made, one of them having the distinction of being the first important mathematical book to be printed. It was published in Venice in 1482 and has beautiful figures printed in its wide margins.

Euclid's book was not translated into English until 1570, when Shakespeare was a boy of six. Although late in the field, it gave good measure, the text, with notes, taking up 928 pages! A reproduction of the title page of this first English edition of the *Elements* will be found as the frontispiece of this book.

Notice the error made in calling Euclid "the philosopher of Megara." In the Middle Ages, and, as can be seen, even in the time of Queen Elizabeth of England, this error was often made. The author of the *Elements* was not the only Euclid; there was another man of the same name, a philosopher, born at Megara, a town on the isthmus between Attica and Corinth in Greece. Writers in the Middle Ages often confused the two Euclids, as has been done in this case. The title page describes the preface as "very fruitfull"; as a matter of fact it is often far from fruitful, while some of Euclid's theorems are altered, others joined together.

After the publication of the first English version, and until as recently as 1900, edition after edition of Euclid's book appeared. So many copies of this book have been sold that probably few other books, except the Bible, have ever had as wide a circulation.

Our pursuit of the story of the *Elements* has taken us right up to modern days. We must now retrace our steps and go back to the time of ancient Greece once more so that we may pick up the thread of our tale of geometry's beginnings.

Even before the birth of Christ, Greek mathematicians had mastered the geometry of the sphere and knew how to handle such things as circles and triangles drawn on the surface of a sphere.

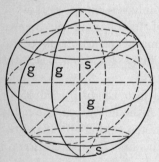

Circles connected with a sphere
(g) Great circles
(s) Small circles

Fig. 22

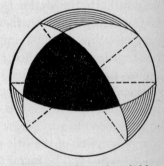

Spherical triangles are bounded by intersecting arcs of great circles.

Fig. 23

It is only natural that the study of the sphere should have occupied a prominent place in Greek mathematics as soon as it was realized that the earth was spherical in shape. Such study arose through the burning curiosity of intelligent Greeks regarding the shape and dimensions of the earth on which they found themselves. In a later chapter, we shall deal more fully with the branch of mathematics known as trigonometry that arose from the study of spheres and circles. At this point we shall merely discuss the purely geometric knowledge of the sphere that was developed by the ancient Greeks. As has been said, Pythagoras was probably the first to realize that the earth was in the form of a sphere. It is certain that by the time of the philosopher Aristotle, that is, about 340 B.C., various attempts had even been made to calculate the circumference of the earth. One such attempt had been made by a mathematician named Eudoxus.

Round about 250 B.C., the greatest mathematician of antiquity, Archimedes, was able to record in a book known as the *Sand Reckoner*, that "certain writers" had stated that the circumference of the earth was "thirty myriads of stadia." The Greek *myriad* was ten-thousand; unfortunately, there was more than one kind of *stadion* used for measuring distance. One kind of *stadion*, however, is believed to have been equal to about one-tenth of a modern mile. If this was the kind of stadion mentioned by Archimedes, "thirty myriads of stadia" or 300,000 stadia, would be equal to about 30,000 miles. If we take the figure based in 1910 by J. F. Hayford on observations made in the United States of America (equatorial semi-axis: 6378.388 kilometers) and do a little multiplication and division, we find that the circumference of the earth around the equator is approximately 24,907 miles. Let us now see how, two and a half centuries before Christ, a Greek mathematician calculated that the circumference was approximately 250,000 stadia, that is 25,000 miles if the stadion mentioned above were used by him, an error of only some 90 miles!

In the third century before Christ, the finest library in the world was at Alexandria in Egypt. It had been founded by the same king of Egypt, Ptolemy, who had established the school of mathematics where Euclid taught. Toward the latter half of that century, a friend of Archimedes named Eratosthenes was its librarian. Eratosthenes was also a mathematician, though other Greek mathematicians did not consider he was quite in the first class; they nicknamed him "Beta," which shows that our modern grading of college students as "A, B, C" etc. is not a very recent innovation. After reading the next few paragraphs, the reader will be able to realize from this classification how high was the standard of scholarship of the Greek mathematicians two thousand years ago.

Despite his rating as merely "B," Eratosthenes may well have made an extraordinarily close approximation of the circumference of the earth. If his stadion was the one that was equal to about one-tenth of a mile, his estimate of the earth's circumference was only 0.4% in error. Even if his result was not as accurate as this, his method was remarkably scientific and its originality would today surely gain for its inventor a higher mark than "B."

There are two occasions during the year when the sun, *sol*, is farthest from the equator, and seems to pause, *sti-*, before returning toward the equator. One of these is called the "winter solstice" (three days before Christmas), the other the "summer solstice" (about June 21st). Long before the time of the Greeks it was known that if a staff were set upright on the earth, its noontime shadow, which always lies due north and south, would be longest at the winter solstice and shortest at the summer solstice.

Eratosthenes found out in some way—it may have been from ancient Egyptian documents in his library—that at noon, at the summer solstice, an upright rod at Syene in Egypt cast no shadow. This fact was confirmed by observing that the water in a deep well at that same place and time completely reflected the sun's rays, the edge of the well casting no shadow on the water below. At the same moment, an upright rod at Alexandria cast a short shadow on horizontal ground.

Eratosthenes knew that Syene was due south of Alexandria and also, of course, that at noon the shadow at Alexandria lay due north and south. He argued that it followed that the rod at Syene, the rod at Alexandria, the center of the earth, and the center of the sun *when directly over Syene*, must all lie in the same plane. So he was able to produce something like the following picture:

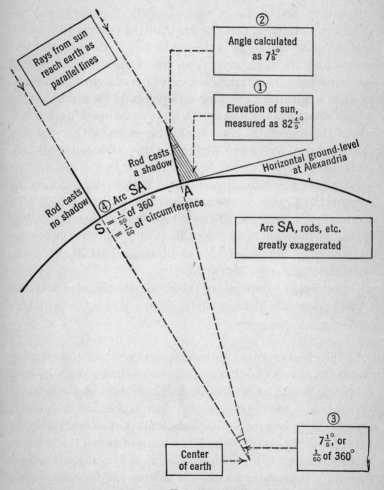

Rays from sun reach earth as parallel lines

② Angle calculated as $7\frac{1}{5}°$

① Elevation of sun, measured as $82\frac{4}{5}°$

Rod casts a shadow

Horizontal ground-level at Alexandria

Rod casts no shadow

④ Arc SA
S $= \frac{1}{50}$ of 360°
$= \frac{1}{50}$ of circumference

A

Arc SA, rods, etc. greatly exaggerated

Center of earth

③ $7\frac{1}{5}°$, or $\frac{1}{50}$ of 360°

Fig. 24

Let us examine this figure; it is really very simple. Eratosthenes knew, of course, that the earth is a sphere and that, in consequence, imaginary lines that continued the directions of the two upright rods would meet at the earth's center. He also knew that the sun's rays are, for all intents and purposes, parallel to each other when they reach the earth. So only an elementary acquaintance with Euclid's geometry was required to determine that the angle at the center of the earth was equal to the angle between the top of the rod at Alexandria and the sun's rays. Since an arc is measured by the angle it subtends or stretches at the center of a circle, and since, as we saw, we are here dealing with points on the earth that are all in the same plane, the arc SA must equal one-fiftieth of the whole circumference. Now Eratosthenes knew that the distance between Syene and Alexandria was 5000 stadia, all such distances in Egypt having been calculated by the *bematists* or surveyors of Alexander the Great and King Ptolemy during the conquest of Egypt. So the circumference of the earth, argued Eratosthenes, must be 50 times 5000 stadia, that is, 250,000 stadia. *If* the stadion used for this calculation was the one we have already mentioned, this would make 250,000 stadia approximately equal to 25,000 miles.

And the man who achieved this result was regarded only as a second-class mathematician in the Golden Age of Greek mathematics!

In this chapter we shall mention only two other great mathematicians of this Golden Age: others will find a place in later chapters, though even then we shall have discussed only a few of the many men who laid the foundations on which our present-day mathematics has been built. Let us first glance at the work of the younger and less famous of two of the greatest mathematicians of all time, Apollonius of Perga. He was born some fifty years after Euclid had written the *Elements*. Little is known about his personal life, except that he studied at the

school in Alexandria where Euclid had taught, and that he became one of the shining lights of that school of Alexandria.

We can imagine Apollonius, inspired by Euclid's example,
making up his mind to gather together and put in order everything that was known about a branch of mathematics that
especially interested him and that is known as *Conic Sections*.
In carrying out this ambition, Apollonius contributed more
to his particular subject than Euclid had done to elementary
geometry, for he thought out a completely new method that
was far better than the method that had been used in dealing
with conic sections by the mathematician Menaechmus, who
had lived about 350 B.C. So good were the methods of Apollonius that they held the field for eighteen centuries, until the
year 1637, when the great French mathematician Descartes
published a book that completely revolutionized the treatment
of the subject, and, for that matter, all Greek geometry. In a
later chapter we shall see how Descartes' work made what had
been a difficult subject extremely simple, and opened up new
mathematical concepts that lie at the root of modern mathematics. Since we no longer use the methods of Apollonius, we
shall merely glance at the meaning of "conic sections," all of
which are nowadays handled much more easily by the algebraic
application of analytic geometry invented by Descartes.

In each of the four figures that follow, the reader will find,
on the left, an oblique cone, the kind used by Apollonius in
order to make his treatment of the subject entirely general;
on the right, a right cone (or cone whose vertex is directly over
the center of its base) which is only a special case, but which
may give the general reader a clearer idea of the meaning of
conic sections. Such reader should imagine a right triangle that
has been cut out from a piece of cardboard, then placed upright on one of its shorter sides, and rotated around the other
shorter side. The solid figure traced out by the right triangle
would be a *right cone* such as is shown on the right of each of the
next four figures. Now imagine such a cone made out of a solid

piece of wood. If a saw were taken and a straight cut made
through the wooden cone in any direction, the shape cut by the
saw would be called a *conic section*, since the word "section"
merely means "cutting."

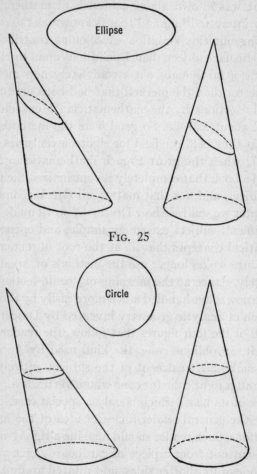

FIG. 25

FIG. 26

The circle is a special form of the ellipse.

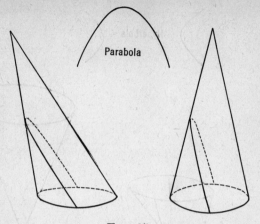

Parabola

FIG. 27

To form a parabola, the saw-cut must be parallel to the slanting edge of the cone.

To obtain the conic section shown on page 56 the cutting must be very similar to that made for the parabola, but *not* parallel to the slanting edge of the cone. Further, this cutting, if extended indefinitely upward, must cut what might be called a *reflection* of the original cone. The two outlines that result form what are known as the two branches of a hyperbola.

We saw (page 41) the reasons that led Apollonius to choose the names parabola, ellipse and hyperbola. For his work on conic sections, Apollonius became known as the Great Geometer.

We now come to the greatest mathematician of antiquity—some would say the greatest who has ever lived, if one bears in mind the amount of mathematical knowledge available to him when he started his work and compare this with the accumulation of such knowledge with which the great mathematicians of the last three hundred years have commenced their studies.

In Sicily, the second largest island of the Mediterranean,

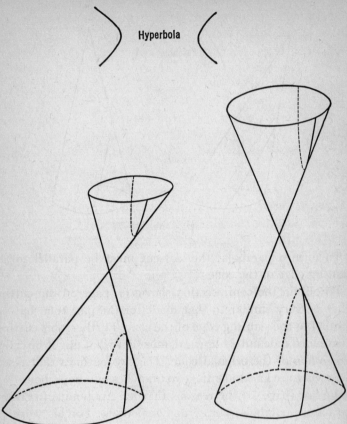

Hyperbola

FIG. 28

stands the ancient city of Syracuse which goes back to the year 700 B.C., when Greeks from Corinth settled there.

In 287 B.C. the great Archimedes was born in Syracuse. He was destined to become his city's most famous son, and perhaps the world's greatest mathematician. Archimedes came of a well-known family—his father was a mathematician and astronomer who may have been related to Hiero, the ruler of

Syracuse—and as a young man he was able to go to Egypt in order to study at the royal school of mathematics in Alexandria where Euclid had taught for many years. Returning home to Syracuse, so great was his ability, energy, and power of application that he brought the mathematics of his day to such a height that no further progress was possible until new mathematical tools called symbolic algebra and analytic geometry had been developed some eighteen centuries later.

As a scientist, he built up the branch of science that deals with the pressure exerted by liquids; he discovered the laws that govern levers, and made a host of practical inventions, such as a machine for raising water to a higher level. It is said that the hold of a large ship belonging to Hiero II, the tyrant, or king of Syracuse, had filled up with water. Hiero appealed to Archimedes, with whom he was on very friendly terms (it is thought the two were related to each other) to find some way of emptying the water. Archimedes promptly invented an instrument consisting of a long tube, open at each end, inside which was a spiral piece of metal, shaped like a corkscrew. By immersing one end in the water, tilting the tube and turning the spiral by means of a handle, the water would flow up the tube and out of the upper end.

Archimedes found ways of moving great weights by means of levers, cog-wheels and pulleys. By means of such devices he is said to have moved a ship that was lying in a drydock. He is said to have declared to Hiero that any given weight could be moved by any given force, however small, and then to have remarked, "Give me a place to stand on and I will move the earth." Plutarch says that "when Hiero was struck with amazement and asked Archimedes to reduce the problem to practice and give an illustration of some great weight moved by a small force, he fixed upon a ship of burden with three masts, from the king's arsenal, which had only been drawn up with great labor by many men, and, loading her with many passengers and a full freight, himself the while sitting far off, with no great effort, but only holding the end of a compound pulley quietly in his hand and pulling at it, he drew the ship along smoothly and safely as if she were moving through the sea."

He invented catapults that could be used at long or short range, machines for throwing showers of rocks through holes in the walls of Syracuse, and long movable poles hanging over those walls and having a kind of iron beak in them; when an enemy ship came near the harbor walls, the poles would be raised in the air and then allowed to crash down into the enemy ship. When, late in Archimedes' life, the Romans came up against these weapons they were so terrified that "if they did but see a piece of rope or wood projecting above the wall, they would cry 'there it is,' declaring that Archimedes was setting some engine in motion against them, and would turn their backs and run away."

Archimedes attached little value to inventions like these. They were, he said, merely the "diversions of geometry at play." Plutarch adds, "Though these inventions had obtained for him the renown of more than human sagacity, he yet would not even deign to leave behind him any written work on such subjects." If Archimedes were living today there can be no doubt that he would be in the forefront of those scientists and mathematicians who are striving to prevent the use, or rather, abuse, of science for the purpose of destroying our civilization.

As every high-school boy who studies science will know, on one occasion a request from King Hiero led to an important scientific discovery. The king, it seems, had sent some gold to a goldsmith, to be made into a crown. When the crown was finished, the king suspected the goldsmith of having substituted silver for part of the gold. Being unable to prove that his suspicion was well founded, he appealed to Archimedes to suggest some way by which the honesty, or dishonesty, of the goldsmith could be proved.

The Roman architect Vitruvius, who tells us the tale, says that while taking a bath, Archimedes hit on a solution of the king's problem when he saw the bath-water overflow. Anyone who knows how helpful to thoughtful meditation it is to lie in a hot bath and half float on the water may think that a more probable version of the story would be that the sudden realization that "when a body floats on water and loses weight, the loss in weight is equal to the weight of water displaced" came to the great mathematician as he was giving a practical demonstration of this law.

Whatever may have been the cause of his sudden inspiration, filled with excitement at having solved the problem and—more important still—of having hit on an important scientific discovery, he dashed naked through the streets of Syracuse crying "Eureka, eureka, I have found it, I have found it." History does not relate whether the goldsmith was found to be guilty or innocent, but his memory, at any rate, has been preserved, thanks to his connection with the discoverer of "the principle of Archimedes."

It is to be hoped, for the sake of other members of his household, that Archimedes had his own private bathroom. He must have spent a great many hours in it. We are told that after taking a bath he would anoint himself with oil and then draw geometrical figures in the oil on his body, musing the while on mathematical problems and "being in a state of entire preoccupation, and, in the truest sense, divine possession with his love and delight in science." He seems to have been exactly the kind of person many people—quite incorrectly—regard as the typical professor. We are told that he would forget about his food when thinking out some problem; we have seen that clothing meant nothing to him; he would be seen sitting for hours musing over geometrical figures he had drawn in the ashes scattered over his hearth. A difficult man to live with, one imagines, but what human mind has ever achieved as much as his?

Although today Archimedes is usually remembered for his mechanical inventions and his work in connection with mechanics and hydrostatics, his greatest work, by far, lay in the field of pure mathematics. As a mathematician, he was supreme and unchallenged.

He invented an improved way of writing large numbers, although he never seems to have thought of a simpler notation than the clumsy Greek alphabetical number-symbols he used so skilfully; he calculated the approximate value of $\pi$, that is, the ratio between the circumference of a circle and its diameter. Today we know that this is a number that cannot be found exactly, although its value can be calculated to any required degree of accuracy (a misguided enthusiast once worked out its value to 707 decimal places). Archimedes proved by a method known as the "process of exhaustion" that the value or $\pi$ lay between $\frac{223}{71}$ and $\frac{220}{70}$, or, as we should say today, between 3.14085 and 3.14286, a remarkable achievement when one considers the kind of mathematical tools at his disposal. Incidentally, in the course of a long and extremely complicated geometric and arithmetical process, he showed that he knew some method for finding square roots. The "process of exhaustion" had been used two centuries before his time by a mathematician named Antiphon in attempts to "square the circle" by drawing a square inside a circle, then doubling the number of sides again and again until the area between the final inscribed polygon and the circle was approximately exhausted. Archimedes improved on this method by finding two limits within which the circumference of a circle must lie. By successively making these limits draw closer and closer to each other he found that the circumference was a little more than $\frac{223}{71}$ times its diameter, and a little less than $\frac{220}{70}$ times its diameter. (He needed the length of the circumference in order to "square the circle," since he had previously proved that the area of a circle is the same as that of the right triangle whose shorter sides are respectively equal to the circumference and the radius of the circle.)

Figure 29 will make his general method clear.

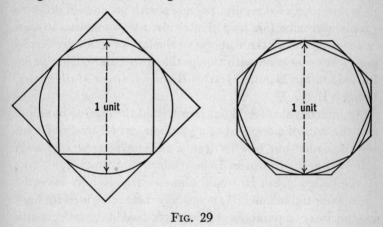

FIG. 29

It is obvious that in each case, the length of the circumference of the circle must lie between the respective perimeters of the inscribed and circumscribed regular polygons shown in the figures. Moreover, it can be shown by calculation or careful measurement that as the number of sides in the polygons increases, the lengths of the perimeters come nearer and nearer to each other. In other words, the length of the circumference lies between limits which move closer and closer to each other. It will be found that if the diameter of each circle is taken as one unit, the circumference will lie between the following limits:

| | Perimeter of inscribed polygon: | Perimeter of circumscribed polygon: | "Gap": |
|---|---|---|---|
| (*4 sides*) | 2.8 units | 4.0 units | 1.2 units |
| (*8 sides*) | 3.0 units | 3.3 units | 0.3 units |
| (*12 sides*) | 3.1 units | 3.2 units | 0.1 units |
| (*24 sides*) | 3.13 units | 3.16 units | 0.03 units |
| (*36 sides*) | 3.14 units | 3.15 units | 0.01 units |

Archimedes used regular polygons with 96 sides in order to get his approximation for $\pi$. The reader who would care to see a full translation of the elaborate calculations made by Archimedes in connection with this problem will find one on pages 50 to 55 in Sir Thomas Heath's *History of Greek Mathematics*, Volume II.

Archimedes also found out how to find the area of an ellipse and the area of a segment of a parabola cut off by any chord. He also found out how to draw a tangent at any point on a spiral; if he had possessed the modern mathematician's tool of symbolic algebra he would almost certainly have invented the differential calculus. As it was, the method he used for finding the area of a parabolic segment was used in the seventeenth century in the development of the integral calculus, as we shall see in later chapters.

Of the many books he wrote, one dealt with spheres, cylinders and cones. It would seem that he considered this to be his greatest achievement, for he expressed a wish that his tomb should be marked with a sphere and a cylinder.

More than a hundred years after the murder of Archimedes, the Roman orator Cicero visited Sicily and found his tomb near one of the gates of Syracuse. It was sadly neglected, and covered with thorns and briars. Cicero had it restored, but today it is nowhere to be found, having perished in the disasters and turmoils that fell upon Sicily during the Middle Ages.

Who can say what far-reaching mathematical idea perished when, in 212 B.C., Archimedes was brutally murdered by a Roman soldier? The just and kindly King Hiero had died in 216 B.C., to be succeeded by his grandson Hieronymus. The new king allied himself with Carthage, the African city-state with which Rome was fighting the bitter Punic Wars. Hieronymus was murdered before he could see the mischief he had done. Syracuse was attacked by a Roman army and fleet under a general named Marcellus. At first, we are told, the Romans were held off, thanks largely to the mechanical surprises prepared for their reception by Archimedes, now an old man of seventy-five. Marcellus was forced to withdraw his troops for a time, but eventually he surprised the Syracusans while they were celebrating a festival to Artemis, the Greek goddess of the moon and of the chase. The city fell to the Romans, and, as was usual in such cases, the massacre of its inhabitants began.

The Byzantine historian Tzetzes tells us that Archimedes had drawn a diagram in the dust, despite the battle raging in the city, and was quietly pondering over some mathematical problem. He saw a shadow fall over his diagram as a Roman soldier approached. "Stand away from my diagram," cried the agitated old mathematician. The answer he received was just what might have been expected from an adherent to the doctrine that might is right. As Alfred Whitehead has put it, "The death of Archimedes at the hands of a Roman soldier is symbolical of a world change of the first magnitude. . . . No Roman lost his life because he was absorbed in the contemplation of a mathematical diagram."

Thus perished the greatest mathematician of antiquity, possibly the greatest mathematician of all time. With the death of Archimedes, the Golden Age of Greek mathematics comes to an abrupt end. Not for eighteen centuries—not, that is, until the seventeenth century—was the torch lighted by Archimedes to be rekindled almost simultaneously in England and Germany.

# CHAPTER III

# The Invention of Algebra

O<small>NE</small> of the oldest mathematical problems in the world is "Hau, its whole, its seventh, it makes nineteen." The word "hau" is not, as might be supposed, a snort of surprised disgust. It was the word used by the ancient Egyptians for any unknown quantity in a mathematical problem. Nowadays we usually use x or some other letter from the end of the alphabet instead of "hau." Put into present-day English, the problem may be stated as "There is a number such that if the whole of it is added to one-seventh of it, the result will be nineteen."

This problem is found in the Ahmes papyrus, of which we spoke on page 13. Since this papyrus is a copy of an older one written about 2200 B.C., the problem is more than 4000 years old. Readers who would care to see the complicated steps by which the problem is solved in the Ahmes papyrus will find a full translation of the Egyptian text in Volume II of Dr. D. E. Smith's *History of Mathematics*, a book that should be found in every reference library.

Those who are in the least familiar with modern algebra will at once recognize the problem as one that can quickly and easily be solved from the equation $x + \frac{x}{7} = 19$. Once the problem is translated into this symbolic, algebraic shorthand its solution presents no difficulty, since, if $x + \frac{x}{7}$ balances 19, then

7 times the left hand quantity must balance 7 times the right hand quantity. In other words, $7x + x$ (or $8x$) must still balance 133. If this is so, then one-eighth of $8x$ must also balance one-eighth of 133, so we find that $x = 16\frac{5}{8}$.

This modern method of solving the problem takes about one-tenth of the time it takes merely to read through the solution as given in the Ahmes papyrus. How does it come about that we have this time- and labor-saving mathematical tool called modern symbolic algebra? There are three distinct stages in the story of its development.

(1) The kind of problems out of which it grew were known and studied from early Egyptian times. These problems formed part of an abstract "science of numbers" that was unknown to all but a select few who took delight in the challenge it presented to their intellects. For thousands of years the solution of a problem of this nature would be written out like a piece of prose or a philosophical argument.

(2) The second stage commenced about the year A.D. 275 and extended into the sixteenth century. In this stage, solutions were still, in the main, written out like a piece of prose writing, but certain abbreviations were made in some of the wrds etc, as we have abbreviated "words" and "etcetera." A symbol indicating subtraction was introduced, as were one or two other such symbols.

(3) The third stage is the one in which we now live. No words or abbreviations of words are used in solving problems. Instead, word-statements are translated into a kind of mathematical shorthand, consisting of symbols and signs. Once these symbols and signs are mastered, a shorthand mathematical statement of this nature can convey to the mathematician a meaning that could only be expressed by a word-statement of considerable length and complexity. By means of alge-

braic symbolism a kind of "pattern" or mathematical "machine tool" is provided, which guides the mind as swiftly and unerringly to an objective as a jig guides a cutting tool on a machine. This kind of algebra began to be developed only some three or four hundred years ago, and then only by gradual stages. Compared with the thousands of years during which mathematical ideas and processes have been growing in men's minds, our present-day algebra is only a recent development.

It will be noticed that the first of these three stages includes the Golden Age of Greek mathematics. A great deal of what is now called elementary algebra—and some not so elementary—was worked out through the medium of geometry by the brilliant mathematicians at whose work we have glanced in Chapter II. Thus, by the time Euclid produced the *Elements*, the subjects of ratio and proportion had been thoroughly worked out geometrically, as had also many facts that we now express algebraically as identities. An "identity" is a special kind of equation, in which both sides balance, no matter what value may be represented by any literal number, or letter representing a number, that may occur in it. For example: $a(b + c) = ab + ac$; $(a + b)^2 = a^2 + 2ab + b^2$. These, and many other identities were proved originally by means of geometric figures and reasoning. Again, in the *Elements*, we find a geometric solution of what would now be called quadratic equations of the type $x^2 + ax = a^2$, and $x^2 = ab$. The solution is indicated, not by a number, but by a line. In the seventh and eighth books of the *Elements*, Euclid deals with what we now call the Theory of Numbers, while in the ninth book he provides a geometric treatment of series and progressions. Book X deals with numbers (treated geometrically, of course) which, as we shall shortly see, had baffled the Pythagoreans, namely, those known as "irrational" numbers. This catalogue of the contents of part of the *Elements* has been given to indi-

cate the extent to which many concepts now classified as algebraic had their origin even in the geometry of Euclid, to say
nothing of the great store accumulated by later Greeks.

Long before the time of Euclid, the Pythagoreans had laid
the foundation of the Theory of Numbers. Nowadays this
branch of mathematics is not an easy one, but it is quite easy
and interesting to find out some of the things the Pythagoreans discovered about numbers, apart from their strange and
fanciful concepts of male and female, lucky and unlucky,
divine and earthly, and so forth.

They called numbers such as 4, 9, 16 etc. "square numbers."
Figure 30 explains what they had in mind in thus classifying
certain numbers (ignore the shaded portions, for the moment).

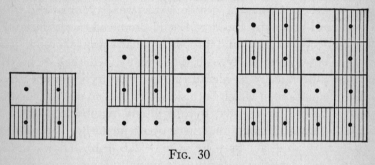

Fig. 30

Now notice some curious facts about these three "square
numbers" (the shaded portions will help you now):

The first square number, 4, is equal to the sum of the first
*two* odd numbers. That is, 1 + 3 gives the square number
whose side is *2*.

The next square number, 9, is equal to the sum of the first
*three* odd numbers. That is, 1 + 3 + 5 gives the square
number whose side is *3*.

The next square number, 16, is equal to the sum of the first
*four* odd numbers. That is, 1 + 3 + 5 + 7 gives the square
number whose side is *4*.

Now go a step further:

The sum of the first *two* odd numbers gives the square number "*two* times *two*," that is, 4.

The sum of the first *three* odd numbers gives the square number "*three* times *three*," that is, 9.

The sum of the first *four* odd numbers gives the square number "*four* times *four*," that is, 16.

The above results suggest that, to pick any number at hazard, the sum of the first *two-hundred* odd numbers would give the square number "*two-hundred* times *two-hundred*," that is, 40,000.

By algebraic reasoning it can be shown that if $n$ is a symbol standing for any number, the sum (s) of the first $n$ odd numbers will be $n$ times $n$. In other words, we say, algebraically, that $s = n^2$. By means of this "algebraic formula" we could find the sum of, say, the first thousand odd numbers without adding them or even writing them down. Here we have another simple illustration of the way modern algebraic symbolism saves time and labor. We have here a mathematical "machine tool," the formula $s = n^2$, which enables us to solve countless problems of this nature without thinking out each problem individually.

The Pythagoreans called certain numbers "triangular numbers." Figure 31 makes it clear why 3, 6 and 10 were so classified.

Now notice some curious facts connected with these three triangular numbers:

The sum of the first two numbers, $1 + 2$, gives the first triangular number, 3.

The sum of the first three numbers, $1 + 2 + 3$, gives the second triangular number, 6.

The sum of the first four numbers, $1 + 2 + 3 + 4$, gives the third triangular number, 10.

Now go a step further. Let us call each group of numbers like

1 + 2, or 1 + 2 + 3, or 1 + 2 + 3 + 4, a "series," and let us call each number in each series a "term."

Now take any one of the three "series" we have been considering. Multiply the sum of the first and last terms in any one of this kind of series by the number of terms in that series, then divide this result by 2. You will find you have the triangular number that is equal to the sum of the terms in that series.

It can be shown algebraically that for any group of con-

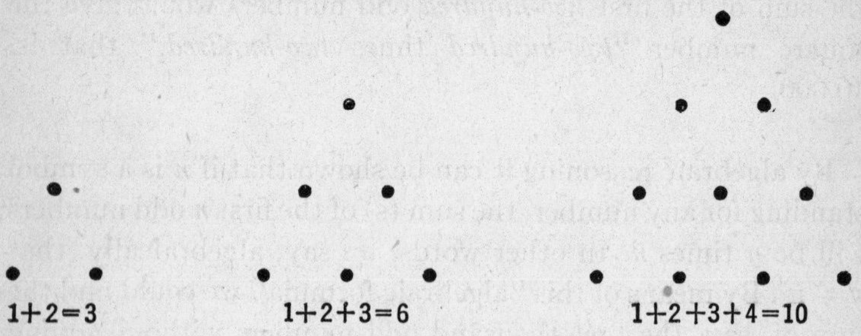

1+2=3          1+2+3=6          1+2+3+4=10

FIG. 31

secutive numbers (not necessarily beginning with 1), if *a* stands for the first number in the series, *l* for the last number, and *n* for the number of terms in the series, then the sum of all those terms (S) can be obtained from the formula $S = \frac{n(a + l)}{2}$, that is, half the answer obtained by finding *n* times the sum of *a* and *l*. Mathematicians call a series of this nature an *arithmetic progression*. Like many other mathematical concepts, it is not really as awe-inspiring as it sounds. The non-mathematical reader can see for himself how easy it is, say, to find the sum of all the numbers commencing with 600 and ending with 1400. The only point where he might trip up is in finding the value of *n*. For instance: there are 3 terms in the series 5, 6, 7. This number is *one more than the difference between the first and the last terms in the series*.

We have already begun to see how helpful the subject we call modern algebra can be.

The Pythagoreans regarded *ten* as the "perfect" number. Ten is the sum of 1, 2, 3 and 4. These numbers include the ratios giving the musical intervals discovered by Pythagoras or one of his followers. They were $\frac{2}{1}$ (the octave), $\frac{3}{2}$ (the fifth) and $\frac{4}{3}$ (the fourth). They also represented to this brotherhood a point (1), a line (2), a triangle, or plane figure (3), and a pyramid, or solid figure (4), thus:

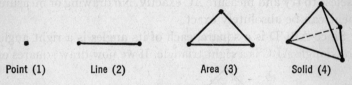

Point (1)     Line (2)     Area (3)     Solid (4)

Fig. 32

They associated certain numbers with the various Signs of the Zodiac, observing that a certain number of stars made up a shape which they thought looked like a bull, another group of stars a shape like an archer, and so on.

Thus it came about that the Pythagoreans at first believed that everything in the universe was connected in some way with a number which had something in common with every other number. Thus, they believed that any two lengths must have some definite length common to each. Thus, if a length of $3\frac{1}{2}$ inches is divided into seven equal parts, and another length, of 5 inches, is divided into ten equal parts, each of the seven equal parts and the ten equal parts will be equal to each other. In other words, $3\frac{1}{2}$ and 5 have a *common measure* $\frac{1}{2}$. It had been taken for granted that any lengths (or the numbers representing those lengths) could be expressed in the same units, provided the process of subdivision were carried sufficiently far.

Then the Pythagoreans ran up against something very mysterious and baffling to them, and something that many people still find difficult to understand, the first time they encounter it. There is no common measure for the length of a side of a square and the length of its diagonal.

We saw in Chapter II that although they may not have known the *general* proof for the "theorem of Pythagoras," they must have known the special case, when the right triangle has its two shorter sides equal in length. Let us draw a square, ABCD, having each side 1 inch long. Now let us see whether we can *calculate* the length of its diagonal AC. It is useless to try and measure AC exactly. No drawing or measurement can be absolutely exact.

Since ABCD is a square, each of its angles is a right angle. So triangle ABC is a right triangle. If we now draw squares on

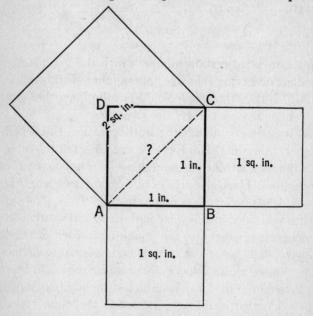

Fig. 33

AC, AB and CB, the sum of the two smaller squares will give us the area of the largest square, the one on AC. Since the area of a square is equal to its length times its breadth, the area of each of the smaller squares will be 1 times 1, or 1 square inch. So the area of the largest square, the one on AC, must be 2 square inches. Then what must be the length of the side AC of this largest square? *It must be a number which, when multiplied by itself, gives the answer 2.* But no such number can be found. We know it must lie on the number-scale somewhere between 1.41 and 1.42, to use modern notation. Or we can go further, and say that it must lie somewhere on the number-scale between 1.414 and 1.415; or further still and say it lies somewhere between 1.4142 and 1.4143, and so on indefinitely. If we conceive of the number-scale as a straight line which is marked off in equal segments by the numbers 0, 1, 2, 3 . . . we can go on subdividing that line into smaller and smaller equal parts and yet never get parts so small that they will exactly represent the number which, when multiplied by itself will give the answer 2. All this profoundly shook the Pythagoreans. They had thought that it was possible to say exactly how many times one measurement was greater than another measurement. For instance, if one line were 4 units long, and another line 1 such unit long, the first line would be 4 times the second line, or, in other words, the ratio between the lines would be $\frac{4}{1}$. But if, as it now dawned on the Pythagoreans, it was not possible to express the length of the diagonal of a square in numbers, it would not be possible to compare that length with any other length. In other words, *its length could not be expressed as a ratio, such as $\frac{4}{1}$.*

Nowadays, we call any number that can be expressed as a ratio (such as $\frac{5}{2}$, $\frac{3}{1}$, 4.8, or $\frac{48}{10}$, and so on) a ratio-nal number; any number that cannot be so expressed (such as the number which when multiplied by itself gives 2) an ir-ratio-nal number, "not ratio-nal number."

So perturbed were the early Pythagoreans at this break-down of their belief that all numbers have some common measure, that it is believed they tried to hush up the puzzling discovery and even threatened to punish with death the first member of their brotherhood who gave away their disturbing secret. Nearly 150 years passed after the death of Pythagoras before the Greek mathematician Eudoxus found a way of geometrically working problems that involved irrational numbers.

Nowadays we simply say that the length of AC in Figure 33 is "the square root of 2 inches," and we write this as "$\sqrt{2}$ inches." The symbol $\sqrt{}$ is of comparatively recent origin. To understand its origin we must first see how the word "root" came into mathematics. The Greeks did not use the expression. They spoke of the "side" of a "square number." Thus they would call 3 the "side" of the square number 9; 4 the "side" of the square number 16, and so on. As we have seen, the Arabs obtained much of their mathematics from the Greeks. When, however, they adopted the simple and convenient Hindu num-ber symbols, their own mathematical reasoning became based to a greater extent on "number" than on geometrical figures. Thus it came about that instead of speaking of the "side" of 16 being 4, they dropped the geometrical notion of a square and conceived of a number as "growing," like a plant, out of a root. Thus, 16 was conceived of as "growing" out of the "root" 4.

After a book by al-Khowarizmi on number-reckoning had become known in Europe, European mathematicians took over the Arab idea of a "root" and translated the Arabic word by the Latin *radix* (compare "radish"; "radical," one who, in his own opinion at any rate, goes to the root of every problem). They also began to speak of *extracting* or "dragging out" the root rather than of *finding* it.

Toward the end of the Middle Ages, during the stage in algebra's development when abbreviations were being introduced, this word *radix* was abbreviated to ℞, the symbol that is still used as an abbreviation for "recipe" in a medical prescription. Thus, ℞ 25 was 5. About a century before the introduction of printing we find a small r being written in place of this ℞, thus, r25 = 5, and it is thought that our modern "radical sign" $\sqrt{\ }$ is simply a copy of the small letter r as written by some copyist before printing was introduced. That is why we now write "the square root of 2" as $\sqrt{2}$.

To return to the later Pythagoreans. They found that there were countless other numbers of the same type as $\sqrt{2}$ which could not be expressed exactly in numbers. This applied to the "side" of any number that was not a "square number."

There is an interesting story connected with the name given by Greek mathematicians to numbers like $\sqrt{2}$, $\sqrt{3}$, $\sqrt{5}$, and so on. Greek mathematicians used the word *logos*, which meant "a word" and also "the mind behind a word" for any number that could be expressed as a *ratio*, such a number being one that their minds could grasp. In fact, the Greek word for "ratio" was *logos*. Any number like $\sqrt{2}$, which, as we have seen, cannot be expressed as a ratio between two numbers, was called *a-logos*, that is, "not logos," "not a ratio number." We must now jump ahead about 1000 years in order to follow up the story of *a-logos*. The Arab mathematician al-Khowarizmi made use of an Arabic translation of the work of some Greek mathematician, who naturally used the word *a-logos* in its technical sense, as indicating "not ratio-nal." Whoever translated the work into Arabic took the word *a-logos*, in its primary instead of its technical sense, as meaning "without a word," and translated it by the Arabic word meaning "deaf." So al-Khowarizmi came to call numbers like $\sqrt{2}$, $\sqrt{3}$, etc. by this Arabic word. Some three hundred years later the European translator Gherado rendered into Latin a book written by al-

Khowarizmi. He found certain numbers described in the Arabic as "deaf," so he translated this by the Latin *surdus*, "deaf." To this day we sometimes call a number like $\sqrt{2}$ a "surd," with its meaningless reference to deafness.

The story of *a-logos* numbers has taken us for a moment into the second stage of the story of algebra. Let us retrace our steps to the time of the Golden Age of Greek mathematics.

Greek mathematicians gave their Science of Numbers the Greek word *arithmētikē*, since *arithmos* meant "number," *techne*, "science." We must not be misled by our present use of the word "arithmetic" into supposing that this *arithmētikē* had any connection originally with the simple number-reckoning we now call by this name. Such number-reckoning was known as *logistic* by the Greeks and was considered by mathematicians as unworthy of their study and attention, being connected with the everyday calculations that were made on an abacus. Eventually, the title *arithmētikē*, or *arithmetica*, as it came to be written in the Middle Ages, ceased to be used for the "Science of Numbers," being replaced, as we shall see, by the Arabic word *algebra*. The title "Arithmetic" did not reappear until the eighteenth century, when, strange to say, it no longer stood for its old "superior" branch of mathematics, for it was then used for the once-despised *logistic*, or number-reckoning. Since the eighteenth century the word "arithmetic" has been used thus, in the sense that it is used today. It is possible, though not certain, that this surprising change in the meaning of a word came about through a mistake regarding its derivation. The word is sometimes found in the eighteenth century as *ars-metrica*, as though it came from the Latin *ars*, "art," *metrica*, "measuring," instead of from the Greek *arithmos*, *techne*, as we saw. Whatever may be the correct explanation of this surprising change in meaning, the word is now always connected with the elementary and practical *art of measure*.

To return to the Greek mathematicians and their work.

During the five centuries that passed after Euclid wrote the *Elements*, they began to work certain problems by using numbers rather than geometric figures. Most of these problems were the kind we should now say lead to equations. It must be remembered, however, that those who worked them had no algebraic symbolism such as we have today, but wrote out their solutions in words written in full.

There is a famous collection of ancient Greek epigrams, or short poems that usually end in a witty phrase, called the *Greek Anthology*. Among these epigrams are forty-six "number problems," some of them thought to have been written at least a thousand years before they were collected in the *Anthology* about A.D. 500. All these problems lead to one kind of equation or another. Here is one of them:

"One-third of a number of apples is to be given to one man, one-eighth to a second man, one-fourth to a third man, one-fifth to a fourth man; a fifth man is to get 10 of them, and a sixth man only 1 of them. How many apples will be required?"

If we let the symbol x stand for the unknown quantity, that is, for the number of apples required, and use our modern algebraic "shorthand" we can at once translate this problem into the equation $\frac{x}{3} + \frac{x}{8} + \frac{x}{4} + \frac{x}{5} + 10 + 1 = x$. This is very easily solved if we multiply every term in the equation by 120, the smallest number that contains 3, 8, 4 and 5 exactly, or the "lowest common multiple" of these numbers.

But a problem like this would be quite difficult if we did not have our modern symbols and methods. Right up to the seventeenth century, problems like this were worked by methods very similar to those set out in the Ahmes papyrus.

Let us glance back at the Egyptian problem we mentioned on page 65. It is even easier than the one just quoted from the *Greek Anthology*, but all the same, there is no easy way of solving it unless we use our modern symbols and methods.

Here in a brief outline is the ancient method by which the

Egyptian problem would have been solved right up to the seventeenth century. Bear in mind that our modern number-symbols and methods of computation make it much easier than it would have been before their introduction.

The Egyptian problem was to find a number such that if that number is added to one-seventh of itself, the result will be 19.

First, choose any number that seems to be likely to fit some of the given facts. In the Ahmes papyrus, the number 7 is chosen. Now see whether this number fits in with *all* the given facts. Clearly, 7 will not do for the unknown quantity, since if you add 7 to one-seventh of itself you get only 8, and not 19. But 19 is $2\frac{3}{8}$ times as great as 8, so the true value of the unknown will be $2\frac{3}{8}$ times as great as the "false" answer 7 with which we started the calculation. Now, $2\frac{3}{8}$ times 7 gives $16\frac{5}{8}$, the true value of the unknown quantity.

This method was known during the Middle Ages as the *Rule of False Position* or simply the *Rule of False*. As late as the middle of the sixteenth century the following lines appear in the *Grounde of Artes*, written by the English mathematician Robert Recorde:

> *Gesse at this woorke as happe doth leade.*
> *By chaunce to truthe you may procede.*
> *And firste woorke by the question,*
> *Although no truthe therein be don.*
> *Suche falsehode is so good a grounde,*
> *That truth by it will soone by founde.*

This method of solving an equation, by which a start is made by supposing a number (you know is most probably false) to be the true answer, was used until some three hundred years ago. Try working the "apple problem" we mentioned just now by this method, and see how long it takes.

We now pass on to the second stage in the story of algebra's growth. Round about the year A.D. 250, an Alexandrian mathematician named Diophantus was flourishing. We do not know when he was born, and we have scarcely any knowledge about his personal life except what is found in an epigram in the Greek Anthology. This says that his boyhood lasted one-sixth of his life; his beard grew after one-twelfth more; he married after one-seventh more; his son was born 5 years later; the son lived to half his father's age, and the father died 4 years after his son. How old was Diophantus when he died?

Since it would be interesting to know at least how long this mathematician lived, we had better work this problem, though we shall not use the *Rule of False* employed by all those who calculated his age during the Middle Ages!

Let the symbol x represent the number of years Diophantus lived, and let the sign $\therefore$ stand for "therefore."

$$\therefore \frac{x}{6} + \frac{x}{12} + \frac{x}{7} + 5 + \frac{x}{2} + 4 = x$$

Now multiply each term by 84, the lowest common multiple of all the denominators.

$$\therefore 14x + 7x + 12x + 420 + 42x + 336 = 84x$$
$$\therefore 756 = 9x$$
$$\therefore x = 84$$

So, if the epigram is based on fact, we do at least know that Diophantus lived to a ripe old age.

During those eighty-four years he won himself the title, given long after his death, of "the father of algebra." It is difficult to see how this claim can be substantiated. It is true that he wrote a book, the *Arithmetica*, which is unquestionably one of the world's greatest mathematical books. Some fourteen centuries later, it was to help mould the mind of Fermat, one of the greatest of French mathematicians. Originally, it consisted of thirteen parts, like Euclid's *Elements*, but only six of them have survived. It deals with number-problems which lead to equations, some of them very difficult ones, involving what we now call quadratic, cubic and bi-quadratic equations, or equations involving the second, third, or fourth power of the unknown. Many of these equations are "indeterminate," that is, they each consist of an equation which contains more than one unknown. So thorough was Diophantus in dealing with these indeterminate equations that they are still sometimes called "Diophantine." But all the same, as has been pointed out by two of the greatest authorities on Greek mathematics, Dr. Nesselmann and Sir Thomas Heath, Diophantus was by no means the first mathematician to work equations such as these. Nor can it be said that the methods he employed were responsible for modern algebraic technique; this was not developed until fifteen hundred years after his time.

The great, outstanding characteristic of modern algebra is that it provides mathematicians with a simple, concise language, in shorthand form, in which to express and clarify mathematical concepts and processes. This mathematical shorthand makes use of symbols and signs which have no outward connection, so far as their appearance goes, with the words or things they represent. It can be mastered with far less strain on the memory than can the shorthand used by a stenographer, yet it enables those who understand it to state and solve problems without using any ordinary words, except for an occasional connecting word such as "since" or "therefore." Important though the work of Diophantus was, it cannot be said that he invented such a system, though this claim is often made on his behalf. The so-called symbols used by him were merely *abbreviations*, which entirely lack the unlimited "generality" and power of our modern symbols.

As we have seen, there are three distinct stages in the story of the evolution of algebra. The first stage extended from the time of the ancient Egyptians to that of Diophantus, around A.D. 250. In this stage, the solution of a problem was written out in words and sentences in full, like a piece of prose, or a philosophical argument. During the last four centuries of this first stage in the development of arithmētikē, Greek mathematicians came to use the word *arithmos* (the Greek word for "number") for the unknown quantity in a problem, writing the word in full, where we should use a symbol like x.

Diophantus apparently grew weary of repeatedly writing the word *arithmos* for an unknown quantity; he abbreviated it to its first two letters, a, r, writing them, of course, in Greek, as αρ. Having to write this abbreviation thousands of times, in course of time he merged the letters into ῳ, then into Ϟ, and finally into ϛ. [This is the theory put forward by Sir Thomas Heath. It is not accepted by all historians of mathematics.]

Similarly, when Diophantus wanted to indicate "*arithmos* times *arithmos*," or, as we should say, the square of the unknown, he wrote the first two letters of the Greek word *dunamis*, "power" (compare "dynamite," "dynamics," "dynamo"), since he evidently regarded "*arithmos* times *arithmos*" as being more powerful than *arithmos* by itself. The Greek capital letters D, U are ΔΥ, so he wrote the abbreviation $\Delta^\Upsilon$. Thus, in his book, $\Delta^\Upsilon$ simply means ϛ times ϛ, or, as we should now say, if x is the unknown quantity, $\Delta^\Upsilon$ meant $x^2$.

Again, since the volume of a cube is its length times its breadth times its height, and since, in a cube, all these three measurements are equal, he called "*arithmos* times *arithmos* times *arithmos*" the "cube of arithmos," just as we do today. Since the Greek word for "cube" was ΚΥΒΟΣ when written in capitals, he abbreviated it to $K^\Upsilon$.

Nowadays, we call $x^2$ either "x squared" or "the second power of x." In this alternative expression we copy the lead given by Diophantus. But we now go further than he did, for we call $x^3$ not only "x cubed" but also "the third power of x"; $x^4$ "the fourth power of x," and so on. Moreover, nowadays, none of these expressions is limited to the unknown quantity;

they can all be applied to any number or *literal number*, by which we mean any letter that stands in place of some number in an algebraic expression.

Up to the time of Diophantus, the only way the Greeks had of writing "10 − 1," or "ten minus one" was ι Λειψις α. The Greek word connecting the Greek letters for 10 and 1 is *leipsis*, "lacking." Once more, Diophantus abbreviated, writing merely the first letter of this word, the (capital) Greek L,Λ. To indicate that it was an abbreviation, he put a stroke through it, and thus obtained a sign Λ, to indicate subtraction. So where we should write "10 − 1" he would write ι Λ α. We must not imagine that Diophantus thus invented a sign which corresponded completely to our modern minus sign. He could write the equivalent of "10 − 1," but "1 − 10" would have been meaningless to him. It was not until some fifteen centuries after the time of Diophantus that the concept of positive and negative quantities entered mathematics and thus gave meaning to an expression such as "1 − 10." This concept will be discussed later in this chapter.

We now must see how it came about that the word "algebra" came to be substituted for "arithmetica" as the title for the Science of Numbers. The Arab mathematician al-Khowarizmi, in addition to writing a book on Hindu-Arabic number symbols, wrote another book on the treatment of equations, basing it on the work of Greek mathematicians. He chose five Arabic words for its title, *al jabr w' al muquabalah*, "the reunion and the opposition." These words referred to the two main processes employed in solving "equation" problems, "reunion" being presumably the bringing together of terms involving the unknown quantity; "opposition" the final stage, when a "reunited" unknown quantity was faced by some number. Thus, to give a very simple illustration, if "three times a certain quantity added to half that quantity is equal to 7" we "reunite" "three times an unknown" with "half the unknown," getting "$3\frac{1}{2}$ times the unknown" and then "oppose" it to 7, getting, as we should say, $\frac{7x}{2} = 7$. Scholars differ, however, as to the exact significance of these terms.

The book was translated into Latin under the awe-inspiring title of *Ludus algebrae et almucgrabalesque* ("The school of al-jabr and al-muquabalah"). Fortunately, this fearsome title was eventually reduced to our familiar word "algebra." It is strange that an Arabic word should have taken the place of the long-established Greek word *arithmētikē*, or its Latin equivalent *arithmetica*. Although Arab mathematicians translated the works of Diophantus and other Greeks into Arabic and studied them thoroughly, they themselves contributed nothing new or original to the subject.

It is interesting to see how this Arabic word *al-jabr* also found its way into Europe through the Moors who conquered Spain. There, for centuries, it was used in a distinctly unmathematical connection. Mathematics certainly plays a very essential part in everyday life, but even the most ardent mathematician would hesitate before declaring that it could mend broken bones! Yet in Spain during the Middle Ages it was usual for a barber to call himself an *algebrista*, or bonesetter, since medieval barbers undertook bone-setting (and bloodletting) as a sideline to their regular business. Even as late as 1565, when Shakespeare was a baby of one year, an English writer, J. Halle, told his readers, "This Araby worde Algebra sygnifyeth as well fractures of bones as sometyme the restauration of the same." If the reader will recollect the meaning of "al-jabr," he will see its connection with the "restauration" of broken bones.

During the Middle Ages, at least three Latin translations of al-Khowarizmi's work on algebra were made in Europe. One was by the well-known translator Gherado, another by an Englishman, Robert of Chester. An English translation of the latter's Latin version of *al jabr w' al muquabalah* was made in 1915 by L. C. Karpinski and may be seen in large reference libraries.

The years from about 800 to about 1450, known as the Middle Ages, were marked by an almost complete stagnation of independent thought, which paralyzed mathematical progress and cast its gloom over European mathematicians as over all other thinkers. A gleam of mathematical light did indeed appear about 1200, when Leonardo Fibonacci ("the son of Bonacci") wrote a book on algebra and the Hindu-Arabic number symbols. Fibonacci was born at Pisa in North Italy, but was educated in North Africa, where his father was in charge of a custom-house. He naturally became acquainted early in life with the Arabic numerals, and in 1202 he published a book on al-Khowarizmi's *al-jabr w' al muquabalah* in which he explained the Arab number-symbols and pointed out their great advantages over Roman numerals, as well as discussing "algebra." Fibonacci calculated the value of $\pi$ as lying between 3.1410 and 3.1427, to use modern notation, a somewhat closer approximation than that made by Archimedes. He also attempted to explain the meaning of an expression such as "5 diminished by 8" which he regarded as a "debt of 3," one of the first attempts to find a meaning for what would nowadays be called a negative number. He also made use of the developments made by the Arabs in trigonometry, with which we shall deal in a later chapter.

This gleam of light, however, soon flickered out, and it was not until about the middle of the sixteenth century, in 1545 to be exact, that the darkness of medieval mathematics began to be dispelled into what was eventually to become a blaze of light surpassing by far even that of the Golden Age of Greek mathematics. From the days of Archimedes to the middle of the fifteenth century very little real advance in mathematical knowledge took place; then, almost overnight, it began to blossom forth. Between the years 1600 and 1700 the vast modern development of mathematics really got under way, and has continued ever since. How can this sudden reawakening be explained? To understand how it came about we must digress and glance at certain historical events that took place in Europe.

The second half of the fifteenth century saw the beginning of a period which was to mark the transition from the Middle Ages to modern times. It is known as the *Renaissance* period, or the period of the re-birth of independent thought and learning. Four events, in particular, though widely separated from each other at first sight, led to this emergence from the intellectual darkness of medievalism.

The first of these events was the capture of Constantinople by the Turks in 1453. When Angles, Saxons, Franks, Goths and other Teutonic tribes had burst into the Roman Empire during the fourth and fifth centuries, those of them who attacked the eastern part of that empire, which had the city of Constantinople as its capital, had been driven back.

In this city, founded in A.D. 330 by the Roman Emperor Constantine on the site of Byzantium, the culture and learning inherited by the Romans from the Greeks had been kept alive all through the Middle Ages. Its scholars had access to priceless Greek documents preserved in its well-stocked libraries, from one of which an Arab caliph had secured a copy of Euclid's *Elements*, as we saw in Chapter II.

For more than a thousand years after its foundation Constantinople had repelled invader after invader; its history during this period may almost be said to be a record of its sieges. But in 1453 the city that had so often stood firm before invaders finally fell before the attacks of Turkish hordes. Its capture produced great repercussions, both practical and intellectual, in Western Europe.

During the Middle Ages, Constantinople had become the

greatest commercial city in the world, being the gateway between East and West. That gateway was now closed, but another and greater was soon to be opened, while, in searching for it, a New World was to be discovered which was to change the course of history.

Some time during the fourteenth century, the Chinese discovery of the magnetic needle, and its application in the form of a crude mariners' compass had been introduced into Europe. No longer were seamen compelled to remain within sight of some coastline; trusting in the mysterious force we call magnetism, they now boldly headed their ships into the open seas.

In this connection, the world owes much to the enlightened foresight of an unusual type of prince. Unlike most of his kind he actually preferred to spend his life encouraging exploration and navigation rather than in slaughtering and robbing his fellow men. Although invited alike by the Pope, the Emperor and the King of England to take command of their armies, Prince Henry the Navigator of Portugal preferred to live on the rocky promontory of Sagres, in the extreme southwestern point of Portugal, in order that he might study mathematics and astronomy, thereby developing the sciences of navigation and map-making. To encourage exploration he made use of the very large revenues that were at his disposal, attracting the boldest and most skillful navigators in the world for the expeditions he organized. His main object was to find an overseas route to India by sailing around the continent of Africa. After the fall of Constantinople his efforts were redoubled, but it was not until after his death that his life-work was crowned with success. On July 8, 1497, Vasco da Gama sailed from Lisbon, sighted Natal on Christmas day (hence the name "Natal"), and finally reached India on May 20th the following year.

Before this great voyage had taken place, Europe had been

amazed and stirred by the discovery of the New World. On August 13, 1476, a young Genoese seaman of Spanish-Jewish descent swam ashore near Prince Henry's promontory of Sagres, after his corsair-ship had been sunk in a sea-fight. The young corsair, then aged twenty-five, remained for many years in Portugal, where he mastered the art of map-making, and became fired by the spirit of discovery that was than stirring Portuguese seamen and merchants. His name was Christopher Columbus. The momentous voyage of the *Santa Maria*, *Niña* and *Pinta* in 1492 was to play a great part in stimulating and broadening men's minds, and to pave the way for new discoveries, not only of land and water, but also of the intellect.

The third event which led to freedom from the fetters of medievalism also stemmed from the fall of Constantinople. This was the expulsion and flight of the many scholars who lived in that city, large numbers of them finding refuge and hospitality in Italy. They came to a Europe whose institutions, that had dominated men throughout the Middle Ages, were now decayed and discredited. The soil was ready for the development of what was best in medieval thought in the light of what was best in the thought of ancient Greece. Aided by these exiled scholars and their priceless manuscripts, Europeans began to rediscover "the glory that was Greece." In doing this, they developed a newborn confidence in their own powers and faculties of independent thought. Thus came about what is known as the revival of learning.

This revival of learning was in turn greatly accelerated by a fourth event that occurred during the latter years of the fifteenth century. This was the introduction of printing into Europe. The vast power of the printing press, combined with the substitution of paper in place of expensive parchment, led to an enormous increase in the number of books that could be distributed, and also to a corresponding decrease in their cost.

Having thus briefly glanced at the great and far-reaching

changes that were taking place in Europe around the year 1500, we are now in a better position to understand the reason why a flood of new mathematical ideas and inventions soon set in, a flood on whose broad waters now sail the proud ships Science, Engineering and Aeronautics.

The first ripple of that flood may be seen occurring in 1545. In Northern Italy, on the Ticino River stands the ancient city of Pavia. After the fall of the Roman Empire, sacked and ravaged again and again—by Attila and his Huns in the fifth century, by Lombards and Franks in the eighth, by Magyars in the tenth—the city had yet risen again and again from its ashes.

In 1501, a boy named Girolamo Cardan was born in that city, the illegitimate son of a learned lawyer. The boy was destined to achieve fame—or notoriety—as mathematician, physician, astrologer, scientist, gambler and breaker of his word. He became a student at the University of Pavia but finished his course at Padua, where he was graduated in medicine. His early efforts to build up a medical practice were so unsuccessful that he and his wife were forced to seek refuge in the poorhouse. Then fortune smiled on him; he was able to cure the child of a senator from Milan. As a mark of gratitude, the senator persuaded the authorities to let Cardan practice as a physician, permission having previously been refused on account of his illegitimate birth. Once installed in Milan as a physician, however, he spent so much time in gambling and in interests outside his profession that his practice suffered. However, he was again smiled on by fortune when he received the appointment of a professorship of medicine at Padua.

Cardan's interests, as has been said, were far from being restricted to medicine. He began to write about mathematics, and this interest led him into correspondence with a mathematician named Niccolo Fontana, better known as *Tartaglia*, "the stammerer." Tartaglia was born at Brescia in 1500.

Twelve years later, when the French captured the town, many of its inhabitants, including Tartaglia's father, were massacred in the cathedral. Young Niccolo was left for dead, but his mother managed to force her way into the charnel-house of a cathedral and carry away his mutilated body. His skull, jaws and palate were split open, but eventually his life was saved by his devoted mother, though he stammered for the rest of his days, owing to his injured palate. So poor were Tartaglia and his mother that he had to make use of tombstones as slates on which to work exercises from a book he managed to obtain. Despite the handicap of such poverty—or perhaps on account of its stimulus—he educated himself to such good effect that eventually he became a lecturer, and then a professor at Venice. While there he discovered a method of solving a cubic equation, or equation such as $x^3 + ax^2 = b$, where a and b represent constants. It was customary in his day for mathematicians to challenge other mathematicians to solve various problems. When Tartaglia announced that he could solve an equation like $x^3 + ax^2 = b$, he was challenged to a contest with an obscure person called Fiore. Each was to draw up thirty problems and hand the list to his opponent. Whichever of them solved the greater number of problems within thirty days was to receive a sum of money deposited with a lawyer. Tartaglia was presented with a group of cubic equations, for whose solution, unknown to his opponent, he had discovered a general rule. In less than two hours he solved all his opponent's problems, while his opponent failed to solve any of those drawn up by Tartaglia.

For some time, Tartaglia kept his method for solving cubic equations to himself, but after much persuasion he disclosed it to Cardan, who solemnly promised not to reveal his secret.

Some years later, to Tartaglia's understandable amazement and indignation, Cardan revealed Tartaglia's method of solution in a book called the *Ars Magna*, published at Nuremberg in 1545. A long and bitter dispute resulted. There can be no question that Cardan broke his solemn promise, even though in his book he gave Tartaglia credit for the part he had played in the matter. This will not be the last bitter and undignified quarrel between mathematicians that we shall encounter.

The *Ars Magna*, besides dealing with the solution of cubic equations, is a comprehensive treatment of the algebra known in Cardan's day. It was the first book to recognize what we now call negative roots of an equation, and the first to set forth clearly the idea of negative numbers, a subject we shall deal with later in this chapter. The book may be regarded as marking the beginning of a new era in mathematics, although it was not written in modern algebraic symbolism.

Today, we remember Cardan principally on account of his method for solving cubic equations, suggested by Tartaglia. In his own day he gained greater renown by a curious book he wrote on astrology. In the Middle Ages this subject was considered as unquestionably scientific. In many European universities of the fifteenth century the only mathematics taught was connected with this subject, although at Oxford, astronomy and not astrology was required, as well as a knowledge of the first two books of Euclid. We shall find that many extremely capable and brilliant mathematicians regarded astrology as a subject worthy of serious study right up to the eighteenth century. In England, Swift gave astrology its death-blow in a famous parody he wrote in 1708 entitled "A Prediction for the Year 1708, by Isaac Bickerstaff, Esq." But in Cardan's day, astrology was treated with respect and awe. Cardan's unscrupulous character is shown by the way he changed the birthday of Luther, whom he hated, in order to be able to give him an unfavorable horoscope.

This extraordinary man Cardan also wrote two books on natural science, both of them very widely read in his day. His views appear fantastic nowadays, but all the same he seems to have recognized the existence of a natural law behind nature.

Doubtless it was the renown he gained from his writings rather than any he may have enjoyed from his medical work that brought him to the notice of no less exalted a personage than Archbishop Hamilton of St. Andrews, Scotland. The archbishop was believed to be suffering from consumption, and Cardan was called in to give him treatment, on the strength of a statement—afterwards admitted by him to be false—that he could cure this complaint. Fortunately for the archbishop, and also for Cardan's reputation, it turned out that he was not suffering from this complaint. On his way home from Scotland, Cardan was received in London by the youthful King Edward VI, whose horoscope he obligingly cast. Unfortunately, his (doubtless) comforting and tactful predictions for the bright and prosperous future of His Royal Highness were upset quite considerably by the much-to-be-lamented death of His Majesty the very next year.

After this pleasant interlude of curing an archbishop of a disease from which he was not suffering, and showing his skill in reading the stars, Cardan's own star appears to have ceased to be in the ascendant. The rest of his life proved to be a series of disasters. His name was disgraced by his sons, one of whom was executed for murder; he gave way more and more to his mania for gambling; his mind became deranged; he lost his professorship, and, after lingering on for several years on a pension for some unaccountable reason granted him by the Pope, he died in 1576, leaving behind him scores of manuscripts, less than a fifth of which have ever been printed. Our interest in Cardan lies not so much in what he actually achieved as a mathematician, but rather in the way in which he prepared the ground for later discoveries which have obscured his own work.

Cardan's many-sided interests—ignoring the disreputable ones—are typical of many of the great mathematicians whom we shall meet in later chapters. Until the beginning of the nineteenth century, if not later, it was possible for one and the same man to keep abreast of—and, indeed, often initiate— new developments in both mathematics and science. Some of them were even able to add philosophy and theology to the list of subjects in which they excelled. Today, so vast is the field, and so highly specialized have the higher branches of mathematics and science become, that no man can hope to be an expert outside his own limited field of inquiry. Today, no man can hope to know even "a little of everything, and everything of something" concerning mathematics and science.

We have now reached the third and last stage in our story of algebra's development: the growth of modern algebraic symbolism. We must now glance at the first fruits of the awakening of independent thought as shown in the work of a veritable host of mathematicians. Fortunately for the reader, it will not be necessary to mention all their names, since their individual contributions were often not very great, though their cumulative contribution has given us our powerful algebraic symbolism which has revolutionized many branches of mathematics.

Instead of drawing up a list of modern algebraic symbols and concepts, and dealing with each in turn, it will be more interesting if we choose a few actual examples of equations as they were written in books of the sixteenth and seventeenth centuries, and discuss the symbols, etc., as they occur. These examples are taken from a long list given in Dr. D. E. Smith's monumental *History of Mathematics*, Volume II, pages 427–431, which should be consulted by the reader who wishes to have further details regarding authorship, title of book, etc.

First, let us glance at the following apparently cryptic statement, which is simply an equation written in 1559.

Let us decipher all this. First, look at the Greek letter $\rho$

(rho). This is a symbol for the unknown, corresponding to the ς symbol of Diophantus and our modern "x."

Now notice the diamond-shaped symbol ◇. This indicates the symbol $\Delta^r$ used by Diophantus, and corresponds to our

$$1 ◇ P 6 ρ P 9 [ | ◇ P 3 ρ P 2 4$$

FIG. 34

modern $x^2$, when indicating the second power of the unknown quantity.

The symbol that looks like part of a square bracket, [, is thought to be an invention of this writer. It stands for our "equals" sign.

The reader can guess the meaning of the P that occurs four times. It stands for the first letter of the Latin word *plus*, and, of course, corresponds to our symbol +, indicating the operation of addition.

So instead of the cryptic statement in Figure 34 we can write $1x^2 + 6x + 9 = 1x^2 + 3x + 24$, or, since "one $x^2$" is equally well indicated simply by "$x^2$," this can be written $x^2 + 6x + 9 = x^2 + 3x + 24$.

Our next example is taken from an Italian book written in 1572. Here it is:

$$1 ⓢ p. 8 ⓣ \text{ eguale à } 20$$

FIG. 35

Here we find no sign for "equals" but the words *eguale à* written in full. But here you will notice a big step forward has been taken toward our modern symbolism. *This writer has almost invented our modern procedure of writing the same letter with different exponents to indicate different powers of the unknown, instead of using entirely different symbols for different powers*, as we saw was done by Diophantus and right up to 1559 (see Figure 34). In the above equation, ℰ stands for our $x^6$; ℰ for our $x^3$. Elsewhere, this writer uses ℧ for x, the unknown (if we wanted to write x with an exponent we should write $x^1$); ℰ stands for $x^2$, and so on.

So Figure 35 simply represents the equation $x^6 + 8x^3 = 20$.

Now consider a third example, written by a French mathematician in 1629:

$$1(4) + 35(2) + 24 = 10(3) + 50(1)$$

You will notice at once that we now have our modern + sign indicating the operation of addition. To indicate that one number was to be added to another, writers in the Middle Ages sometimes used the Latin word *et* ("and"), as in "5 et 8." Instead of "et," the symbol or ligature "&" would sometimes be written. If this symbol is written by hand quickly it easily becomes ⅌, which we now write as +. This sign +, however, did not originate in connection with mathematics. It was used by merchants until the fifteenth century, when mathematicians first began to employ it. Previously, it was a sign used in warehouses to indicate *excess*. Thus, if a bale of goods was 2 (pounds, or whatever it may have been) overweight, and its correct weight should have been 15 pounds, the mark "15 + 2" would be written on the bale.

Secondly, it will be seen that this equation has the "equals" sign =. We can fix the exact date when this sign was first used. In a book entitled *Whetstone of witte*, the first algebra book written in English (1557), its author, Robert Recorde, explains that he has invented the symbol = "bicause noe 2 thynges can be moare equalle." This Robert Recorde studied at both Oxford and Cambridge, taking a degree in medicine at the latter university in 1545. Later, he became physician to Edward IV and to Queen Mary, while he held a government post in Ireland at some time during his career. The *Whetstone of witte* closes dramatically with the following dialogue:

*Master:* But harke, what meaneth that hastie knockyng at
the doore?

*Scholar:* It is a messenger.

*Master:* What is the message; tell me in mine eare. Yea, sir,
is that the matter. Then is there noe remedie but
that I must neglect all studies and teaching, for to
withstande those daungers. My fortune is not so
good, to have been quietly permitted to rest but a
little lōger.

Recorde was taken away and died in prison—some say for
debt, others, on account of complaints on his conduct when in
Ireland.

To return to our equation written in 1629. The numbers
written in parentheses stand for exponents indicating various
powers of the unknown. Sometimes circles were used instead of
parentheses. So the equation is simply

$$x^4 + 35x^2 + 24 = 10x^3 + 50x.$$

Now let us look at an equation written by the great French
mathematician Descartes in 1637. There are several points of
interest here. Descartes wrote:

$$yy \, \propto \, cy - \frac{cx}{b}y + ay - ac$$

The symbol $\propto$ was always used by Descartes for "equals,"
Recorde's symbol = not having been everywhere adopted in
the seventeenth century. Descartes' symbol was often used in
his day.

The next point to notice is the use of a sign for *minus,* the
Latin word meaning "smaller," to indicate the operation of
subtraction. The origin of the minus sign — is not known. It
was used by merchants to indicate a *deficiency* long before it
was used by mathematicians. Thus, "8 — 3" written on a bale
would indicate a deficiency of 3 (yards, or whatever it might
be). Clearly, no merchant would be likely to come across the
puzzling statement "3 — 8"! This would indicate that the

bale contained material that was 8 yards short of the correct
length of 3 yards, which just doesn't make sense. But mathematicians from very early times ran up against statements like
this in their process of solving "equation" problems. For
centuries they ignored such statements as being absurd. Like
the merchant, being accustomed only to the primitive number-
scale 1, 2, 3, 4, 5 . . . they were at a loss to explain such a
statement. In the *Arithmetica* of Diophantus the equation (in
modern symbols) $4x + 20 = 4$ is curtly dismissed as "absurd,"
since no number on the only number-scale known to Diophantus would serve for the value of the unknown x. Before a
statement like "$3 - 8$" could have any meaning, another
mathematical concept had to be invented: the idea of *direction*
on the number-scale. We shall deal with this aspect of *minus*
(and of *plus*) later in this chapter. All through mathematics
we find one generation labeling some idea as "absurd" just because it doesn't make sense to them. A few generations later,
the same idea is accepted as obvious. All that has happened is
that some bright individual has thought out some new line of
approach to the problem, and perhaps invented some mathematical device that makes it all crystal clear. Maybe our
grandchildren will smile in kindly incredulity when they read
that only a few extremely skilled individuals really understood Einstein's theory of relativity in 1948. As we shall see,
even the great Descartes labeled some numbers as "imaginary." Today, those numbers are no more imaginary than the
bread and butter they earn for electricians.

To return to Descartes' equation,

$$yy \not\sim cy - \frac{cx}{b}y + ay - ac$$

It will be seen that he uses more than one letter, in fact, he
uses no fewer than five letters, y, c, b, x, and a. Each of these
letters is a "literal number," or symbol standing for some
number. This form of symbolism had been introduced about

1590 by Vieta, whose work will shortly be discussed. It is customary, though not an invariable rule, to use one or more of the letters at the end of the alphabet for the unknown(s), and other letters of the alphabet for numbers, which, in any particular problem, would be known. Consider, for example, the equation $s = n^2$. This equation, as we saw, is a "pattern," or *formula*, which enables us to find an unknown quantity s, if we know the value which the literal number n represents in some particular instance. On page 69 we saw how this formula enables us to find the sum of any series of odd numbers commencing with 1. The unknown quantity is s, the required sum. The symbol $n^2$ merely tells us that, to find s, we must multiply by itself the number of terms (n) in the series we are considering. The literal number n is understood to have a kind of "elastic" value, being able to represent any number, great or small, in any particular problem. Thanks to this symbolism, algebra now supplies us with innumerable mathematical "machine tools" like this formula $s = n^2$. As has already been said, they guide our minds in working problems which, without their aid, might be cumbersome, laborious, and sometimes insoluble.

It will be noticed that Descartes does not make use of the exponent 2 in order to indicate "y times y," or the second power of y. He simply writes two y's together. Here we have one of the earliest examples of the modern procedure for indicating that two literal numbers are to be multiplied together. They are simply written together, without any intervening $+$ or $-$ sign. Thus, a times b is written as ab. Note that this algebraic method is entirely different from the arithmetic method. Although cp means c times p, yet 56 does not mean 5 times 6, since we understand that whenever we use Hindu-Arabic number symbols they represent counters on an abacus and that therefore 56 means 5 tens added to 6 units. Again, although $3\frac{1}{2}$ means $3 + \frac{1}{2}$, the algebraic cp can only mean c times p.

Descartes' method of indicating y times y by the expression yy, instead of the modern $y^2$, was often used until a couple of centuries ago. In American colleges in the eighteenth century, $x^2$ was written as xx, $x^3$ as xxx.

Let us now see how mathematicians overcame the difficulty that caused Diophantus to declare that the equation $4x + 20 = 4$ was "absurd." We shall see that the difficulty lay, not with the equation, but with the inability of the primitive number-scale to handle any but numbers starting with zero and continuing through 1, 2, 3, 4 . . . in an endless series. After being dubbed "absurd" for thousands of years, equations like the one just quoted at last came into their own, as mathematicians slowly came to realize that in many problems, the essential idea is not merely magnitude, but the *order* in which things lie. If the non-mathematically-minded reader will bear with an example that looks particularly trivial and childish, he may quickly grasp the idea of the new concept that was introduced into the primitive number-scale. By this new concept, the ideas of *direction* and *relative position* were linked to the number-scale, which was now extended into one having *no beginning* as well as no end.

Imagine we are among a crowd of onlookers watching a large hotel on fire. We hear a cry of distress. We see a would-be rescuer emerge from a sixth floor window on to the fire escape. He rushes up 18 steps, peers through a window, evidently sees nothing, and then climbs down 5 steps to look in at another window. Here we shall leave him, since, as mathematicians, we are, of course, supposed to be interested only in calculations.

Even a small child would know that the would-be rescuer is now 13 steps above his starting point. How would he know this? By working the calculation $18 - 5 = 13$. Like Diophantus, he would say that the minus sign shows that 5 is to be subtracted from 18.

But there is another, and quite different interpretation possible. The facts we have considered make it clear that in the statement $18 - 5 = 13$, the number 18 indicates an upward movement in this particular problem, and the number 5 a downward movement. *So the minus sign may be regarded as indicating that the number following it is to be measured in a direction exactly opposite to that indicated by the number 18.*

How would this idea have worked if our would-be rescuer had run 5 steps up and then 18 steps down the fire escape? We should have indicated these movements by writing $5 - 18$. This gives us the kind of problem that baffled ancient mathe-maticians. Obviously, if *minus* can only indicate subtraction, we, too, must remain baffled. But since we have agreed that a minus sign also indicates a change of direction, the statement makes sense, since it tells us that the climber, having gone up 5 steps, then took 18 steps *in the opposite direction*. But can there be any answer to "$5 - 18$"?

Well, let the would-be rescuer make his 18 downward steps in two movements, the first a downward movement of 5 steps, the second, another downward movement of the remaining 13 steps. We can now say that the number of steps from his start-ing point at which he finishes his three movements can be indicated by $5 - 5 - 13$. Clearly, the first two of these move-ments bring him back to his starting point, so the "$5 - 5$" part of the statement can be ignored, leaving the answer $-13$. So $5 - 18 = -13$. But what meaning can be attached to this $-13$? Obviously it indicates *the number of steps below his start-ing point at which the climber finishes*. If then we agree that when calculating distances up and down a ladder, or any graduated scale, a *minus* sign may indicate either a downward movement or a position below some starting point, the ex-pression $5 - 18 = -13$ has a meaning which it could not have with the elementary number-scale of arithmetic.

Now let us consider another case. Suppose the climber had run up 4 steps, paused, then run up another 7 steps. We should then calculate his final position, relative to his starting point, as $4 + 7 = 11$. What does this $+$ sign indicate? Diophantus would have answered "addition." We should now say "Yes, but it may also indicate an *upward* movement." So if we agree that a *minus* sign indicates a downward movement or a position below some fixed starting point, a *plus* sign will indicate either an upward movement or a position above that same starting point. We can now label the starting point as 0, the steps above the starting point as $+1, +2, +3, +4, \ldots$ and the steps below that starting point as $-1, -2, -3, -4, \ldots$ Numbers marked like this, with a $+$ or $-$ sign, are called *directed numbers*, or *signed numbers*. A directed number having a $+$ sign is called a *positive* number; one having a $-$ sign, a *negative* number. As we have seen, Cardan was the first mathematician to deal clearly with the meaning of negative numbers.

Let us now return to the equation $4x + 20 = 4$, which Diophantus considered "absurd." Using our new concept, it is clear that x must stand for a negative number, the number $-4$. A possible problem that would lead to this equation would be "What movement must be made by a man standing on a ladder, if four times that movement combined with twenty steps upward would bring him to a position that was four steps above his starting point?" Since the answer is "4 downward steps," we see that the equation makes perfectly good sense after all.

These directed or signed numbers may be used whenever two movements occur in exactly opposite directions. Thus, on a horizontal scale, movements to the right, or positions to the right of a fixed starting point can be indicated by positive numbers; movements to the left, or positions to the left of that starting point, by negative numbers.

Again, when a line rotates around a fixed point in a clockwise direction (the minute hand of a watch, for example) it is customary to label the angle through which it passes as being a negative quantity. When a line rotates in a counterclockwise direction, the angle through which it passes is labeled as a positive quantity. The whole concept of positive and negative is based on the idea of *movements back and forth*, or positions that result from such movements. For this reason, the development of the idea of directed numbers opened out a great new field for mathematical research, a field that was necessarily closed to earlier mathematicians who did not have this concept. It is difficult to say exactly when the modern concept of directed numbers came into being. We have mentioned that in the sixteenth century Cardan made use of negative numbers; we shall see from a quotation from Napier (page 184) that in 1614 negative numbers were regarded as indicating "less than nothing." But we shall also see that Napier definitely connected them with a point moving in a direction opposite to that in which it traced out positive numbers. It is very possible that it was this application by Napier, which appeared in a book read by every great mathematician in Europe, that led to our present concept of "directed numbers."

No story of the development of symbolism in algebra would be complete without mention of a distinguished Frenchman, François Vieta. He was born in 1540 in the old French province of Poitou. He was a wealthy man who held various legal appointments for many years, but spent his leisure time, like Thales, in the enjoyment of mathematics. Vieta was a kindly and generous person, as is shown by the fact that he once entertained a scientist for several weeks, although that scientist opposed his opinions. He even paid his visitor's traveling expenses. His generous unselfishness is shown in the way he would send copies of the mathematical papers he wrote to scholars all over Europe. A rich man, he was able to have them printed at his own expense, a procedure to which the average mathematician cannot hope to aspire.

We did not include his very important use of algebraic

symbolism among the specimens that were given a few pages back, since it did not prove to be entirely acceptable to other mathematicians. We saw, however, how Descartes (1596–1650) made use of letters of the alphabet as symbols. He owed this concept to Vieta, who by 1590 was using letters as symbols both for constant quantities as well as for the unknown(s) in an equation. But Vieta followed a rigid rule whereby the unknowns were always indicated by the vowels a, e, i, o, u (and y), while the constant quantities were always indicated by consonants. Although this rigid rule was discarded by other mathematicians, Vieta was responsible for the modern use of literal numbers, or letters that stand in the place of numbers. This fact was recognized by John Wallis (1616–1703), the distinguished English mathematician and professor of geometry at Oxford, whose work was later to influence the great Isaac Newton. In tracing the development of algebra, Wallis says that Oughtred, the English mathematician (around 1630) "who affected brevity, and to deliver what he taught as briefly as might be, and reduce all to a short view" carried Vieta's "improvement" still further. "Thus what Vieta would have written

$$\frac{A \ quadrate, \ \text{into} \ B \ cube}{CDE \ solid} \quad Equal \ to \ \text{FG} \ plane,$$

would with him [Oughtred] be thus expressed

$$\frac{\text{Aq Bc}}{\text{CDE}} = \text{FG.''}$$

Oughtred's symbolism for the mathematical concepts of "square" and "cube" would nowadays, of course, be further abbreviated, in our modern symbolism, as $\dfrac{A^2B^3}{CDE} = FG$.

We shall meet Vieta again when we discuss the developments that took place in trigonometry during the second half of the sixteenth century. In algebra, he not only improved the symbolism in the way we have seen, but wrote an important book on algebra called *In Artem Analyticam Isagoge,* "An Introduction to the Art of Analysis [algebra]," the earliest work on symbolic algebra, and another book on the theory of equations, which was not published until after his death. He was the first to give a formula for the sum of what we now call an infinite convergent series such as

$$1 + (\tfrac{1}{4}) + (\tfrac{1}{4})^2 + (\tfrac{1}{4})^3 + \ldots + (\tfrac{1}{4})^n + \ldots$$

This actual series, or rather, its equivalent, had been solved in geometric form by Archimedes. Vieta's formula enables any such series to be summed. Thus, if a is the first term, and r the common ratio, or ratio between any term and its immediately preceding term, then (in modern symbolism)

$$a + ar + ar^2 + ar^3 + \ldots + ar^n + \ldots = \frac{a}{1 - r},$$

where r is a fraction (less than 1). Vieta was thus one of the first mathematicians to see that certain algebraic statements have a distinct "pattern," just as geometric figures have their own pattern. This was to lead to important developments in the seventeenth and subsequent centuries.

He was the first to show that the value of $\pi$ could be found from a *formula* instead of from a complicated geometric figure. He gave the remarkable formula

$$\frac{2}{\pi} = \sqrt{\tfrac{1}{2}} \cdot \sqrt{\tfrac{1}{2} + \tfrac{1}{2}\sqrt{\tfrac{1}{2}}} \cdot \sqrt{\tfrac{1}{2} + \tfrac{1}{2}\sqrt{\tfrac{1}{2} + \tfrac{1}{2}\sqrt{\tfrac{1}{2}}}} \ldots$$

The development of algebraic symbolism paved the way for the development of *analysis,* the most fundamental element in modern mathematics. It is difficult to define the precise boundary between arithmetic and algebra. Possibly the essential difference between the two subjects may best be suggested by a simple illustration. In the first place, the area of a rectangle 4 inches long and 3 inches high would be found by dividing that particular rectangle into squares, each 1 square inch in area, there being three rows of squares, each row containing four squares. The next mental step would be to note that in this particular problem, all the intermediate steps could be omitted and the same result obtained by multiplying together the numbers 4 and 3. Then comes the transition to algebra. Attention is now directed, not to the figures 4 and 3, but to the essential *process* followed, namely, that if A stands for the area of a rectangle in square units, and l and h respectively for its length and height in corresponding linear units, then the area of *any* rectangle will be indicated by the formula, or rule A = lh.

The analysis of the problem has revealed the essential process that lies behind the solution of all such problems. A generalization that is founded on rigorous analysis may be accepted as true in all cases. It is this kind of analysis that lies behind modern mathematics. Without the aid of the symbolism we have been discussing, it would often be impossible to express concisely the abstract processes that lie behind arithmetical examples of those processes. Symbolic mathematical shorthand, the language of algebra, enables extremely complicated processes and concepts to be expressed in a concise and simple manner that is easily and quickly grasped by the mind once this "algebraic language" has been mastered.

The reader may have noted that Vieta called his book on algebra "An Introduction to the Art of Analysis." Vieta disliked the term "algebra" and wished to substitute "analysis." This suggestion, however, was not fully followed. Today, the word "analysis" is used for certain branches of higher mathematics such as the calculus.

We have now traced the development of algebra to the stage at which analysis enters. In subsequent chapters we shall discuss the work of other mathematicians in developing such analysis and in applying algebraic concepts and symbolism to other branches of mathematics.

## *A NOTE ON EQUATIONS, FOR THE UN-MATHE-MATICAL READER.*

A mathematical statement such as $3x + 1 = x + 5$ is known as an *equation*, since the value of the expression on the left-hand side is *equal to* that of the expression on the right-hand side.

Imagine a pair of scales having two weights in the left-hand pan, one of them marked "3x ounces," the other "1 ounce." In the right-hand pan are two other weights, one of them marked "x ounces," the other "5 ounces."

Now imagine that the weights on the left balance those on the right, as indicated in the given equation. It will readily be seen that any of the following processes can now be applied *without disturbing this balance:*

1. An equal weight can be added to each side.
2. An equal weight can be subtracted from each side.
3. The whole of each side can be multiplied by any number (if x ounces balance 5 ounces, then 3x ounces must balance 15 ounces)
4. The whole of each side can be divided by the same number.
5. The square root of each side may be taken. (This applied to any root).

We can now "solve" the equation $3x + 1 = x + 5$, that is, we can find the value (or values) of x that will make $3x + 1$ equal to $x + 5$. Thus:

$$3x + 1 = x + 5$$

$\therefore 2x + 1 = \quad 5$ [By applying (2) and subtracting **x** from each side]

$\therefore 2x \quad = \quad 4$ [By applying (2) and subtracting 1 from each side]

$\therefore \ x \quad = \quad 2$ [By applying (4) and dividing each side by 2]

The number 2 is said to be the "root" of this particular equation, or the value that "satisfies" this equation.

Remember that a *minus* sign means "diminished by." Thus, $2x - 9$ means "9 less than whatever may be the value of $2x$." So if we add 4 to $2x - 9$ the result will be $2x - 5$; if we subtract 4 from $2x - 9$ the result will be $2x - 13$.

Remember that the square root of a number is the number which, when multiplied by itself, will give that number. When the reader has read the section on "directed numbers" he will see that the product of two negative numbers is a positive number. So the square root of 9 is not only $+3$, it is also $-3$, since $-3$ times $-3$ equals $+9$. These two results are indicated as follows:

$\sqrt{9} = \pm 3$, read "the square root of nine equals plus or minus 3."

# CHAPTER IV

# The Development of Trigonometry

TRIGONOMETRY, as we know the subject today, is a branch of mathematics that is linked with algebra. As such, it dates back only to the eighteenth century.

When treated purely as a development of geometry, however, it goes back to the time of the great Greek mathematician-astronomers who flourished some two hundred years before and after the commencement of the Christian era.

If regarded simply as "tri-angle-measurement," which is all the *word* tri-gono-metry implies, its roots go back to Egyptian days four thousand years ago. This title, however, was not given to the subject until 1595, when it was first used by a mathematician named Pitiscus.

It is obvious that the builders who constructed the Pyramids of Egypt must have been familiar with triangle-measurement. However, the Egyptians do not appear to have had more than the practical working knowledge of the geometric properties of triangles, etc., which we discussed in Chapter II. It cannot be said that they invented anything that can definitely be regarded as trigonometry. It is true that in the Ahmes papyrus there is a reference to a *seqt*, or *seqet*, a word whose meaning is obscure. Some think this *seqt* corresponded to a certain trigonometric concept, but there is no definite evidence to support this conclusion. The *seqt* was probably a geometric measurement which made sure that the faces of a pyramid in course of construction all arose at the same desired slope with the base.

We can, however, associate the Egyptians with the discovery of certain facts, connected with shadows, which, centuries later, were to form the basis of trigonometric discoveries and inventions by Arab mathematicians. These facts were originally discovered in the course of observations of the shadows cast by the brilliant Egyptian sunshine. We shall meet them in due course.

In order to trace the story of trigonometry from its real, geometric, beginnings we must commence by glancing at the contributions made to the subject—directly or indirectly—by four mathematician-astronomers, Aristarchus, Hipparchus, Menelaus and Ptolemy, whose work marks the definite beginning of what we mean by trigonometry.

Ever since thinking man has been on the earth he has been striving to solve the riddle of the universe. We have seen that men were led to study the properties of spheres and circles as through long centuries they watched the ceaseless procession of the stars, which seemed to them to be imbedded in a spangled curtain that was continually being drawn across a vast celestial sphere. We have seen how Greek geometry reached its culminating point with Archimedes and Apollonius, and how through the medium of this geometry a great store of knowledge about the Science of Numbers was accumulated, which was later to be equipped with algebraic symbolism.

After the death of Archimedes, no further progress in "pure" mathematics (mathematics that is not applied to some other branch of science) was possible, however, until quantities had ceased to be tied to geometric figures, and the restrictions thus imposed had been lifted by the application of modern algebraic analysis to the development of mathematical concepts and processes. As we have seen, that day was to wait for many centuries. Meanwhile, mathematicians turned their attention to the application of geometric knowledge to the field of astronomy, a branch of science that is completely dependent on mathematics.

In 280 B.C., one of these mathematicians, a Greek named Aristarchus of Samos, made an observation of the summer solstice that was mentioned—and made use of—by the astronomer Hipparchus, 145 years later. Thanks to this clue, we can fix the approximate date when Aristarchus lived. It is thought that he was about twenty-five years older than Archimedes, and a little younger than Euclid. Today, he is remembered as astronomer rather than as mathematician, since it was he who first concluded that it was the earth that revolved around the sun, and not, as was universally believed, the sun around the earth. To the Greeks of his day, however, Aristarchus was known as "the great mathematician," while the writer Vitruvius includes him among the few great men possessing a profound knowledge of geometry, astronomy, music and all other branches of "science."

Only one book of his survives, a work *On the Sizes and Distances of the Sun and Moon*, and it is only through the *Sand Reckoner* of Archimedes that we know of his theory of the earth's movements. This intriguing title for a mathematics book relates to an attempt made by Archimedes to estimate the number of grains of sand in the universe; incidentally, it gave him an opportunity to use his newly invented method of writing very large numbers. In discussing the universe, Archimedes tells us about the theory of Aristarchus, who disagreed with Aristotle and those who held that the earth was the fixed, unmoving center of the universe, as it appears to be. He tells us that Aristarchus declared "that the fixed stars and the sun remain unmoved, that the earth revolves about the sun in the circumference of a circle, the sun lying in the middle of the orbit." If we substitute "ellipse" for "circle" we have here our modern theory of the movement of the earth, a theory which illustrates the dictum laid down by the philosopher Parmenides, a follower of Pythagoras, about 500 B.C., that the evidence of our senses is less reliable than the evidence of logical reasoning.

Aristarchus was born eighteen centuries before his time; not until 1543 were his views to be vindicated by fellow scientists, not until some considerable time later were they to be accepted by men in general.

In 1499, a German student, whose father had originally been a Polish citizen, graduated in medicine at the University of Padua where Cardan was to follow in his steps a few years later. The student, Nicolaus Copernicus, whose real name was Nicolaus Koppernigk, attended courses in mathematics (largely astronomy in those days) as well as in medicine. It may seem incredible to those familiar with modern courses in medicine and mathematics that any one student could graduate in both these subjects. It must be remembered, however, that in the fifteenth century the amount of knowledge to be acquired was relatively very small, compared with that of today. Moreover the only requirement for graduation in those times was attendance at lectures; there was no searching examination of students. There is no question, however, that Copernicus mastered mathematics and astronomy, for not only does he rank today as one of the great astronomers of all time, but he earned his bread and butter as a professor of mathematics.

In 1543 Copernicus lay on his death-bed. Just before he lapsed into complete insensibility a newly printed book was placed in its dying author's hands. It was the book—today world famous—in which he had revived the theory of the movement of the earth that had been laid down by Aristarchus nearly three hundred years before the beginning of the Christian era. During the intervening eighteen centuries men had clung to the opinion held by Aristotle.

The Copernican System, as it is called (though if justice were done, it would be called the System of Aristarchus), was not generally accepted for many years after the death of Copernicus in 1543. For one thing, it is contrary to the apparent evidence of our senses; for another, the Roman Catholic Church did its utmost to suppress it, even forcing the great Galileo, on June 22, 1633, to withdraw his support of the "new" theory under threat of torture by the Inquisition. Certain scholars of that Church admitted the truth of this theory, but feared that the faith of their followers would be weakened should they learn that man is not the center of all things in the universe.

Shakespeare evidently still held to the view of Aristotle in 1596, when he wrote *The Merchant of Venice*, for he makes Lorenzo say to Jessica

". . . Look how the floor of heaven
Is thick inlaid with patines of bright gold.
There's not a star that thou behold'st
But in his motion like an angel sings."

Such, then, is the main ground for the respect and admiration in which we hold the name of Aristarchus of Samos today. His mind, eighteen centuries ahead of his time, is yet another example of the brilliant independence and originality of ancient Greek thought and scholarship.

In this chapter, however, our main interest in "the great mathematician" lies in the methods he used in an attempt to calculate the relative distances of the sun and moon from the earth. Although his final conclusions were inaccurate, owing to the crude instruments at his disposal, the method he employed involved calculations which paved the way for the development of the first real trigonometric concept.

His method was based on his realization of the fact that since "moonlight" is merely a reflection of the sun's rays, the respective centers of the sun, of the moon, and of the earth must lie at the corners of a triangle that will be right-angled at the moon's center *when half the moon is visible from the earth*.

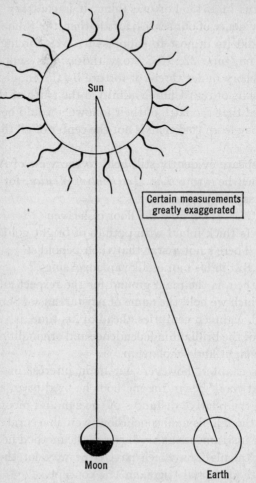

[The distance between earth and moon is enormously exaggerated for the sake of clarity. The angle at the center of the sun should be only one-sixth of one degree, approximately.]

FIG. 36

Choosing an early morning when the moon, so far as he could judge, was exactly half-visible, Aristarchus estimated the size of the angle at the earth's center that lay between imaginary lines joining that center to the centers of sun and moon. With his crude instruments he estimated that it was, as we should say, 87 degrees [it should have been 89 degrees 42 minutes]. Using the geometry of Euclid, he easily calculated the other acute angle in the triangle to be 3 degrees.

Armed with these facts, he then proceeded by a masterly and complicated application of Euclidean geometry to calculate that the distance of the sun from the earth is more than eighteen times, but less than twenty times the distance of the moon from the earth. Owing to the inaccuracy in the measurement of the angle, his result is far from the truth [the sun is 388 times farther away from the earth than is the moon], but what interests us is that his remarkable geometric reasoning made use of concepts which we now describe as trigonometric. Using only geometric notions of angles (expressed as fractions of right angles), arcs of circles and chords in circles, he virtually employed the modern concepts of circular measure and of values that nowadays would be expressed in trigonometric language. Mathematically-minded readers who would be interested to see these elaborate calculations (and others connected with the size of the sun and of the moon) will find a translation of them set out in *A History of Greek Mathematics* (Volume II), by Sir Thomas Heath.

So much for Aristarchus "the great mathematician." We now come to the real inventor of trigonometry, Hipparchus, who is regarded as the "father" of this subject.

We are ignorant of most of the events in his life, except for knowing that he was born at Nicaea in Bithynia (the city where a famous church council was to meet some four and a half centuries later to draw up the "Nicene" creed, still familiar to church people today), and that the years when most of his work was done were those between 161 B.C. and 126 B.C. As is the case of so many of the really great men of antiquity, he was not considered worthy of inclusion in Plutarch's *Lives*, which were practically limited to lives of warriors, politicians and orators. Had Hipparchus been expert in any of these deeply respected occupations he would doubtless be included among some heroes whose memory Plutarch saved from well-merited oblivion. Being merely the greatest astronomer of antiquity and the father of trigonometry, he naturally was not among Plutarch's candidates for immortality.

Since most of the books written by Hipparchus have perished, we have to form our estimate of his greatness from references to his work made by other mathematicians and astronomers. One of these, Ptolemy, whom we shall shortly meet, made use of a catalogue of fixed stars, more than 800 in number, the position of each of which in the celestial sphere had been fixed by Hipparchus by calculating celestial angular measurements that correspond to latitude and longitude on earth. This Ptolemy was a mathematician, astronomer and geographer who must not be confused with the king who lived some four hundred years before his day, and who founded the great library at Alexandria.

Had the Roman masters of Europe paid greater attention to a discovery made by Hipparchus, much trouble and confusion for their successors might have been averted. In 135 B.C. he detected an error in the number of days allocated to the calendar year, which should coincide as nearly as possible with the solar year, that is, with the number of times the earth spins round on its axis while making one complete orbit of the sun. It makes no difference to this calculation, of course, whether the view of Aristarchus or that of Aristotle is held; Hipparchus, like all subsequent astronomers up to the time of Copernicus, accepted the mistaken opinion of Aristotle.

No one knows who first discovered that the noontime shadow of an upright rod is longest at the winter solstice (see page 50) and shortest at the summer solstice. Although the historian Herodotus tells us that the Greeks obtained their knowledge of a sundial from the Babylonians, it is known that this instrument was used by the Egyptians as early as 1500 B.C. for recording the passing of time, to use an expression that conflicts with most philosophical concepts of "time." By keeping a record of the number of days that elapsed while the shadow cast by an upright rod passed from its shortest to its greatest length and then back again to its shortest length, ancient peoples learned to measure the length of the year—one of the roots from which astronomy sprang—while observations of the hour-by-hour movement of the shadow enabled them to measure the daily passing of time.

We still call the "rod" on a sundial the *gnomon*. This word has had a long and varied history. It was given by the Greeks to the "rod" on a sundial because it "gave them knowledge" about the passing of time. *Gnomon* is derived from the Greek word meaning "to know," which is also found in our word "a-*gnostic*," "one who does not know (whether God exists)." Then the word came to be applied to an instrument used by mathematicians for drawing lines at right angles to each other—this time, a reference to the relative position of a sundial's gnomon and its shadow. Later, the word was used, in the form "gnomon-wise," where we should use the word "perpendicular." Still later, the Pythagoreans used it to describe each L-shaped odd number that helped to build up each "square number" such as 4, 9, 16 and so forth (see Figure 30, page 68).

Hipparchus knew that Aristarchus had made an observation of the hour when the shadow of the *gnomon* was shortest, namely, at the summer solstice in the year 280 B.C. Hipparchus, 145 years later, found that the summer solstice in 135 B.C. occurred some eleven hours earlier in calendar time that it would have done if each of the intervening 145 years had coincided with $365\frac{1}{4}$ calendar days, the then-accepted length of the year.

From this observation he calculated that the solar year coincided with 365 days, 5 hours, 55 minutes, 12 seconds. With modern instruments of precision it is found that he was only 6 minutes 26 seconds out, the time required for a complete orbit of the sun being 365 days, 5 hours, 48 minutes, 46 seconds.

When, in 46 B.C., Julius Caesar, the Roman dictator, reformed the calendar, the discovery made by Hipparchus was ignored both by Caesar, an amateur astronomer himself, and by Sosigenes, the astronomer who "assisted" him. They allocated 365 calendar days to each "common" or ordinary year, and one extra day to every fourth year, thus assuming there were exactly 365¼ days in each solar year. Incidentally, Julius Caesar managed to secure immortality on this occasion, at any rate, by changing the name of the fifth Roman month from *Quintilis* to *Julius*, hence our name "July." He also decreed that the year should commence with *Januarius*, originally the eleventh Roman month, instead of with March. This accounts for the contradiction in terms of the names *September*, *October*, *November* and *December* for our ninth, tenth, eleventh and twelfth months, when they *mean* seventh, eighth, ninth and tenth, respectively. Incidentally again, the successor of Julius Caesar, the Emperor Augustus Caesar, not to be outdone, modestly persuaded the Senate to substitute his name for *Sextilis* which had been the sixth Roman month, hence our "August." Those who despise Latin and the classics would probably be surprised if they knew how much Latin they speak every day, and how much history lies hidden in words.

Because the Julian calendar, as it is called, ignored the discovery of Hipparchus that the solar year was a little less than 365¼ days, the *vernal equinox*, a day in March when night, *nox*, is equal, *equi*, to day, began to creep back on the calendar.

In 1582, in order to restore the vernal equinox to its proper place in the calendar, Pope Gregory XIII reformed the Julian calendar, omitting ten days in a single block. It was not until

1752 that English prejudice against change—witness today the prejudice of the English-speaking peoples against changing their medieval weights and measures to the simple, time and labor-saving metric system—was finally overcome. By that time it was necessary to omit eleven days, one more than had had to be omitted in 1582, September 2, 1752 being immediately followed by September 14th, 1752. This naturally led to riots in England, where a warm reception awaits (or used to await) the government official who tries to interfere in a man's private life. Maybe there were even more non-mathematically-minded English then than there are today; anyhow, large numbers of them decided they were being robbed of eleven days of their lives. So they rioted, raising the slogan "Give us back our eleven days."

It was not until the end of World War I that Russia could be persuaded to fall in line with other nations and abandon the Julian calendar. They then had to omit the unlucky number of thirteen days in order to bring their calendar in line with that of more co-operative nations. All this trouble, confusion and mental distress could have been avoided if only Julius Caesar had paid greater respect to the discovery made by Hipparchus, and followed it up.

To prevent future errors, the Gregorian calendar laid down that, as in the Julian calendar, every year whose number is exactly divisible by 4 should be a "leap year," having one extra day tacked on to February (surely "pause year" would have been a more appropriate title?), but that, in order to take into account the (corrected) calculation made by Hipparchus in 135 B.C., a centennial year should only be a "leap" year if it were a multiple of 400. Thus, 1600 was a leap year, 1700, 1800 and 1900 were *not* leap years, 2000 will be a leap year, and so on. Even this does not quite square matters. By the year 4905 the calendar year will have crept a whole day away from the true solar year and something will have to be done about it.

All this discussion of the calendar error has taken us far away from the days of Hipparchus, who first pointed it out. Possibly, however, the discussion has brought home to some non-mathematically-minded readers one of the many essential services rendered by mathematics to civilization. Without this Queen of the Sciences our lives would be lived in chaos and uncertainty.

This is not the place in which to discuss the more technical and complicated details of the astronomical discoveries made by Hipparchus. Some of them, especially that which concerns the "precession of the equinoxes" were of such great importance that they gained for him the reputation of being the greatest astronomer of antiquity. [The earth, not being a perfect sphere, but a slightly unbalanced spheroid, wobbles on its axis as it rotates. This wobble causes a slow, continuous change in the direction of the earth's axis, and therefore of its equator, known as *precession* ("going ahead"). Hipparchus estimated that this change in direction amounted—as we should say—to .0102 degrees every year: today we estimate that it is .0156 degrees every year.]

We now come to the invention of trigonometry by Hipparchus, a stroke of genius to which we owe even more than we do to his astronomical discoveries. It all arose out of the measurement of chords in a circle.

Our word "chord," indicating a straight line joining two points on a circle, comes from the Latin word *chorda*, which meant a bowstring, before being taken over by medieval mathematicians. *Chorda* in turn had come into Latin from the Greek *chordē*, which meant, primarily, the intestine of an animal, and then either the gut used for a string on a musical instrument such as a lyre, or the string by which an arrow was shot from a bow. The bow itself was called *arcus* in Latin, and medievalists also took over this word to describe any part of the circumference of a circle. We still call such curved line an "arc" in consequence.

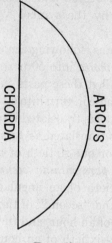

Fig. 37

We are told by Theon of Alexandria (a mathematician who lived toward the end of the fourth century A.D., and whose daughter Hypathia was murdered by a "Christian" mob on account of her knowledge of "pagan" science) that Hipparchus wrote a treatise on "chords in a circle." This work, he says, filled twelve books, that is, parchment rolls. In a book called the *Syntaxis*, or *Almagest*, as it became known to the Arabs and to medieval Europeans, Ptolemy explains how the lengths of chords were calculated in his day. He doubtless obtained his methods from Hipparchus. *The length of a chord was connected with the size of the arc whose ends it joined.* Thus, as we shall see, the length of a chord came to be connected with an *angle*.

Let us first see how the size of an arc was measured. Suppose a radius to make one complete turn, or revolution. In doing this, it was considered to have made 360 "steps"; each "step" was called by the Greeks a *moira*, or "part," by medieval mathematicians a degree (*de-gradus*, "a step away from"). The connection between a degree and a complete revolution, or circle, was indicated by the symbol ° chosen for the word "degree(s)."

Greek mathematicians, following the example of the Babylonians, divided each *moira* into 60 parts. Ptolemy, whom we shall shortly meet, called these parts "first small parts." He then divided each of these in turn into 60 "second small parts." When Ptolemy's book was translated into Latin, his Greek for "first small part" was translated as *pars minuta prima*, hence our word "minute" for one-sixtieth of a degree; his "second small part" became *pars minuta secunda*, hence our word "second" for one-sixtieth of an angular minute. Hence also our words "minute" and "second" of time, for the "first small part," or one-sixtieth of an hour, and the "second small part," or one-sixtieth of one-sixtieth of an hour. Hence also the abbreviation for "first small part," one stroke, thus ′ and for "second small part," two strokes, thus ″. [These Babylonian sub-divisions were also used by the Greeks for sub-divisions of other units besides those connected with angular measure.]

Now let us see how a connection was found between the size of an arc and an *angle*. Figure 38 shows three concentric circles, or circles having the same center, here marked O.

Imagine a line OP rotating in a counter-clockwise direction from an initial position OX to the position shown in Figure 38. Let us suppose that OP has then moved through one-sixth of a complete turn or revolution. The measure of arc AB, and of arc CD, and of arc EF would then be given by this same angle, namely, one-sixth of 360 *moirai*, or degrees, each of these arcs having the same *angular* measurement, although their *linear* measurements would obviously all be different. If, however, the chords AB, CD and EF were drawn in Figure 38, the units in which their linear measurements were taken by the Greeks would vary in like proportions as the linear measurements of the arcs.

The unit of length in which a chord was measured was obtained from the diameter *of its own circle*. This diameter was divided into 120 parts. Thus, if a chord were half the length of the radius of its own circle, it would be said to contain 30 parts, and so on. Now the circumference of a circle, or an arc of 360

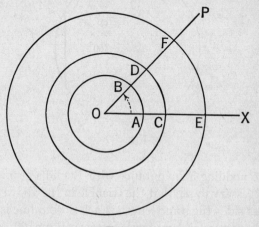

Fig. 38

degrees, is always $\pi$ times the length of the diameter of that circle. So it was possible to draw up a table giving the lengths of chords, as so many "parts" of a diameter, and connecting each of those lengths with the size of the arc whose ends were joined by the chord in question, the arc-measurement being in angular units.

Instead of speaking of *moirai*, we shall in future speak of "degrees," while we shall always indicate the size of an arc by the number of degrees, etc., it subtends at the center of its circle.

Armed with these definitions and explanations we are now in a position to understand how Hipparchus drew up his first

"Table of Chords in a Circle." Let us commence with a very simple example: that of the length of a chord joining the ends of an arc that subtends an angle of 60° at the center of its circle. We will indicate the length of this chord by the abbreviation "crd. 60°."

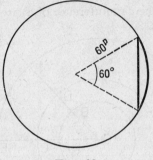

FIG. 39

A mere nodding acquaintance with Euclid's geometry is all that is necessary to see that the triangle in the above figure has each of its sides the same length. Each dotted line is a *radius*, or half-diameter, and must therefore contain 60 of the 120 "diameter-units" used by the ancient Greeks. So the length of the chord, being here equal to the radius, will be 60 diameter units. If we agree to indicate these units, or "parts" of a diameter by a small p written above and to the right of a number, we can express this result as

$$crd\ 60° = 60^p$$

We will spare the reader the more complicated geometry required in some of the calculations that follow. If, however, he remembers with enjoyment the geometry he learned at school, he may care to amuse himself by checking (by Euclidean geometry) the accuracy of the results obtained by Hipparchus (or Ptolemy?) more than twenty centuries ago. After an hour or so he may begin to hold the genius of Hipparchus and other Greek mathematicians in still greater respect.

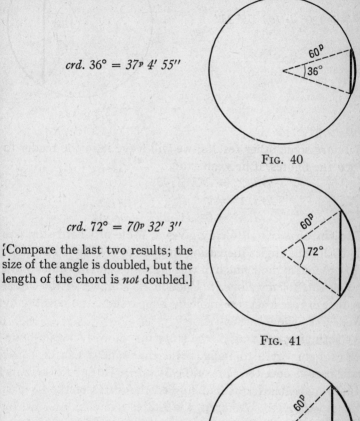

*crd.* 36° = *37ᵖ 4′ 55″*

Fig. 40

*crd.* 72° = *70ᵖ 32′ 3″*

[Compare the last two results; the size of the angle is doubled, but the length of the chord is *not* doubled.]

Fig. 41

*crd.* 90° = *84ᵖ 51′ 10″*

Fig. 42

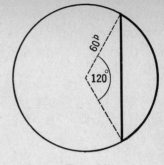

$$crd. \ 120° = 103^p \ 55' \ 23''$$

FIG. 43

Here are some other results; we will leave it to the reader to draw the figures, if he wants to:

$$crd. \ 2° = 2^p \ \ 5' \ 40''$$
$$crd. \ 1° = 1^p \ \ 2' \ 50'' \ (nearly)$$
$$crd. \ \tfrac{1}{2}° = 0^p \ 31' \ 25'' \ (nearly)$$

In the *Syntaxis*, Ptolemy gives a Table of Chords for arcs that subtend angles increasing from $\tfrac{1}{2}°$ to $180°$ by steps of $\tfrac{1}{2}°$. We cannot say how much of this ingenious and laborious work is due to Ptolemy himself. Undoubtedly, much of the initial spade work, at least, was done by Hipparchus, and possibly by Menelaus, whom we shall shortly meet.

Continuing our trail of the story of "chords," we find ourselves transported to India. Some three and a half centuries have passed since the time of the *Syntaxis*. During those years, Hindu mathematicians had studied the works of the Greeks, and especially the *Almagest*, the Arabic name, as we saw, by which Ptolemy's *Syntaxis* was known in the Middle Ages. They knew the Greek method of calculating the length of a chord and doubtless obtained from it an idea that led, as we shall now see, to an important trigonometric development.

We must now make the acquaintance of the Hindu mathematician-astronomer Aryabhata. He was flourishing in A.D. 500 at Patalipatua on the Upper Ganges in India, where he made many complicated calculations that we should now describe as being rather of an arithmetical or algebraic nature than purely geometric, advancing the study of *arithmētikē* in certain respects.

In trigonometry, Aryabhata made two very far-reaching changes in his calculations of the lengths of chords in a circle. First, he substituted the length of a *half-chord* for that of a chord; secondly, he used the same unit of measurement for the arc (that is, the angle at the center of the circle), the radius, and the half-chord, using angular minutes for each.

How is it possible to use angular measure for the length of a straight line? Well, just imagine a piece of string equal in length to the radius of a circle placed on the circumference of its circle. The angle at the center of the circle subtended by the ends of the string will be equal to the angular measure of an arc equal in length to the radius. How could this angular measure be calculated? It all hinged on knowing the value of $\pi$, which we first discussed on page 60. [Note that this Greek letter was not used for this ratio until early in the eighteenth century.]

It had been known from very early days that there was a connection between the length of the diameter of a circle and its circumference. The Babylonians and the Hebrews seem to have muddled along as best they could by assuming that $\pi$, the number of times the diameter is contained in its own circumference, was equal to 3. Thus, in the Old Testament (1 Kings, VII, 23) there is a description of a "molten sea," presumably a metal basin of some kind, whose dimensions are given as "ten cubits from the one brim to the other . . . and a line of thirty cubits did compass it round about." The same dimensions of this same "molten sea" are given again in 2 Chronicles, IV, 2. The Egyptians knew better than this, even by the time of the Ahmes papyrus, and therefore presumably by 2200 B.C. They found, doubtless by actual measurement, that, as we should say, the value of $\pi$ was 3.1605. Archimedes, as we saw in Chapter II, was able to calculate the value of $\pi$ as lying between 3.140 and 3.142, to use modern notation. Aryabhata came even nearer the true value of $\pi$, calculating this to be $\dfrac{62832}{2000}$, or 3.1416 as we should say today.

Knowing that the circumference of any circle is approximately 3.1416 times the length of its diameter, or 6.2832 times its radius, it is a simple matter to divide 21,600, the number of minutes in the 360° measure of the whole circumference, by this 6.2832. The answer will be the approximate number of angular minutes in an arc (of *any* circle) equal in length to the radius of that circle. In this way Aryabhata found that the approximate angular measure of the radius of any circle was 3438 angular minutes, a value that will suggest to mathematical readers the familiar, and more exact 57°17′ 44.8″ or 3437.747′ of our modern "radian."

In order to understand Aryabhata's use of a *half-chord*, the non-mathematical reader is advised to study Figure 44 carefully. It is important that he should do so, since Aryabhata's method is the one which, with modifications, is followed today. The all-important point, from the modern standpoint, is that Aryabhata introduced a *right triangle*. It is this right triangle that is the basis of all our present "trigonometric functions."

Instead of considering the length of the chord that is connected with, say, an angle of 30°, as the Greeks would have done, Aryabhata found the length of half the chord that subtended an angle of 60° at the center of the circle. He then associated that length with half the angle, namely, with 30°.

It will be seen from Figure 44 that this half-chord is not equal to the length of a chord XY that would be formed if the ends of the arc of 30° were joined. So there is a much greater difference than appears at first sight between a Hindu (and modern) half-chord, used trigonometrically, and the Greek "chord" of Hipparchus and Ptolemy. The half-chord now associated with an angle is *not* half the chord that subtends that angle at the center. *It is half the chord of twice that angle.* As we should say today, if A is an acute angle,

$$\sin A = \tfrac{1}{2}(\text{crd. } 2A)$$

Readers who may not be familiar with this abbreviation "sin A" should refer back to this sentence after reading the paragraphs that follow.

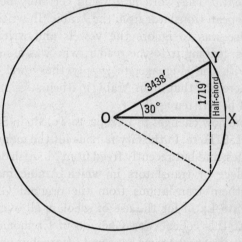

Fig. 44

Aryabhata naturally called his "half-chord" by a Hindu name. This was the word *jiva*, to give it one of many variable spellings. Thus, he calculated that the *jiva* of 30° was 1719′; the *jiva* of 15° was 890′ (a more exact number would be 889.76); the *jiva* of 7°30′ was 449′ (more exactly, it would be 448.72′). These values appear in a book written by him, in which the rules appear in the form of verse couplets. It is called the *Aryabhatiyam*.

Our story of "chords" now takes us to Arabia. Certain Arab mathematicians followed Aryabhata's lead, even to writing the

Hindu word *jiva*, in Arabic characters, as *jiba*. Except for its technical, mathematical association with the length of a half-chord, this word *jiba* was meaningless in Arabic, and would certainly be meaningless to any European translator who was unfamiliar with its highly technical meaning. Now, there is another Arabic word *jaib*, which has the same consonants *jb* as *jiba*, but which has nothing whatever to do with chords of a circle since it means "bosom," "curve," "opening at the neck of a garment." This word *jaib* would certainly be known to every European translator from the Arabic. In writing Arabic, the practice was to ignore the vowels and write only the consonants, leaving it to the reader, who was assumed to be familiar with the language, to supply the vowel sounds. It follows, therefore, that in an Arabic mathematics' manuscript, *jiba* would be written as *jb*.

The scene now changes to Europe, to Toledo in Spain about the year 1150. Here, in the city famous for the manufacture of sword blades, and but recently freed from Moorish domination, was a college of translators in which Arabic manuscripts, many of them translations from the original Greek, were rendered into Latin for the use of scholars all over medieval Europe. At this college was Gherado of Cremona, a distinguished translator whom we have met before, but who was not, please note, a distinguished mathematician. He spent many years translating Arabic versions of the works of Aristotle, the *Elements* of Euclid, the *Sphaerica* of Menelaus, a book we shall meet with later in this chapter, the *al-jabr* of al-Khowarizmi, the *Syntaxis* or *Almagest* of Ptolemy, and many other Arabic manuscripts. Among the latter was an Arabic work on trigonometry. When Gherado came across the word *jiba*, abbreviated to the letters *jb*, he must have shaken his head in puzzled bewilderment. The only Arabic word he knew that contained the two consonants *jb* was *jaib:* but *jaib* meant "bosom."

What on earth could this have to do with the length of half a chord? In the end he appears to have decided that what seemed right and proper to Arab mathematicians was good' enough for Gherado, for he proceeded to translate *jb* by the Latin word *sinus*, "bosom," "curve." Thus it comes about that every time we speak of the *sine of an angle* today we are perpetuating an error made 800 years ago. The *sine of an angle* is one of the basic concepts of trigonometry. *Sine* is nowadays abbreviated to *sin*, pronounced as "sign."

Nowadays the sine of an angle is not the length of a half-chord, as it was until the eighteenth century. It is a *ratio*. How that ratio is obtained will be explained in a moment. By the time of the greatest of Swiss mathematicians, Euler, who lived from 1707 to 1783, the *sine of an angle* was generally treated in this way, as a *ratio*. Since the time and work of Euler, whom we shall meet in a later chapter, it has always been treated as such. It was Euler who finally transformed trigonometry from a geometric to an algebraic basis. The beginning of this tremendously important transformation dates from about 1550; its completion was due to Euler.

The basic concept and first step that eventually led to this change seems absurdly simple—and unimportant—at first glance. Of course, it is easy to be wise after the event—when some bright person has thought of it—but it is strange that no one thought of the simple method we now have of writing decimal fractions until the sixteenth century. Once this was done, the sine of an angle ceased to be a length and became a *number*.

If the reader will look at a modern Table of Sines, he will find that "sin 44°30'," to take one example, is given as ".70091." Let us see what this means. First, remember it is not a length, as were the values of sines and chords from the time of Hipparchus to that of Euler, it is a *ratio*. Now a ratio, being just an ordinary *number* and not a quantity, can be obtained regardless of the units in which the two quantities whose magnitudes are being compared may happen to be given, provided that each of these quantities is expressed in similar units. Moreover, once it has been obtained, a ratio can be used just as an ordinary number, without reference to "inches," or "minutes," or "cubic feet," and so on. In other words, a ratio is algebraic and not geometric. Thus, the ratio between 1719 angular minutes and 3438 angular minutes gets away from angles and circles and becomes just the *number* $\frac{1719}{3438}$, or $\frac{1}{2}$, or .5; the ratio between 3 inches and 12 inches gets away from the lengths of lines and becomes just the *number* $\frac{3}{12}$, or $\frac{1}{4}$, or .25. It was the development of decimal-fractions and Napier's method of writing them which enabled any fraction to be expressed, to any desired degree of accuracy, in an easily-handled form, and thus paved the way for the substitution of ratio numbers in place of lengths in trigonometry.

*By using a ratio, in decimal form, instead of a length for the sine of an angle, the first step was taken in changing trigonometry from a geometric to an algebraic subject.* As a consequence, mathematicians, scientists, architects, surveyors and countless others now have another most powerful mathematical tool at their disposal.

How can we express the sine of, say, 44°30′ as a ratio? Where can we find the two quantities involved in every ratio, one for the numerator, the other for the denominator? If you will look again at Figure 44, you will see that the value of the sine, or *jiva*, as a length, came from one of the sides of Aryabhata's right triangle. Note that this side was *opposite the angle whose "jiva" or sine was to be found.* Note further that the length of a second side in this triangle was also, indirectly, involved, even in Aryabhata's time, since the number of minutes in which he expressed the length of his half-chord depended on the number of minutes he had chosen for his radius. Here is the clue that enables us to find the two quantities for our ratio number, simply from a right triangle: we can dispense altogether with Aryabhata's circle, and with the terms "radius" and "half-chord." All we need is a right triangle that has one of its acute angles equal to the angle whose sine is required. For the numerator of our fraction (or ratio) we shall require the length of the side opposite this acute angle, since this side corresponds to Aryabhata's "half-chord"; for its denominator we shall need the length of the hypotenuse, or longest side of our right triangle, since this corresponds to Aryabhata's "radius." If we wanted to give ourselves unnecessary work (nowadays) we could calculate each of these sides in angular minutes, or in sixtieths of a radius, or in tenths, or thousandths, or millionths or ten-millionths or even ten-billionths of a radius—all these units have been used, and discarded now that we have decimal fractions. Why not just measure the two lines in inches, and have done with it? The *ratio*, being just a number, will not be affected by the kind of unit in which *each line* is measured, as we saw just now.

Suppose then that we want to find a rough approximation of the value of sin 44°30′, but have no Table of Sines available. First, draw two lines (of indefinite length) which intersect at a point 0 at an angle of 44°30′. Choose either one of these lines, and on it mark off CA equal to, say, 2 inches—any other measurement will do. From A draw a line at right angles to the unmarked arm of the angle, and let B be the point where it cuts that arm. [See Figure 45.]

Compare this figure with Aryabhata's figure on page 127. You will see that if you were to draw a circle in Figure 45, having O as center and OA as radius, AB would be the *jiva* of 44°30′, as the Hindus would have put it.

You will notice, however, that instead of giving OA (Aryabhata's *radius*) the angular measure of 3438′ as the Hindus would have done, we have simply marked it with its linear measure of 2 inches. Let us now measure AB, also, of course, in inches. Provided our work is reasonably accurate, we shall find that, as exactly as we can measure with an ordinary ruler, AB will be 1.4 inches long. All that now remains is to compare

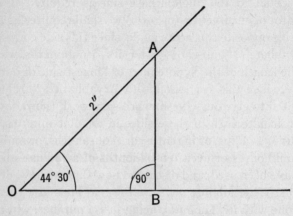

Fig. 45

the length of AB with the length of OA, and thus follow the idea developed in the sixteenth and seventeenth centuries, which was, in effect, "Let us get rid of all these various units of length in which we have for centuries indicated the sine of an angle, and let us substitute a ratio number." So all we have to do is to calculate the value of the ratio

$$\frac{\text{length of side opposite our angle}}{\text{length of our hypotenuse}}.$$

From the dimensions in our figure we see that

$$\sin 44°30' = \frac{1.4}{2} = .7.$$

Naturally, since this result is based on construction and measurement, it would not be sufficiently accurate to use in a careful mathematical computation. As we saw, our modern Tables of Sines, which do not depend on drawing or measurement, give sin 44°30′ as .70091.

We said that the length chosen for OA was immaterial. If we were to make OA equal to 3 inches we should then find that AB was 2.1 inches, but the *ratio* $\dfrac{AB}{OA}$ would still be $\dfrac{2.1}{3}$, or .7; if we were to make OA equal to 4 inches, AB would then become 2.8 inches, but the *ratio* would remain $\dfrac{2.8}{4}$, or .7.

How would Aryabhata have expressed sin 44°30′? He would have found that "*jiva* 44°30′ = 2407′."

So the ratio between the *jiva*, or half-chord in minutes, and the radius, also in minutes, would be $\dfrac{2407}{3438}$. If we work this out in modern style, we get .7001, which is not very far off our modern value of .70091 for sin 44°30′.

How would Hipparchus have expressed sin 44°30′? We saw that sin A = ½(crd. 2A), so sin 44°30′ = ½(crd. 89°), as will be seen from Figure 46:

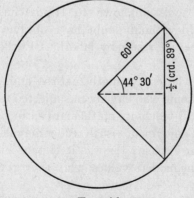

Fig. 46

Hipparchus would (doubtless) have said that

$$\text{crd. } 89° = 84^p \, 6' \, 28''$$
$$\text{so } \tfrac{1}{2}(\text{crd. } 89°) = 42^p \, 3' \, 14''$$

To write this in modern fashion we must work out the ratio

$$\frac{42^p \, 3' \, 14''}{60^p}$$

since the length of the radius, as taken by Hipparchus and the Greeks, was 60 of the 120 parts into which they divided the diameter.

$$\text{The numerator of this fraction} = 42 + \frac{3}{60} + \frac{14}{(60)^2}$$
$$= 42 + .05 + .0036$$
$$= 42.0536 \text{ parts of a diameter}$$

$$\text{The denominator} = 60 \text{ parts of a diameter.}$$

So, working out the ratio $\dfrac{42.0536}{60}$, we find that this Greek re-

sult of calculating sin 44°30′ would give .70089 as against .70091 in modern tables. The author must confess that a dislike for unnecessary work caused him to calculate the $84^p \, 6' \, 28''$ by mathematical tools unknown to Hipparchus. Hipparchus, however, would without doubt have obtained a similar, or perhaps more exact result by laborious Euclidean geometric methods.

The reader who enjoys mathematics—and, strange as this may sound to some who have been subjected to a certain type of mathematical teaching, mathematics can be a most satisfying source of enjoyment—such reader may find it interesting to see how near Ptolemy (or was it Hipparchus?) and Aryabhata got to the modern values, when they gave the following results:

$$\text{crd. } 60° = 60^p; \textit{jiva } 30° = 1719' \, (\sin 30° = .5)$$
$$\text{crd. } 36° = 37^p \, 4' \, 55'' \, (\sin 18° = .30902)$$

*jiva* 15° = 890′ (sin 15° = .25882)

crd. 72° = 70ᵖ 32′ 3″ (sin 36° = .58779)

crd. 90° = 84ᵖ 51′ 10″ (sin 45° = .70711)

*jiva* 7° 30′ = 449′ (sin 7°30′ = .13053)

crd. 120° = 103ᵖ 55′ 23″ (sin 60° = .86603)

*jiva* 11°15′ = 671′ (sin 11°15′ = .19509)

crd. 12° = 12ᵖ 32′ 36″ (sin 6° = .10453)

*jiva* 3°45′ = 225′ (sin 3°45′ = .06540)

After this mathematical interlude, let us resume the story of trigonometry's beginnings. The trail laid by *sine* and its forebears through the ages has taken us far from the Greece of Hipparchus. It is hoped, however, that the journey may have given the reader a clearer bird's-eye view of this section of trigonometry's development than would have been the case had the story of *sine* been told in disconnected fragments as we passed chronologically through the ages.

What use did Hipparchus and later Greeks make of these Tables of Chords? That they must have been considered of great usefulness is evident by the mere fact of their existence. Who in his senses—and the reader will surely agree that Greek mathematicians of ancient days were very much in their senses—would spend laborious hours in calculating by geometric methods the length of the chord of every half-degree from ½° to 180° if great usefulness would not result?

Quite apart from their value in astronomical calculations—their main use—they were used for the solution of plane triangles, or triangles drawn on a flat surface such as this page. If we are given certain facts (*data*, "the things given") about a triangle, such as the length of each of its sides, or the length of two sides and the size of the angle included between them, and so on, we may then calculate the remaining parts of the triangle. This process is called "solving the triangle" or the "solution of the triangle."

Nowadays, the solution of plane triangles is a simple matter if we work up to it step by step. But it was not so simple for the Greeks. To solve a plane triangle they imagined it as being inscribed in a circle. Then each side of the triangle would be a chord of that circle, and each angle of that triangle would equal half the arc lying between the ends of the side opposite that angle.

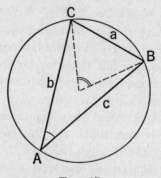

Fig. 47

Very little geometric knowledge is needed to show that angle A is half the angle at the center of the circle, which in turn is the measure of the arc CB. So angle A equals "half arc CB." The value of a Table of Chords like the one drawn up by Hipparchus will now be manifest. The mathematically minded reader will see the obvious connection between Figure 47 and our present familiar formula, for plane triangles, $\dfrac{a}{\sin A} = \dfrac{b}{\sin B} = \dfrac{c}{\sin C}$. This, and many other "modern" formulas (in their original and more complicated forms) were known and used by the Greeks. Mathematicians of the period we are exploring, however, were mainly occupied in applying geometry to astronomy. So they naturally paid greater attention to the solution of *spherical triangles*. Before we glance at the trigonometry connected with such triangles let us bear in mind that a great deal of *geometric* knowledge of a sphere was in the possession of mathematicians two thousand years ago. By the time Euclid wrote the *Elements* there was a great store of such knowledge. He made use of propositions relating to a sphere that were so well known in his day that he merely stated them as accepted facts and did not give their proofs.

Certainly by the year A.D. 100, or some 350 years after Eratosthenes had calculated the circumference of the earth, as we saw in Chapter II, the geometry of the sphere had been thoroughly investigated. For instance, the two kinds of circles that can be drawn, or imagined, on the surface of a sphere had been classified as *great circles* and *small circles*. If an orange is cut into two exactly equal parts, the cut made by the knife on the outside of the peel will be a great circle. The mathematical definition of a great circle is "the intersection of a sphere with a plane passed through its center, and having the same center and radius as the sphere." A *small circle* of a sphere is any other circle drawn on the surface of that sphere which does not comply with this definition. All the "parallels of latitude" marked on a globe, with the exception of the equator, are *small circles*. The equator is a *great circle*. Every circle that passes through both north and south poles is a *great circle*. The shortest distance between any two points on the surface of a sphere is the shorter arc of the great circle that passes through those points. That is why navigators have to learn all about "great circle sailing."

That these, and many other geometric facts about spheres, were thoroughly well known by A.D. 100 is clearly shown by the way in which Menelaus of Alexandria, the "father" of spherical trigonometry, introduced the subject of the geometry of spheres in the first two of three books that make up a most important work of his, called the *Sphaerica*.

He does not trouble to define these circles (and other matters connected with a sphere) but assumes that his readers are already familiar with them. He starts off by defining a *spherical triangle* as "the area enclosed by arcs of great circles on the surface of a sphere."

The non-mathematical reader can easily grasp the connection between great circles and spherical triangles if he will place three rubber bands in the positions of great circles anywhere around a ball. (If the bands do not slip, they may be assumed to be roughly in the position of great circles.) The first two of these bands will divide the surface of the spherical ball into four parts, each of which is called a *lune* (Latin, *luna*, "moon"). When the third rubber band is placed in position, it will divide each lune into two *spherical triangles*, provided it does not pass through the point of intersection of the first two bands. It follows that, in general, three great circles divide the surface of their sphere into eight spherical triangles. It is possible for "three arcs of intersecting great circles" to enclose an area which has one of its bounding arcs greater than a semi-circle and one of its angles greater than 180°. We need not solve such a "triangle," however, since the arcs that bound it also form parts of related triangles, each of whose sides is less than a semi-circle and each of whose angles is less than 180°. Menelaus recognized this, since he definitely limits his discussion to triangles whose sides are each less than a semi-circle.

In the third book of the *Sphaerica*, Menelaus produced the world's oldest-known work on spherical trigonometry. In it he laid the foundations of a branch of mathematics that is essential, not only for astronomers and geographers, but also for all navigators.

The details of spherical trigonometry are too technical for discussion in a book of this nature, but very little mathematical background is required to understand the general principles of the subject that underlie its application to navigation.

The main object of every navigator is to be able to locate his exact position on the earth's surface. To do this, he must know his latitude and longitude. The reader who is unfamiliar with the exact meaning of these terms should glance ahead at pages 149–153 before proceeding further.

The navigator requires no knowledge of trigonometry in order to be able to find his longitude, provided he knows Greenwich time no matter where he may be on the earth's surface. Nowadays he finds this either by radio or by having an accurate chronometer set to Greenwich time. In 1714 the English government offered prizes of £10,000, £15,000 and £20,000 (enormous sums in those days) for chronometers sufficiently accurate to enable longitude to be determined within 60, 40 and 30 miles respectively. A Yorkshire watchmaker named John Harrison, whose father was a carpenter, won the highest prize, though the whole of it was not awarded to him until 1767.

Since the earth revolves through 360° every 24 hours, it revolves through 15° every hour, or 15′ every minute, or 15″ every second. Now suppose it is "sunrise" at, say, 5 A.M. at Greenwich and everywhere along the Greenwich meridian. The town has just swung into the sun's rays. It will still be "dark" at all places between the Greenwich meridian and the meridian 180° to the west of Greenwich, but "light" at all places between the Greenwich meridian and the meridian 180° to the east of Greenwich. Since the sun appears to move from east to west, we know that the earth spins from west to east. So every place on a meridian 15° west of Greenwich swings into the "sunrise" an hour later than Greenwich; every place on a meridian 15° east of Greenwich swings into the "sunrise" an hour before Greenwich.

Suppose then that a navigator on a ship finds that noon, when the sun is directly over the ship's meridian, occurs when Greenwich time is 2 P.M. He knows that his longitude is twice 15°, or 30° *west* of Greenwich. since his "local time" is 2 hours *behind* Greenwich time. If his local time were noon when Greenwich time were 9 A.M. he would know that his longitude was three times 15°, or 45° *east* of Greenwich, since his "local time" was 3 hours *ahead of* Greenwich time.

To find one's latitude is not such a simple matter, since it involves spherical trigonometry. It is determined by observation of the stars. It simplifies an understanding of the apparent movement of the celestial bodies if the universe is regarded from the point of view of Aristotle, that is, as though the earth were the fixed center of the universe while around it revolved the stars, seemingly embedded in the transparent surface of a vast celestial sphere whose center is the earth's center. Since all our "star measurements" are necessarily angular ones it is perfectly justifiable to imagine the stars as being thus embedded in the surface of a celestial sphere, no matter what may be their actual distance from the earth.

Beneath each star, *at any given moment*, there will be a point on the earth which is directly under that star. This point on the earth is called the star's *sub-stellar point* at that particular moment. As each star appears to move around the heavens, so its sub-stellar point can be imagined as moving across the surface of the earth, tracing out an imaginary line parallel to the earth's equator, and therefore one of innumerable parallels of latitude. The exact position of every prominent star and of its sub-stellar point has been worked out by spherical trigonometry and can easily be found in an air or nautical almanac. This is an example of the kind of work done by Prince Henry the Navigator of Portugal and his mathematicians, and by the mathematicians appointed by Charles II of England in 1675 to work at the observatory he had just built at Greenwich, near London. King Charles did this "for the advancement of navigation and nautical astronomy," so essential for a nation dependent on overseas commerce, as well as for control of the seas.

Figure 48 shows the earth, enormously exaggerated, as it is situated (apparently) at the center of a vast celestial sphere. The point marked P is the north celestial pole, the position of the Pole star, which may be regarded as situated directly

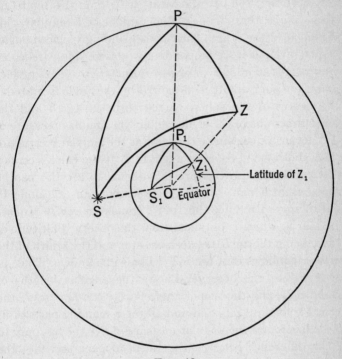

FIG. 48

above $P_1$, the north pole of the earth. This is the only star that does not appear to move (actually it does apparently move around in a tiny circle, but we will ignore this), since the axis of the earth points almost directly toward it.

The point marked Z is the zenith, or point on the celestial sphere directly above an observer, say, on a ship at the point marked $Z_1$ on the earth.

The point marked S is the position of some star as it appears from the earth to be imbedded in the surface of the celestial sphere. The point marked $S_1$ is the sub-stellar point of that star on the earth.

Now note that the two spherical triangles in this figure are the same *shape*, that is, one of them might be a photographic enlargement of the other. Their correspondingly placed angles are equal and their correspondingly placed sides are equal *when measured in angular measure as arcs of great circles*, since the length of such an arc is measured by the angle it subtends at the center of the sphere. Since both the earth and the celestial sphere have the same center, the angular measure of arc PZ, for instance, will be the same as the angular measure of arc $P_1Z_1$, both being equal to angle POZ at the earth's center.

The angular measure of arc $P_1S_1$ (equal to arc PS) can be obtained from a nautical almanac, so too, can the angle $P_1$ (equal to angle P). Since the arc SZ equals the *zenith distance* of the star S, which is obtained from the observed altitude of the star, being the angle between the star and the zenith of the observer, it follows that arc $S_1Z_1$ will also be known. Thus, in triangle $P_1Z_1S_1$ the observer knows the angular lengths of $P_1S_1$ and $S_1Z_1$, and the size of angle $P_1$. He can now solve the spherical triangle $P_1Z_1S_1$ and find all the remaining parts of it. Once he has found the angular measure of $P_1Z_1$ he has only to find the difference between that measurement and 90°, the angular measure of the arc of the great circle from the North Pole to the Equator, of which $P_1Z_1$ forms part. This difference is shown in our figure by the dotted arc below $Z_1$. This will obviously equal the observer's latitude.

The Greek method of solving certain cases of oblique spherical triangles (triangles that did not contain a right angle) was to split them up into right spherical triangles. They used (in more complicated form, of course) several of the formulas we use today for the solution of these right triangles. Our present formulas were not completely developed until 1614, when Napier, whom we shall meet in a later chapter, drew up the "Rules of circular parts" we still use. These "Napier's Rules" occurred incidentally in a book about an invention that amazed and delighted mathematicians, namely, that of logarithms.

The possibility of the direct solution of an oblique spherical triangle does not appear to have occurred to the Greeks, and it was not until the tenth century that the Arabs began to investigate this matter. Not until the end of the sixteenth century did Vieta and Pitiscus lay the final foundations of our present-day methods, by developing some of the formulas we now use, and it was not until after Napier's death that his four "analogies" (formulas involving "like" ratios) were published.

Enough has been said about spherical triangles to indicate yet once more the debt we owe to the great Greek mathematicians who first developed the subject. It was the genius of Menelaus, eighteen centuries ago, that first put this powerful and practical tool into the hands of astronomers, geographers and navigators.

It must be remembered, however, that all the trigonometric calculations and all the trigonometric reasoning carried out by the Greek mathematicians were limited to values given in Tables of Chords. In consequence, many of their methods were necessarily much more roundabout than those that have arisen since the development of no fewer than six different kinds of trigonometric tables from the idea implanted by the original Greek Table of Chords.

Before we discuss the work of the last Greek mathematician of interest in this chapter it will save a good deal of clumsy circumlocution if we digress from the Greeks for a moment and jump to the year 1620 just to pick up a word which will obviate long-winded expressions like "the chord of 180°-minus-the-angle-we-are-discussing."

During the sixteenth and seventeenth centuries the circle used by Aryabhata, as we saw, was replaced by the simpler right triangle of modern trigonometry. Now, in every right triangle, the sum of the two acute angles must be 90°, since the sum of all three angles in any triangle is 180°. For this reason, the two acute angles in any right triangle are said to be *comple-*

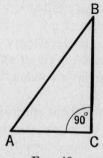

Fig. 49

*ments* of each other. The Latin word *compleo* means "I fill up," "I complete," so the complement of any acute angle is the acute angle needed to "fill it up" to 90°. Thus, 80° is the *complement* of 10°, and so on. Let us draw triangle ABC, right-angled at C.

Since the angle at C equals 90°, *angle B is the complement of angle A*. We have already discovered that the sine of an angle is equal to the ratio $\dfrac{\text{length of side opposite that angle}}{\text{length of hypotenuse}}$. Applying this fact, we see that "the sine of the complement of A," or, in other words, the sine of angle B in Figure 49 (which represents *any* right triangle) will be the ratio $\dfrac{AC}{AB}$. In the early seventeenth century, Edmund Gunter, who played an important part in the application of Newton's invention of logarithms to the development of the slide rule, preferred to call *the sine of the complement of A* by the shorter expression *complement sine of A*. In writing, he shortened this still more to *co. sine A*. Soon, other mathematicians dropped the period, writing and calling it *cosine A* which, since the end of the seventeenth century has been shortened, in writing, still further to *cos A*, though this is still usually read as "cosine A."

We see then, that in Figure 49,

$$\sin A = \frac{BC}{AB}; \cos A = \frac{AC}{AB}$$

$$\sin B = \frac{AC}{AB}; \cos B = \frac{BC}{AB}$$

that is, sin A = cos B; sin B = cos A.

Instead of defining the cosine of an angle as "the sine of its complement" it will be seen that we can forget all about the complement and simply say that the cosine of an acute angle in a right triangle equals the ratio $\dfrac{\text{side adjacent to that angle}}{\text{hypotenuse}}$, it being understood that "side adjacent to," means "*shorter* side adjacent to." It is well to remember, however, that *the sine of any acute angle is always exactly the same as the cosine of its complement*. This fact makes it possible to condense tables of sines and cosines. If the values of the sines of angles from 0° to 45° are given at intervals, say, of 10′, they will serve, *when read in reverse order*, for the values of the cosines of angles from 45° to 90°. Similarly, if the values of the cosines of angles from 0° to 45° are given, they will serve, *in reverse order* for the sines of angles from 45° to 90°.

We now come to the astronomer-mathematician-geographer Ptolemy, who lived about A.D. 150.

Once again the story of a great man must commence with

the now monotonous but still regrettable statement that we know practically nothing of his private life. All we can say for certain is that Ptolemy was connected with Alexandria, that he did much astronomical work between A.D. 125 and 150, and that he wrote several books, one of which is world famous. There is an unreliable legend that he lived for forty years on the elevated terraces of the temple of Serapis at Canopus, near Alexandria, and that pillars were erected there with a record of his astronomical discoveries carved in them. There were also untrustworthy legends about him handed down by the Arabs, who held his work in the highest respect. According to one of these legends he lived to be seventy-eight years old.

Ptolemy's great book was called by him *Mathēmatikēs Suntaxis* (Syntaxis), "The Mathematical Collection," hence the title *Syntaxis* for the work. Like Euclid's *Elements* and the *Arithmetica* written a hundred years later by Diophantus, Ptolemy's work consisted of thirteen books. It dealt with astronomy, plane and spherical trigonometry, geometric facts and methods required for preparing a Table of Chords, and an actual Table of Chords itself. The *Syntaxis* was accepted by Greek scholars as the greatest book on astronomy ever written, hence they came to call it "The Great Collection," to distinguish it from other, less important books on astronomy. Later, the Arabs showed their respect and admiration for the book by calling it not merely "great," or even "greater," but *al-majisti*, "The Greatest," combining the Arabic *al*, "the," with an Arabic form of the Greek *megistos*, "greatest." Hence the Latin title *Almagest*, by which the *Syntaxis* became known throughout Europe during the Middle Ages. An Arabic version was translated into Latin by Gherado of Cremona in 1175 with the title *Almagest*, and many other Latin translations were made. The book has been printed in both Greek and Latin several times, the latest Greek version appearing as recently as 1913.

The *Almagest* contains detailed particulars of the astronomical investigations made by Hipparchus, while it elaborates Ptolemy's explanations of the movements, as he thought, of the heavenly bodies around the earth. This *Ptolemaic System*, as it is called, was accepted without question by European and Arab astronomers until it became superseded in the late sixteenth and early seventeenth centuries by the Copernican System, or, as some of us would prefer to call it, the System of Aristarchus.

It is evident from the way in which the subject is presented that little of the trigonometry contained in the book was Ptolemy's invention. His main contribution to the subject, somewhat like that of Euclid's main contribution to geometry, was to select, condense and arrange all that was known about trigonometry in his day and thus establish and preserve for others the methods and formulas then in use. It is probable that he corrected and extended the Tables of Chords that had been drawn up by Hipparchus and Menelaus. He invented the geometric theorem known today as "Ptolemy's theorem," familiar to all mathematically-minded readers. This proves that if a quadrilateral whose sides are respectively a, b, c and d units in length and in this order, and whose diagonals are respectively x and y units in length, is inscribed in a circle, then xy = ac + bd. Mathematically-minded readers will be able to see how this theorem, as applied by Ptolemy to trigonometry, gave him (in the complicated form of "chords") the equivalent of one of the most important of all modern trigonometric formulas. The non-mathematical reader should by now be able to grasp the paragraphs that follow, although he may find that the change from the Greek use of chords to the modern use of sines and cosines requires a certain amount of algebraic manipulative practice.

Suppose α and β are respectively the angular measurements of two overlapping arcs in a circle, and that they terminate at the same point, α being greater than β.

Ptolemy drew the diameter from the point where the two over-lapping arcs terminated, and then completed the inscribed quadrilateral shown in our figure, also drawing its remaining diagonal.

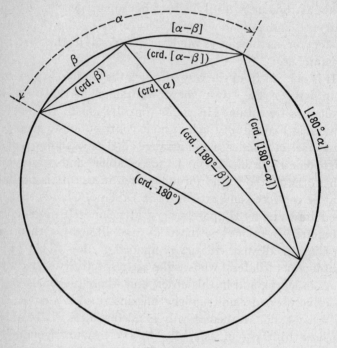

FIG. 50

Applying the theorem now called by his name, he then found [crd.$(\alpha - \beta)$] from the equation

$$(\text{crd. } \alpha) \cdot [\text{crd.}(180° - \beta)] = [\text{crd.}(180° - \alpha)] \cdot (\text{crd. } \beta) + [\text{crd.}(\alpha - \beta)] \cdot (\text{crd. } 180°)$$

In order to transform this equation into its modern form, first put $\alpha = 2\theta$, and $\beta = 2\phi$. This makes the equation become

$$(\text{crd. } 2\theta) \cdot [\text{crd.}(180° - 2\phi)] = [\text{crd.}(180° - 2\theta)] \cdot (\text{crd. } 2\phi) + [\text{crd. } 2(\theta - \phi)] \cdot (\text{crd. } 180°)$$

But we know that $\sin \theta = \frac{1}{2}(\text{crd. } 2\theta)$, so $(\text{crd. } 2\theta) = 2 \sin \theta$.
Similarly, $(\text{crd. } 2\phi) = 2 \sin \phi$; $[\text{crd. } 2(\theta - \phi)] = 2 \sin (\theta - \phi)$
Again, $[\text{crd.}(180° - 2\phi)] = [\text{crd. } 2(90° - \phi)]$
$$= [\text{crd. } 2(\text{complement of } \phi)]$$
$$= 2 \sin (\text{complement of } \phi)$$
$$= 2 \cos \phi.$$
Similarly, $[\text{crd.}(180° - 2\theta)] = 2 \cos \theta$, while, if we take the
length of the radius of the circle as 1 unit, $(\text{crd. } 180°) = 2$.

So we may now write our equation as
$$(2 \sin \theta) \cdot (2 \cos \phi) = (2 \cos \theta) \cdot (2 \sin \phi) + [2 \sin (\theta - \phi)] \cdot (2)$$
$$\therefore \ 4 \sin \theta \cos \phi = 4 \cos \theta \sin \phi + 4 \sin (\theta - \phi)$$
$$\therefore \ \sin \theta \cos \phi = \cos \theta \sin \phi + \sin (\theta - \phi)$$
$$\therefore \ \sin (\theta - \phi) = \sin \theta \cos \phi - \cos \theta \sin \phi$$
which mathematical readers will at once recognize as one of
the most important and essential formulas in modern trigonometry.

It may interest some readers to discover for themselves how
Ptolemy applied his theorem to find $(\text{crd. } AC)$ in Figure 51,
given $(\text{crd. } AB)$ and $(\text{crd. } BC)$, and drawing the diameters
AD and BE. They can then see how this trigonometric application of his has led to our familiar formula
$$\cos (\theta + \phi) = \cos \theta \cos \phi - \sin \theta \sin \phi$$
[It can easily be proved that $(\text{crd. } DE) = (\text{crd. } AB)$. Having
found a formula, from quadrilateral BCDE, in terms of chords,
let $2\theta = $ arc AB, $2\phi = $ arc BC, and then proceed as in the
previous example.]

As a geographer, Ptolemy followed the example of earlier
geographers in dividing the surface of the earth by a network of
"parallels of latitude" and "meridians of longitude," as they
are now called. A parallel of latitude is any small circle (see
page 137) that is parallel to the equator; a meridian of longitude is half of any great circle that passes through both North
and South Poles. The word "meridian" took its rise from the
fact that at *noon* every day the shadow of a pole will always

lie in the direction north-south. At that moment, noon, the sun is directly over every point on an extension of that shadow that reaches from North Pole to South Pole. So the half of a great circle lying between North and South Poles came to be called a *meridian*, since every point on that line would have

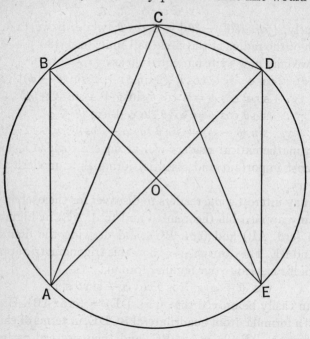

FIG. 51

noon at the same instant every day. The Latin *meridies*. "noon," is a contraction of *medius*, "middle" and *dies*, "day."

The Greeks and their medieval successors conceived of the *width* of the world as running from north to south, its *length* from east to west. Presumably, this was because the line of the Mediterranean Sea marked the "length" of the world to the ancients. Thus it came about that Ptolemy used a Greek word meaning "width" for a measurement north or south of a fixed line, the equator, which word of his was later translated by the Latin *latitudo* (from *latus*, "broad"), hence our word "latitude" for a measurement to the north or south of the equator. Ptolemy's word for "length" was translated by the Latin *longitudo* (from *longus*, "long"), hence our word "longitude" for a measurement to the east or west (for the past three hundred years) of the meridian through Greenwich. The reason why this Greenwich meridian was chosen as the starting point for measurements of longitude is suggested on page 140.

Since these terms "latitude" and "longitude" refer to distances on the curved surface of a sphere, they are measured in angular units, by reference to angles at the center of that sphere.

In Figure 52, the latitude of point A is *north* (of the equator) and is equal to the angular measure of arc BA, which in turn is equal to the angle BOA at the center of the earth, this angle being measured on the plane through the North Pole, the point A, the South Pole and the center of the earth. Only a portion of this plane is shown in the figure, the portion bounded by the meridian through A and the axis of the earth. Latitude north of the equator is sometimes indicated by a *positive* number: thus, $+60°$ means "60° north of the equator."

At E, the latitude is south (of the equator) and equals the angular measurement of arc CE, that is, it equals angle COE. Latitude south of the equator is sometimes indicated by a *negative* number: thus, $-48°$ means "48° south of the equator."

At each of the points B, C and D the latitude is 0°, since each of these points is on the equator.

Notice the only *small circle* shown in this figure. Every point on this small circle, H for instance, has the same latitude as A. Any small circle like this, drawn parallel to the equator, is called a "parallel of latitude."

Now for longitude. Longitude, as we saw, is measured east or west of the meridian through Greenwich. As in the case of

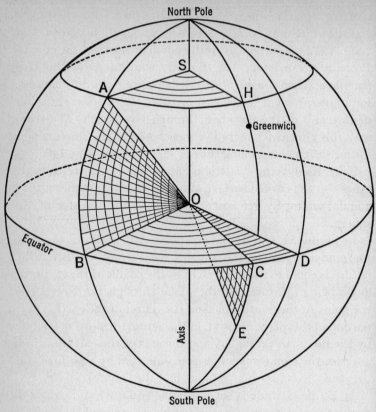

FIG. 52

latitude, it is an angular measurement. The longitude of A might be measured by the angular length of arc HA *with reference to the angle at the center of its own circle*, namely, angle HSA, but this might lead to errors. In practice, the arc HA of the small circle has often to be handled in nautical miles, 1 nautical mile being the average length on the earth of an arc of an earth's *great circle* equal to 1 minute. Since HA is not an arc of a great circle, the number of nautical miles along arc HA

will not be the same as the number of minutes of arc in HA.
To avoid possible confusion it is better to take an arc of the
great circle we call the equator. It will be seen that the angular
measure of arc CB, namely, the angle COB, is the same as the
angular measure of arc HA on its own circle, namely, the angle
HSA. Both these angles are known as *dihedral* angles. If non-
mathematicians will visualize the angle between the flat surfaces or faces of a section of an orange they will be visualizing
a dihedral angle. This kind of angle is simply the angle lying
between two intersecting planes. It will be seen that dihedral
angle HSA equals dihedral angle COB, so the angular measure
of arc CB, being, say, 82°, will equal the longitude of A (west
of Greenwich). This will also be the *angular* measure of arc
HA with reference to the small circle through A and H, as we
have seen. But the length HA in nautical miles will not be the
same as the length CB in nautical miles. Now, on the *equator*,
an arc is an arc of a great circle of the earth, so if the angular
measure of CB is 82°, or 4920′, the distance between C and B
will be 4920 nautical miles. But how can a sailor calculate the
number of nautical miles between A and H if he wishes to sail
on a course that will be parallel to the equator? If the reader
will look at Figure 52 he will see that the line SA lies in a plane
that is parallel to the plane of the equator, on which OB lies.
He will also see that SA and OB also both lie in the same plane,
the one bounded by the meridian through A and the axis of
the earth. So SA and OB are parallel lines in the same plane.
It follows that angle SAO = angle BOA = latitude of A. Let
us call the radius of the earth R nautical miles, that is to say,
let any one of the lines AO, BO, CO, or DO equal R nautical
miles.

Now let trigonometry come to our aid. Since ASO is a triangle right-angled at S,

$$\frac{AS}{AO} = \cos \text{ (angle SAO)} = \cos \text{ (latitude of A)}$$

That is,

$$\frac{AS}{R} = \cos \text{ (latitude of A)}$$

So

$$AS = R \cdot \cos \text{ (latitude of } A\text{)}$$

Suppose the latitude of A is 60°. From a table of cosines we find that cos 60° = .5

$$\therefore AS = .5R = \tfrac{1}{2} BO$$

Since $AS = \tfrac{1}{2}$ BO, the circumference of this particular parallel of latitude is half that of the equator. In other words, each minute of arc on this 60° parallel has half the *linear* measure of each minute of arc on the equator.

Now BC = 4920 nautical miles (see page 153)

$$\therefore AH = .5(4920) = 2460 \text{ nautical miles.}$$

It will be seen that if x stands for the latitude along any parallel of latitude, then *each minute of arc on that parallel of latitude will contain cos x nautical miles*.

Before we leave the nautical atmosphere of the last few pages to return to Ptolemy in sun-drenched Alexandria—or was it Canopus?—let us glance at the sailor's measure of speed, the *knot*.

A knot is a *speed* of 1 nautical mile per hour. Its name takes us back to the early days of sailing ships. Before the invention of more accurate and more complicated gadgets, a ship's speed through the water was found by heaving overboard a log of wood, to which was attached a line divided into equal portions by knots. By counting the number of knots paid out during a known period of time, the speed of the ship through the water would be roughly measured. Hence the word "knot" became associated with a ship's speed. Later, a *knot* was associated with a *speed of 1 nautical mile per hour*. The log of wood that used to be thrown overboard originated the expression "log book," in which, to this day, a record is kept of the ship's daily run.

To return to Ptolemy. He applied his knowledge of geometry and trigonometry to map-making. The average man who glances at a map does not realize the difficulty of representing the curving surface of a sphere on a flat surface, even with the aid of intricate mathematics, by means of which it can only be partially overcome. Ptolemy knew infinitely more about such things as *orthogonal projection* (see his book, the *Analemma*) and *stereographic projection* (see his book, the *Planisphaerium*) than do most of us. He seems to have applied these mathematical concepts primarily to maps of the stars. It was, however, from Ptolemy that Renaissance map-makers learned their job, without which the great navigations of the fifteenth and subsequent centuries could not have taken place. Unfortunately, although Ptolemy had all the necessary mathematics at his disposal, he based his map of the earth on a calculation of the earth's circumference made by Posidonius about a century after Erastosthenes had estimated it to be 250,000 stadia. Posidonius calculated that it was only 180,000 stadia, and for some reason this erroneous calculation was adopted by the geographer Strabo (about 50 B.C. to A.D. 20) and later by Ptolemy. Since the latitude of few places was accurately known, and since the only way of calculating longitude at that time was by observations of eclipses (a method suggested by Hipparchus), Ptolemy had to rely almost entirely on calculations of distances made by travelers (estimates which were largely guesswork), since even the use of the log at sea had not then been introduced. The materials on which he had to work were unworthy of his theoretical skill in map-making, his methods of transferring the outline of a country from a spherical surface to the plane surface of a map differing very little from those in use today. Figure 53 is his map of the world, as then known to Europeans.

The obvious errors in the above map notwithstanding, it is vastly better than those drawn in the Dark Ages that descended on Europe after his day. Map-making fell back into a second childhood; even the belief that the earth was a sphere was banned by the church, and people were taught that the world was a flat disk surrounded by ocean. As the knowledge of Greek died out in Western Europe, the vast stores of mathematical and scientific knowledge amassed by centuries of

FIG. 53

*Ptolemy's map of the world (c. A.D. 150)*

Greek philosophers, mathematicians, astronomers and geographers faded away. It was not until the thirteenth century that map-making began to recover, not until the fifteenth century that Ptolemy's principles of map-making were reintroduced into Europe. The demands of navigation brought about further improvements, and Ptolemy's *Almagest* became widely known once more in Europe, being one of the earliest books to be printed. In 1500 a Basque named Juan de la Casa, a companion of Columbus, drew a map of the world which for the first time showed the recently discovered coast of America.

With the story of Ptolemy we come to the end of the contribution made to trigonometry by the Greeks. From his day until the Renaissance the only real advance in the subject came from the Hindus and the Arabs. After the fall of the Roman Empire in the face of attacks by hordes of barbarians, all branches of mathematics, as we have seen, suffered from the stagnation that paralyzed thought in Europe.

We have already seen the far-reaching results of the work done in India by Aryabhata in developing ideas that were to lead to our modern concept of the sine of an angle. We now come to the story of the invention of two other trigonometric ratios, which, like the sine, grew out of *lengths*.

As early as A.D. 400 Hindu writers were showing an interest in the lengths of shadows, but it was left to the Arabs to develop the idea of trigonometric "lengths" connected with shadows. By such a "trigonometric length" we mean one in which the length of a shadow is connected with the size of an angle.

Before World War II, there was an Arabic manuscript in Berlin—whether it exists today is doubtful—written toward the end of the ninth century. It contained a list of the lengths of two kinds of shadows, both equally important, and both treated separately, though side by side. One kind gave the length of the shadow cast on horizontal ground by an upright gnomon; the other, that cast on a vertical wall by a "turned" gnomon, or one that had been placed horizontally so as to form a sundial on the wall of a building. Medieval writers came to call the *shadow* cast by an *upright* gnomon the *umbra recta,* that cast by the *"turned"* gnomon the *umbra versa.*

Figure 54 shows both kinds of sundials. Imagine that the one on the left is on horizontal ground in the garden of a house that also possesses the one on the right, on one of its walls. The gnomon on the right has been purposely made the same length as the shadow (*umbra recta*) on the left for reasons that will appear shortly. Since the sundials are side by side, the

altitude of the sun will be the same in each case. Moreover, as
we saw when discussing Eratosthenes and his calculation of
the earth's circumference, the sun's rays are parallel to each
other when they reach the earth, to all intents and purposes.
So *in a case like this*, the shadow on the right (*umbra versa*)

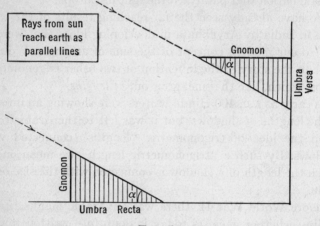

Rays from sun
reach earth as
parallel lines

Gnomon

Umbra
Versa

Gnomon

Umbra   Recta

FIG. 54

will be the same length as the gnomon on the left. This reciprocal connection appears to have escaped the notice of Arab
and medieval mathematicians, probably because it would be
very unlikely for a "turned" gnomon to equal the length of a
neighboring "umbra recta." In any event, they did not develop the idea as we do today, and as we shall shortly do in this
book.

Toward the end of the sixteenth century, the "shadow"
names *umbra recta* and *umbra versa* began to give place to other
terms. A writer called Thomas Fincke wrote a book in 1583
in which he called the *umbra versa*, still a length and not yet a
ratio, by the name of "tangent." The most probable explanation for his choice of this term is suggested in Figure 55.

If the "turned" gnomon on the right of Figure 54 is regarded as the radius of a circle, and if that radius is regarded as having rotated through the angle α in Figure 55, the *umbra versa* will form part of the tangent to the circle at the point where the gnomon-radius meets the circle. The name "tangent" was adopted by the well-known mathematician Pitiscus in 1595

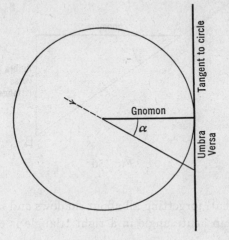

FIG. 55

and has been used ever since. "Tangent of A" is now abbreviated to "tan A."

It was during the lifetime of Pitiscus that mathematicians were just beginning to develop the idea of ratios instead of lengths in trigonometry. Since the sixteenth and seventeenth centuries mathematicians were familiar with the Arab custom of stating the length of a shadow as a certain number of times the length of its gnomon; it was natural that in turning the tangent of an angle into ratio form, its length should be compared with the length of the gnomon-radius in Figure 55. Thus, in the right triangle shown in Figure 56, if BC is the *umbra versa*, or "tangent," and AC the *gnomon*, or "radius," the ratio between these two lengths that can be connected with the

angle A (which would be the altitude of the sun if we were
discussing a turned sundial) will be

$$\tan A = \frac{BC}{AC}.$$

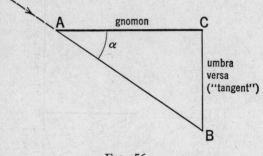

FIG. 56

So we see that, forgetting all about shadows and sundials, the
tangent of an acute angle in a right triangle is equal to the
ratio

$$\frac{\text{side opposite that angle}}{\text{(shorter) side adjacent to that angle}}.$$

Now, in our last figure, angle B is the complement of angle A.
So the *tangent of angle B* will be the same thing as the *tangent
of the complement of angle A*. So, using our new definition of a
tangent ratio, we see that

$$\tan B = \textit{tangent of the complement of } A = \frac{AC}{BC}.$$

Like that other long-winded expression "sine of the complement of A" and like Alice in Wonderland, on the occasion
when she remarked "I must be shutting up like a telescope,"
the clumsy expression "tangent of the complement of A" came
to be called the "complement tangent of A" which in turn
came to be written as "cotangent of A" (again, it was Edmund

Gunter, the originator of the word "co.sine" who thought of this one), and finally as "cot A."

Forgetting all about complements of angles now, we can define the cotangent of any acute angle in a right triangle as

$$\frac{\text{(shorter) side adjacent to the angle}}{\text{side opposite the angle}}.$$

Reverting to Figure 56 once more, we see then that

$$\tan A = \frac{CB}{AC}; \quad \cot A = \frac{AC}{CB}$$

$$\tan B = \frac{AC}{CB}; \quad \cot B = \frac{CB}{AC}$$

In other words, the tangent of an angle equals the cotangent of its complement, and is also the reciprocal of its own cotangent. The last part of this statement simply means that if a tangent ratio of an angle is written upside down, it gives the cotangent ratio of that same angle. [If the product of two numbers equals 1, each number is the reciprocal of the other. Thus, the following pairs of numbers are respectively reciprocals: $\frac{3}{5}$ and $\frac{5}{3}$; 2 (or $\frac{2}{1}$) and $\frac{1}{2}$; .8 and 1.25; $\frac{a}{b}$ and $\frac{b}{a}$.]

Notice that although *tan x* is the reciprocal of *cot x*, this reciprocal relationship does *not* apply to *sin x* and *cos x*, since these ratios do not involve the same pair of sides of a right triangle as do tan x and cot x.

Let us return for a moment to shadows and sundials in order to clear up one point that was put off until the meaning of the terms "tangent" and "cotangent" had been discussed. How did Arab and medieval mathematicians actually express the lengths of shadows? First, consider the length of the umbra recta shown in Figure 57.

In this figure BC represents the known length of the gnomon, CA the length of the *umbra recta* that has to be deter-

mined when the altitude of the sun is known to be A°. In the
Middle Ages, this would be given in tables as

$$CA = BC \cdot \frac{\text{sine of complement of A}}{\text{sine of A}}.$$

Mathematical readers will see that this is equivalent to saying
that the length of the *umbra recta* was equal to the length of

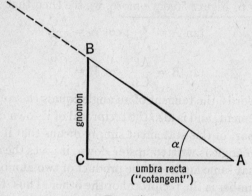

FIG. 57

the gnomon multiplied by the cotangent of the altitude of the
sun. Those who may not know why $\dfrac{\text{"sine of complement of A"}}{\text{sine of A}}$
is the same as "cot A" can easily find out by looking at Figure
58 and the explanation that goes with it. For simplicity, small
letters have been used for the lengths of the sides of the triangle, each small letter following the capital letter at the angle
opposite its side.

It will be seen that

$$\frac{\text{sine of the complement of A}}{\sin A} = \frac{\cos A}{\sin A} = \frac{\frac{b}{c}}{\frac{a}{c}} = \frac{b}{\not c} \cdot \frac{\not c}{a} = \frac{b}{a} = \cot A.$$

Readers may be interested to find out for themselves how

medieval mathematicians, knowing only *sines*, would have expressed the length of the *umbra versa* when the length of the gnomon and the altitude of the sun were known. In modern terms, the length of the *umbra versa* would be the length of the gnomon multiplied by the tangent of the altitude of the sun.

Greek mathematicians, as we have seen, had Tables of

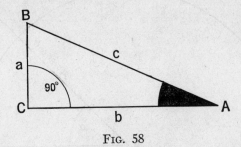

FIG. 58

Chords, but they had nothing corresponding to the tables of cosines, tangents and cotangents that we possess. Nevertheless, so capable were they that they were able to express the equivalent of a cosine, as some readers may have found out on page 149, while a hint of the equivalent of a tangent occurs as early as Aristarchus, as we hinted on page 113.

During the Middle Ages, tables of the lengths of sines and of the equivalents to tangents and cotangents became available to mathematicians.

The introduction of the mariner's compass into Europe and the consequent long voyages undertaken across open seas greatly stimulated the study of navigational mathematics. In the fifteenth century, trigonometric tables, which included values of two new ratios, were prepared for navigators. One of these ratios is now called the *secant*, though at first it was usually called *hypotenusa*, being so known to Copernicus and to his fellow-worker Rheticus. In a book of trigonometric tables published by Rheticus in 1551, values of this new ratio were included, under the title of *hypotenusa*. In 1583, Thomas Fincke, the inventor of the word "tangent," called this new ratio the "secant." Although this term was not immediately adopted by other mathematicians (Vieta, for example, in 1593

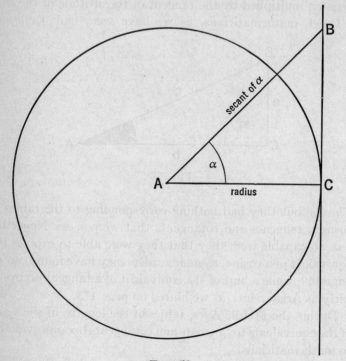

FIG. 59

preferred to use the word *trans-sinuosa*) it eventually came into general use. The probable reason for Fincke's choice of this name is suggested in Figure 59.

Although, in geometry, a secant is a line that cuts a circle at two points, sixteenth-century mathematicians agreed to accept this word as sufficiently descriptive of AB in the above figure.

Ignoring the circle in Figure 59, and thinking only of the right triangle in that figure, we nowadays express the secant of angle A *as a ratio* by comparing the length of the hypotenuse AB with that of AC, the shorter side adjacent to the angle we are discussing. "Secant" is abbreviated to "sec."

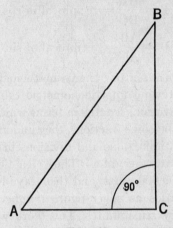

FIG. 60

It will be seen that in Figure 60, sec A $= \dfrac{AB}{AC}$, that is, the ratio between the length of the hypotenuse and that of the shorter side adjacent to A.

Further, we see that since B is the complement of A in this figure,

$$\text{sec B} = \frac{AB}{BC} = \text{"secant of the complement of A"}$$

$$= \text{"cosecant of A."}$$

In America, "cosecant" is abbreviated to "csc"; in England, to "cosec." No final agreement on this abbreviation has yet been reached.

We see, then, that in Figure 60,

$$\sec A = \frac{AB}{AC} = \text{reciprocal of } \cos A;$$

$$\csc A = \frac{AB}{BC} = \text{reciprocal of } \sin A;$$

$$\sec B = \frac{AB}{BC} = \text{reciprocal of } \cos B;$$

$$\csc B = \frac{AB}{AC} = \text{reciprocal of } \sin B.$$

In the sixteenth century many mathematicians occupied themselves in drawing up trigonometric tables. In order to avoid giving the various lengths in terms which would involve difficult and cumbersome fractions, they undertook stupendous arithmetical multiplications and divisions in order to obtain greater and greater accuracy. Thus, Rheticus divided the radius into 10,000,000 units, and then gave lengths of all six trigonometric ratios as seven-figure numbers for angles at intervals of every ten minutes. This work was published in 1551. In 1579 Vieta extended these tables so as to give the values of all these ratios at intervals of every minute.

Rheticus was a professor of mathematics who was an enthusiastic supporter of Copernicus. It was he who superintended the publication of the book that was handed to the dying Copernicus (see page 110). His real name was George Joachim, but he is always known as Rheticus because he was born in part of the Austrian Tyrol that had originally been settled by the Rhaeti tribe. After the publication of his trigonometric tables in 1551 he undertook the still more exacting task of drawing up ten-figure values of all six ratios, based on a radius of 10,000,000,000 units, for angles at intervals of every ten seconds. He died before they could be published, but in 1596 they were printed at the expense of the Elector Palatine,

Frederick IV (the ruler of the Palatinate, a district on the Rhine). As a mark of appreciation they were published under the title *Opus Palatinum*, by which name they have been known ever since. These tables are considered the finest achievement of the greatest computer of this type of trigonometric tables. It may well have been the thought of the enormous labor involved in drawing up tables like these by methods that involved the constant multiplication and division of huge numbers that induced Napier to look around, and—after a search of twenty years—to find an ingenious way by which multiplication could be effected by addition, and division by subtraction. We shall glance at this invention of Napier in our next chapter. It is said by Pitiscus that Rheticus employed computers to work with him *for twelve years* in order to produce his great tables. There is a copy of the *Opus Palatinum* in the New York Public Library (Fifth Avenue); the trigonometric tables occupy 735 pages, each closely printed page being 9 inches by 15 inches.

Instead of speaking of the sine, cosine etc. as "trigonometric ratios connected with angles," we can use the neater expression "functions of angles." When two variable quantities are connected in such a way that the value of one of them depends on the value of the other, the first of these quantities is said to be a *function* of the second. Since the value of the first quantity depends on the value assigned to the second quantity, it is called the *dependent* variable, while the second quantity is called the *independent* variable.

We shall meet with the term "function" in other branches of mathematics besides trigonometry. Thus, in algebra, "8x," for example, is a function of x (if x can vary in value in any one problem) since the value of 8x depends on the value assigned to x. In the same way, $2p^2 + 5p - 9$ is a function of p, if p is a variable. It will be seen that *sin A* must be a function of A, since the value of *sin* A depends on the value of the angle A. Similarly, cos $\phi$ is a function of $\phi$; tan $\theta$ is a function of $\theta$, and so on.

In mathematical shorthand, "function of x" is written "f(x)." This symbol may indicate any expression in terms of x, such as 8x, or 5x$^2$, or 9x$^3$ — 4x + 3, and so on. If we meet the expression "f(p) = 5p$^2$ + 2p — 8" it simply means that the particular function of p we are to consider is 5p$^2$ + 2p — 8. The symbols $f(x)$, $F(x)$, $\phi(x)$ were used by Euler in the eighteenth century.

So when we speak of "tables of trigonometric functions" we shall simply mean tables of the values of sines, cosines, tangents, cotangents, secants and cosecants of angles.

In the chapter that follows, we shall see how a surprising labor-saving invention, originally intended to simplify the use of tables of trigonometric functions, had far-reaching consequences in other branches of mathematics.

# CHAPTER V

# The Invention of Logarithms

*"Seeing there is nothing (right well-beloved Students of Mathematics) that is so troublesome to mathematical practice, nor doth more molest and hinder calculators, than the multiplications, divisions, square and cubical extractions of great numbers, which besides the tedious expense of time are for the most part subject to many slippery errors, I began therefore to consider in my mind by what certain and ready art I might remove those hindrances."* (Napier: the opening words of the *Descriptio*.)

IT IS probably true that no great mathematical invention, with one solitary exception, has resulted from the work of any one individual. One mathematician sows a seed which starts a train of thought in the minds of others. Eventually, it may be after years and even centuries have elapsed, the seed develops into full and vigorous life, and, as a consequence, mathematical knowledge and power are advanced another step. This is the normal course of events. The one solitary exception is the invention of logarithms.

In July, 1914, less than a week before the first great tragedy of modern times, the outbreak of World War I, delegates arrived in Edinburgh from all over the world to attend an international congress held to commemorate the publication, three hundred years previously, of a small book of 147 pages, 90 of them filled with mathematical tables. The book, written by John Napier, of Merchiston, near Edinburgh, was entitled, in the scholars' language of his day, *Mirifici Logarithmorum Canonis Descriptio*, "A description of an admirable table of logarithms."

In his inaugural address to this international congress, Lord Moulton said, "The invention of logarithms came to the world as a bolt from the blue. No previous work had led up to it; nothing had foreshadowed it or heralded its arrival. It stands isolated, breaking in upon human thought abruptly, without borrowing from the work of other intellects or following known lines of mathematical thought. It reminds one of those islands in the ocean which rise suddenly from great depths and which stand solitary, with deep water close around all their shores."

To the preparation of this little book of 147 pages Napier had devoted twenty years of severe and steady labor. Seldom, if ever, were twenty years better spent. They were to exert a profound influence on methods of calculation and to be of inestimable value to mankind. Thanks to Napier's mathematical genius, power of concentration, and tenacity of purpose, mathematicians, scientists, astronomers, actuaries, engineers and countless others were to be saved untold hours of time-consuming mechanical computation. More than this, whole fields of mathematical knowledge, then unknown, were to be opened up, illuminated and clarified by the concept invented by Napier.

John Napier was born in 1550, his father, Alexander Napier, being then only sixteen years old. His family was old and respected, well known for its sense of responsibility to its own community as well as for its sturdy defense of its own individual rights. Several of John Napier's forebears had been provost (mayor) of Edinburgh, an office, in those wild and stormy days, that demanded ability, strength of character, and considerable Scottish tenacity of purpose.

Napier was educated at home until being sent, at the age of thirteen, to the University of St. Andrews. This was the usual age of entry to a university in the sixteenth century. He was not graduated at St. Andrews, but left Scotland and studied abroad, again a normal procedure in those days for the son of a Scottish man of means. He remained abroad for several years, but there is no record as to where or what he studied. In 1572 he married and settled down to live the life of a country gentleman on an estate in Stirlingshire owned by his father.

Scotland was then torn by bitter religious hatreds and quarrels, and Napier, true to the age in which he lived, threw himself into them with burning zeal. Presumably alarmed by the menace to his beloved Protestantism presented by Roman Catholic Spain, an alarm only temporarily dispelled by the defeat of the Spanish Armada in 1588, he emulated Archimedes in devising terrifying instruments of war which, as he quaintly put it "by the grace of God and worke of expert craftsmen" he proposed to build "for defence of this Iland." These weapons included a burning mirror with which he proposed to destroy the enemy's ships; a piece of artillery "destroying everything round the arc of a circle" and guaranteed by its designer "to kill thirty thousand Turks without the hazard of one Christian" (a truly splendid Christian weapon, though not from the point of view, possibly, of thirty thousand unbelieving Turks); a round metal chariot, a kind of forerunner of the tank, propelled by man-power and so constructed that its occupants could move it rapidly and easily while firing through small holes in it; and finally, "devises for sayling under water, with divers other devises and stratagemes for harming of the enemyes."

Napier's destructive weapons seem to have missed fire, not advancing further than the plans he drew up (and which are still in existence). Not so a book he published in 1593 in defense of Protestantism, in which, by thirty-six propositions, each duly proved by reference to the Apocalypse, he showed to his own complete satisfaction, and apparently to the complete satisfaction of thousands of readers, that the Pope was Antichrist and that the Creator proposed to end the world between the years 1688 and 1700.

The book proved an immense success, passing through twenty-one editions; to his dying day Napier regarded this book as his greatest service to mankind; no international congress, however, assembled to honor its tercentenary.

It was shortly after the publication of this book that Napier turned his mind to mathematics. After twenty years, he produced, in 1614, the book which has brought him undying fame and respect, and earned for him the gratitude of mankind. (One of the delegate speakers who honored the memory of Napier in 1914 was Salih Mourad, the representative of Turkey!)

In Napier's day, as we have seen, the sine of an angle was still regarded as a length. To avoid clumsy fractions, this length was calculated in very small units. As we saw in our last chapter, a compiler of values of trigonometric functions would choose a very large number such as ten million, or even ten billion, for the number of units in the radius. By calculating the length, say, of the half-chord, or sine, in terms of these units, he would be able to tabulate its value to a very close approximation without using fractions.

In trigonometry, it is often necessary to find the product of two sines. Since, under the system we have described, the values of these sines would be represented by numbers which might involve seven or even more figures, their multiplication would require the expenditure of much time and labor. Napier decided to try and find a method by which this labor might be lessened—a remarkable undertaking, when it is remembered that multiplication had for centuries been regarded as an essential and unavoidable process, and still more remarkable when it is remembered that no modern algebraic symbolism or analysis was then available for Napier. Fortunately, however, although armed only with arithmetic, and, later, with geometric representation of ratio and proportion, Napier possessed such power of application and so indomitable a will that he was able to overcome all handicaps, and discover not merely simple processes in place of multiplication, division, extraction of roots, etc., but also some of the most important and fundamental ideas and principles later to be established in other branches of mathematics. At the outset of his quest, he was concerned only with the multiplication of sines, but as his work progressed, Napier came to realize that he had lighted on concepts that were by no means restricted to trigonometric computations, but had a much wider field of application.

Let us leave Napier and his laborious arithmetic for the moment, and discuss the meaning and significance of logarithms, *from the modern point of view*. Thanks to modern algebraic ideas and symbolism this is a simple task. Without this equipment, it bristles with difficulties and complications, as even the cursory glance we shall give Napier's methods will show us.

If we may use the language of metaphor, we can liken Napier to a pathfinder who alone and with crude climbing equipment clambered to the summit of a high mountain. The path he discovered was steep and difficult, but by his aid others were able to follow in his footsteps. It does not detract in the least from the greatness of his achievement that having arrived at the top of the mountain, he and his friend Henry Briggs were then able to see a better track to the summit on which they stood, a track they subsequently always followed. When death robbed the world of Napier, his friend continued to guide newcomers along the better track, and to make that track still easier. As time went by, and algebraic concepts and symbolism were developed, the invention of new equipment, unheard of in Napier's day, made both the ascent of this track and also the improvement of it extremely easy matters.

To acquire enough of this necessary modern equipment to understand the significance of logarithms is very simple. It requires no greater mathematical background than that presented in Chapter III of this book, since a logarithm nowadays is simply an exponent. In Chapter III we saw how "a times a" was first written as aa, then as $a^2$. Similarly, "a times a times a" was written as aaa, then as $a^3$. Suppose we wish to multiply $a^2$ by $a^3$. This will be equivalent to multiplying aa by aaa, that is "a times a" by "a times a times a." Clearly, this result can only be aaaaa, or $a^5$. Now omit the intermediate steps. We have found that

$$a^2 \times a^3 = a^5.$$

In other words, the product of the *second* and *third* powers of the letter a is the *fifth* power of that letter. This is an example of one of the laws of exponents, laws that were, if not completely unknown, at least not formulated or generally known in Napier's day. This particular law, which applies to powers of any letter, is that the *product* of two or more powers of the same letter is another power of that letter which is obtained by *adding* the given exponents of the letter.

The ramifications of the laws concerning exponents extend throughout modern algebra. The easiest way for the non-mathematician to grasp the significance of some of them is to study particular cases in which the letter a is given a definite value, such as 2. Consider the series of numbers

2, 4, 8, 16, 32, 64, 128, 256, 512, 1024, etc.

These numbers may nowadays be written as

$2^1$, $2^2$, $2^3$, $2^4$, $2^5$, $2^6$, $2^7$, $2^8$, $2^9$, $2^{10}$, etc.

(1) By multiplication, we know that, say, $8 \times 64 = 512$.

In other words, using the lower line of numbers, $2^3 \times 2^6 = 2^9$.

Now, here, we have made use of *logarithms*. We could, if we wished, say that "3 is the logarithm of 8 to base 2; 6 is the logarithm of 64 to base 2; 9 is the logarithm of 512 to base 2," although it would not be a practical proposition to use 2 as a base since no logarithmic tables have been calculated to such base; it would therefore be impossible to look up the logarithms of numbers such as 3, 5, 7, 9, 10, 11, 12, 13, 14, 15, 17, etc. to base 2. Most logarithmic tables are based on 10. To this base, the logarithm of 10 is 1, the logarithm of 100 is 2, the logarithm of 1000 is 3. Our tables tell us that the logarithm of, say, 5 to this base 10 is .69897. All this means is that $10^{0.69897} = 5$.

Our illustration of logarithms to base 2 is, however, a perfectly good example of the law that states "the logarithm of a product equals the sum of the logarithms of the factors of that product." Thus, $2^3 \times 2^5 \times 2^7 \times 2^4 = 2^{19} = 524288$ (from a table of logarithms).

*By using logarithms we have changed the process of multiplication to that of addition.*

(2) By division, we know that, say, $256 \div 4 = 64$. In other words, $2^8 \div 2^2 = 2^6$. This is an example of the law that states "the logarithm of a quotient equals the logarithm of the dividend minus the logarithm of the divisor," or, since $2^8 \div 2^2$ means the same thing as the fraction, $\dfrac{2^8}{2^2}$ "the logarithm of a fraction equals the logarithm of the numerator minus the logarithm of the denominator."

*By using logarithms, we have changed the process of division to that of subtraction.*

(3) By arithmetic we know that $\sqrt{1024} = 32$. In other words, $\sqrt{2^{10}} = 2^5$: the logarithm 10 has been divided by 2 to find the logarithm of the square root.

By arithmetic we know that $\sqrt[3]{64} = 4$. In other words, $\sqrt[3]{2^6} = 2^2$: the logarithm 6 has been divided by 3 to find the logarithm of the cube root.

These are examples of the law that states "the logarithm

of the root of a number equals the logarithm of that number divided by the index of that root." [Remember that $\sqrt{2^{10}}$ stands for $\sqrt[3]{2^{10}}$]

*By using logarithms, the extraction of any root can be performed by a simple process of division.*

So much for the meaning and significance of logarithms. As presented in modern algebraic symbolism their simplicity makes us liable to underestimate the magnitude of Napier's achievement. The subject was far from simple as approached along the only lines open to him.

Let us glance at the way in which Napier expressed his concept of a logarithm. In a short book called the *Constructio*, published in 1619, two years after his death, Napier explains how he reached his conclusions, and calculated the tables given in the *Descriptio*. In the latter book he gave only such explanations as would enable mathematicians to grasp his new concept and experiment with his tables. He added the modest remark that he did not intend to explain his methods unless other mathematicians found his invention to be of value.

The *Constructio* shows how Napier gradually developed his ideas over a long period of time. One gets the impression that the germ of his idea grew from a consideration of arithmetic and geometric progressions. An arithmetic progression is a series of numbers, or terms, such as the particular example we considered on page 70. In general, these terms must increase (or decrease) in such a way that the difference between any term and the term that precedes it is always the same. [Napier does not mention decreasing arithmetic progressions, as the only type he made use of was the progression 0, 1, 2, 3, 4, 5, 6, 7. . . .]

A geometric progression is a series of numbers, or terms, which increase or decrease in such a way that the ratio between any term and the term that precedes it is constant. Thus, the numbers 1, 2, 4, 8, 16, 32, 64, 128 . . . form a geometric progression with common ratio $\frac{2}{3}$. Similarly, the numbers 729, 243, 81, 27, 9, 3, 1 form a geometric progression with common ratio $\frac{1}{3}$.

Napier was doubtless familiar with a fact that had been known to mathematicians certainly ever since the time of Archimedes, namely, that in a geometric progression commencing with 1, the product of any two terms is itself one of the terms in the progression. Take, for example, the progression 1, 3, 9, 27, 81, 243, 729 . . . If we label each of the terms in numerical order, commencing with zero as the label of the first term, it will be seen that the product of the term (for example) labeled 1 and the term labeled 3 gives the term labeled 4; the product of the term labeled 2 and the term labeled 4 gives the term labeled 6, and so on. Clearly, there is some connection between the numbers forming the geometric progression and those forming the arithmetic progression 0, 1, 2, 3, 4 . . .

A geometric progression was Napier's starting point in his long quest. It has been argued that a geometric progression was therefore the seed from which the concept of logarithms grew, and that Napier's invention must accordingly be classed with other mathematical discoveries as being the product of many minds. But the whole concept of his logarithms was so far removed from the concept and implications of a geometric progression that it would be equally far-fetched to credit the inventor of the number scale with the invention of logarithms simply because Napier made use of that number-scale.

Napier's first idea seems to have been to draw up a geometric progression commencing with the terms 10,000,000, 9,999,999, and continuing down to the region of zero, each successive term being $\dfrac{9,999,999}{10,000,000}$ of its preceding term. By labeling these terms by successive terms of an arithmetic progression he would have linked together a geometric progression with "label numbers" forming an arithmetic progression. The sum of the "label numbers" of any two terms in his geometric progression would have given the "label number" of the product of those two terms, which would then have been found alongside its "label number." Before we see how Napier discovered the impractibility of this plan, let us find out why he chose 10,000,000 for the first term in his geometric progression.

In the *Constructio* he gives us the reason for this choice. It was the number of units chosen, in the best trigonometric tables of his day, for the length of the radius on whose length the length of the sine depended. He says, "Instead of 100,000, which the less experienced make the greatest sine [*sinus totus*, the sine of 90°, which equalled the radius] the more learned put 10,000,000, whereby the difference of all sines is better expressed. Wherefore also we use the same for radius and for the greatest of our geometrical proportions."

This raises an interesting question. What table of sines did Napier use? There were several he may have possessed. He tells us he was occupied for twenty years in compiling the 90 pages of logarithmic tables in the *Descriptio*. Since he published this book in 1614, he must have commenced working on it about 1594. In that year there were several trigonometric tables in existence. One of these was the table, or *canon* published in 1551 by Rheticus. This table, however, as we saw, gave the values only at ten-minute angle intervals, so it would have been useless for Napier's purpose, which was to supply logarithms for the sines of angles differing only by one minute. Vieta, however, had extended this table, in 1579, to include values of the functions of angles between 0° and 90° at intervals of one minute. Since both these tables were based on a radius of 10,000,000 units, it seems probable that Napier used Vieta's extension of the original tables drawn up by Rheticus in 1551. The great *Opus Palatinum* of Rheticus was not published until 1596, as we saw, and Napier cannot have been aware of its existence when he discussed the choice of radius made by

"more learned" mathematicians. Otherwise, when emphasizing
the greater accuracy obtained by taking 10,000,000 units for
the radius he would surely have given first place to tables
based on a radius of 10,000,000,000 units, as were those in the
*Opus Palatinum*. His expression "less experienced" was possibly a reference to the compilers of the first two tables of
trigonometric functions published in England, one in 1590, the
other in 1594. His words "more learned" almost certainly refer
to Rheticus and Vieta.

Having chosen 10,000,000 as the first term in his geometric
progression, Napier proceeded to calculate one-hundred suc-
cessive terms, each term after the first being $\dfrac{9,999,999}{10,000,000}$ of the
term preceding it. If the continuation of this plan had proved
possible, an enormous array of numbers in geometric progression would have been available, each so close to the preceding
term that every value given in a table of sines would have been
included, as well as millions of other numbers. By choosing
this common ratio, Napier saw he would get a progression in
which the second term, 9,999,999, would be 1 less than the
first, while the "gap" between each succeeding pair of terms
would gradually become smaller and smaller. As the calculations proceeded, however, the number of terms required to fill
the gap between any two consecutive integers would become
greater and greater, until eventually the computation would
involve many millions of separate calculations. In the *Constructio*, Napier reproduces the actual figures he used in the
earliest stage of his work before he abandoned this procedure.
It is here that we come across the first known example of the
use of a period for indicating decimal fractions.

Decimal fractions are the most important development of
arithmetic since the introduction of Hindu-Arabic number-
symbols. They enable parts of a whole to be added, subtracted, multiplied and divided, etc., as whole numbers, and

thus avoid the clumsy and complicated methods involved in handling other fractions. Their use was first clearly advocated by a mathematician named Simon Stevin of Bruges, better known as Stevinus, in a work published in 1582 and called *La Practique d' Arithmetique*. Many previous mathematicians had almost, but not quite, hit on the idea of decimal fractions. For instance, tables of square roots had been drawn up for numbers which had first been multiplied by 1,000,000. The roots as given in the table were, of course, 1,000 times too great, but by this method it was possible to avoid the use of fractions, at least for approximate values of the roots. We have seen the somewhat similar method adopted by compilers of values of trigonometric functions. The idea ʻhat lies behind our present "decimals" was only gradually reached, the process of thought involved in its development covering hundreds of years. Stevinus had suggested a clumsy notation for decimal fractions, whereby 23.548, for instance, would be written as

$$23 \; ⓪ \; 5 \; ① \; 4 \; ② \; 8 \; ③ \; .$$

Napier seems to have been the first writer to use a period to mark the end of the whole numbers, and to realize that the decimal fractions occupied places which could be regarded as lying on an extended abacus, to the right of the units' wire. In the *Constructio*, Napier said, "In numbers distinguished by a period in their midst, whatever is written after the period is a fraction, the denominator of which is unity with as many ciphers [zeros] after it as there are figures after the period." (Macdonald's translation). Here is yet another example of a very simple idea that was to have tremendous consequences. In this connection, it must be remembered that the *Constructio* was not published until two years after Napier's death. So it is impossible to say with certainty whether these sentences were inserted by Napier or by Briggs, who revised the work before publication. The fact that Napier does not use a decimal point or its equivalent in his *Descriptio* seems to indicate that this simple yet fruitful invention is due to Briggs. On the other hand, it is difficult to imagine how Napier's calculations (which we shall now consider) could have been carried out without the use of the decimal point.

In order to calculate the terms of his geometric progression with as little labor as possible, Napier successively subtracted from each newly added term an easily computed fraction of that term, namely one-ten-millionth of it. An extract from the *Constructio* will make his method clear:

[First term of required geometric progression: 10,000,000.

Common ratio: $\dfrac{9,999,999}{10,000,000}$

Subtract $\dfrac{1}{10,000,000}$ of each term successively.]

$$
\begin{array}{r}
10000000.0000000 \\
1.0000000 \\
\hline
9999999.0000000 \\
.9999999 \\
\hline
9999998.0000001 \\
.9999998 \\
\hline
9999997.0000003 \\
.9999997 \\
\hline
9999996.0000006
\end{array}
$$

Napier proceeded in this way until he reached the hundredth term, which was approximately 100 less than the first term, being 9,999,900.0004950.

At this point, Napier seems to have realized that some other method would be necessary. It was at this stage that he introduced a geometric representation of ratio and proportion in order to discover more about the nature of the problem he was investigating. In other words, he began to apply *analysis* to his problem, though he had no algebraic symbolism as a language in which to express the steps in his analysis. His original system of logarithms and his methods of computation have long been abandoned; we need only glance at them sufficiently to enable us to grasp their underlying principles.

Napier's study of the problem led him to imagine the movement of a point along a line whose length represented 10,-000,000. Suppose AZ in Figure 61 is the line, and suppose a point moves from A toward Z in such a way that its initial velocity at A steadily decreases. The successive distances covered in equal intervals of time would become less and less, but the ratio between any two adjacent pair of these distances

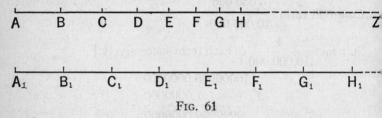

FIG. 61

would always be the same, since the point was conceived of as moving with a steadily decreasing velocity. Notice how Napier is here giving a "generalized" picture of a geometric progression; he is applying analysis to the problem and getting away from arithmetic with all its lack of generalization. In Figure 61, the points marked A, B, C, D . . . may represent not only successive positions of the moving point after equal intervals of time, but also the positions on a number scale of the terms 10,000,000, 9,999,999 and so on of Napier's geometric progression. The whole line AZ represents the first term, 10,000,000, the length BZ the second term, 9,999,999, and so on.

Napier then drew another line (the lower line in Figure 61) and imagined a point moving along it *without* change of velocity, its velocity throughout being the same as the initial velocity of the first moving point.

We may regard the distances marked $A_1B_1$, $B_1C_1$, $C_1D_1$ . . .

as equal time-intervals. Napier argued that when the point on the upper line had reached B, the point on the lower line would have reached a point, $B_1$, a little farther from $A_1$ than B was from A. The reason would be that while both points started with equal velocities, the point on the upper line was continually decreasing in velocity, while the other point continued with unchanged velocity. Taking AB as the unit in which both lines were to be measured, Napier estimated that $A_1B_1$ would equal 1.0000001. He therefore gave this "label number" to 9,999,999 and thus came to associate the length $A_1B_1$ with the length BZ, since this represented 9,999,999.

Instead of using an expression like "label numbers," Napier first called the numbers represented by $A_1B_1$, $A_1C_1$, $A_1D_1$ . . . "artificial numbers." Later, however, he invented the word "logarithms," using two Greek words, which we have already frequently met in other connections, the words *arithmos*, "number" and *logos*, "ratio." It is impossible to say exactly what he had in mind when making up this word. Seven years after his death, his friend and co-worker Henry Briggs said, "They seem to have been called logarithms . . . because they exhibit to us numbers which always preserve the same ratio to one another."

In Napier's original plan, the line AZ, which represented the *sinus totus*, or radius of 10,000,000 units, was arbitrarily given zero as its logarithm. Napier regarded 10,000,000 units as the distance of the moving point from Z after the expiration of no period of time. As he puts it "By the definition of distance nothing will be the logarithm of radius." By similar reasoning, he concluded that the length represented by $A_1B_1$ was the logarithm of the length represented by BZ; that $A_1C_1$ was the logarithm of CZ; that $A_1F_1$ was the logarithm of FZ, and so on, the smaller the number, the larger its logarithm. Later on, when he saw that he had hit on a concept that could be applied to numbers generally, and not merely to values of sines, he decided that for numbers greater than 10,000,000 the line AZ would have to be extended backwards and the moving point regarded as moving to the left. The logarithm of such a number was regarded by him as "defective," this being his word for the modern term "negative." He says, "Therefore we call the Logarithmes of the sines Abounding [positive] because they are always greater than nothing and set this marke + before them, or else none. But the logarithmes which are lesse than nothing we call Defective or wanting, setting this marke — before them." (*Descriptio*, Wright's translation.) We shall see how this concept was reversed when an improved type (the modern "common" logarithm) was brought forward by Napier and Briggs. Nowadays, the logarithm of any number greater than 1 is positive, that of any number less than 1 negative.

In order to find a method within the bounds of practical possibility whereby to calculate his logarithmic table, Napier made use of proportion. Without giving a rigorous proof, he showed that if $\dfrac{a}{b} = \dfrac{c}{d}$, then $\log b - \log a = \log d - \log c$. This proposition, which applies to modern logarithms as well as to those invented by Napier, is stated by him in the words, "The logarithms of similarly proportioned sines are equidifferent. This necessarily follows from the definitions of a logarithm and of the two motions. For since by these definitions arithmetical increase always-the-same corresponds to geometrical decrease similarly proportional, of necessity we conclude that equidistant logarithms . . . correspond to similarly proportioned sines." This statement is of great importance; it enabled Napier to select whatever logarithms were necessary for his table of sines and it—and other propositions developed from it—had to be applied before his logarithms could be used.

In the first (1614) edition of the *Descriptio*, the logarithms are given as seven-figure numbers. Later editions gave them to one figure less, probably because a small error in the early stage

of Napier's work, by accumulation, produced errors in the last
figure of his final logarithms. Here is a copy of the top and bottom lines of a page in the 1616 edition:

Deg 30

| m | Sine | Logarth | +\|−<br>Diff | Logarth | Sine | |
|---|---|---|---|---|---|---|
| 0 | 500000 | 693147 | 549306 | 143841 | 866025 | 60 |
| | | *[29 lines, here omitted]* | | | | |
| 30 | 507538 | 678183 | 529252 | 148930 | 861629 | 30 |

Deg 59

Values of the logarithms of functions of angles from 30°0′ to
30°30′ are found by reading down the lefthand column and
then across that line from left to right. Thus, log sin 30°30′ =
678183; those from 59°30′ to 59°60′ (that is, 60°) by reading up
the righthand column and then across from right to left. Thus:
log sin 60° (or 59°60′) = 143841.

It will be seen that these tables provide logarithms for values
of other functions besides sines. Bearing in mind that the sine
of any acute angle equals the cosine of its complement, it
will be seen that column 5 not only gives the logarithms of the
sines of angles in column 7, but also the logarithms of the cosines (as we should now say) of the angles in column 1. Similarly, column 3 gives not only the logarithms of the sines of
angles in column 1, it also gives the logarithms of the cosines
of the angles in column 7.

Many points of interest are suggested by the middle column.
This is a column of "differences" between the numbers in
columns 3 and 5. Since (to use modern terms) $\tan \theta = \dfrac{\sin \theta}{\cos \theta}$, it

follows that log tan $\theta$ = log sin $\theta$ — log cos $\theta$. So 693147 — 143841 will be "log sin 30° — log cos 30°" and will equal log tan 30°. On the other hand, 143841 — 693147 will be "log sin 60° — log cos 60°" and will equal log tan 60°. Now 143841 — 693147 gives a *negative* answer, but the digits in that answer are the same as those in the logarithm for tan 30° This explains the + and — signs in the table. All the angles in column 1 of the table lie between 0° and 45°; the values of their tangents are less than the value of the *sinus totus;* their logarithms (in Napier's system) were consequently positive as indicated by the + sign on column 1's side of the table All the angles in column 7 lie between 45° and 90°; their tangent values are greater than that of the *sinus totus;* their logarithms, consequently, in Napier's system, were negative as is indicated by the — sign on column 7's side of the table

Modern logarithmic tables of functions of angles could still be drawn up in this fashion, but with —|+ instead of +|— It has been found, however, that it is easier to change negative logarithms of functions of angles into positive numbers. This is done by adding 10, temporarily, to the negative logarithm. For example, using modern logarithms to base 10, a modern table gives

$$\log \tan 60° = + \ .23856$$
$$\log \tan 30° = +9.76144$$

In using these modern tables it has to be understood that 10 has been added in order to get the number +9.76144. Now 9.76144 — 10 = —.23856, which is the real logarithm of tan 30° in our present system. It will be seen that the digits in this number are the same as those in the logarithm of tan 60° So both "log tan 30°" and "log tan 60°" might both be indi
$$-|+$$
cated by printing the single entry .23856. Since, however, it is easier to work with positive logarithms, an extra column is now added so that only positive numbers appear in them.

Napier's tables occupied 90 pages of the little book in which he—almost timidly—submitted the results of twenty years' work to the judgment of other mathematicians. He told them that if they found his idea to be of value he would explain how he worked out the tables; he knew there must be defects and errors in his work. "Nothing," he said, "is perfect at birth." He was not kept long in suspense regarding the reception his work was to receive; it met with instant and admiring appreciation. An eminent mathematician of Cambridge University, Edward Wright, and a still more famous professor of mathematics at Gresham College, London, Henry Briggs, were especially interested. Wright had written several works on navigation and he at once saw the value of logarithms in navigational calculations. He lost no time in translating Napier's *Descriptio* into English. Before publishing the translation, he submitted it to Napier for his approval. When the translation was published, it contained a note written by Napier himself: "But now some of our Countreymen in this Island well affected to these studies, and the more publique good, procured a most learned Mathematician to translate the same into our vulgar English tongue, who after he had finished it, sent the Coppy of it to me, to bee seene and considered on by myselfe. I having most willingly and gladly done the same, finde it to bee most exact and precisely conformable to my minde and the originall." Edward Wright died in 1615 and his translation of Napier's book was published by his son, Samuel Wright, in 1618.

On March 10, 1615, Henry Briggs wrote to a friend that Napier "hath set my head and hands a work with his new and admirable logarithms. I hope to see him this summer, if it please God, for I never saw book that pleased me better, or made me more wonder." He adds that he was "wholly taken up and employed about the noble invention of logarithms lately discovered." That summer he spent a month with

Napier at Merchiston Castle, which Napier had inherited from his father. In 1624, seven years after Napier's death, Briggs published logarithmic tables under the title *Arithmetica Logarithmica*. In the preface, he mentions some important conversations that took place between him and Napier on the occasion of this visit. These conversations brought forth our modern logarithms. Having laboriously achieved his original object, Napier saw that certain changes in the structure he had erected would result in great simplifications and advantages. Regarding that twenty-year-old structure merely as a temporary scaffolding, Napier and Briggs proceeded to erect a new structure. When the new structure was completed, the scaffolding, without which it could not have been erected, was abandoned and today is merely of great historic interest.

The possibility of changes in his original ideas had been foreshadowed by Napier in the *Descriptio*. There he states that the choice of zero as the logarithm of the *sinus totus*, or radius, was purely arbitrary. "It was indeed left at libertie in the beginning, to attribute nothing, or 0, to any sine or quantitie [for its logarithm]." (Wright's translation.) Briggs, explaining that the logarithms in his *Arithmetica Logarithmica* are different from those in the *Descriptio*, says, "I myself, when expounding [Napier's original logarithms] in London to my auditors in Gresham College, remarked that it would be much more convenient that 0 should be kept for the logarithm of the whole sine, but that the logarithm of the tenth part of the same whole sine . . . should be 10,000,000,000 [that is, 1 followed by as many zeros as were desired: 7 for 7-figure tables, 10 for 10-figure tables, and so on]. And concerning that matter I wrote immediately to the author himself; and as soon as the season of the year and the vacation of my public duties of instruction permitted I journeyed to Edinburgh, where, being most hospitably received by him, I lingered for a whole month. But as we talked over the change in the logarithms he said that he had for some time been of the same opinion and had wished to accomplish it; he had however published those he had already prepared until he could construct more convenient ones if his affairs and his health would admit of it. *But he was of opinion that the change should be effected in this manner, that 0 should be the logarithm of unity and 10,000,000,000 that of the whole sine;* which I could not but admit was most convenient by far. So rejecting those [tables] I had previously prepared, I began at his exhortation to meditate seriously about the calculation of those logarithms." In his *Arithmetica Logarithmica*, published, as has been said, seven years after Napier's death, Briggs gave tables in which zero was taken as the logarithm of 1, while he fixed the logarithm, not of the whole sine, but of 10, as the basis of the system, choosing 1 (followed by fourteen zeros) as its logarithm. The addition of all these zeros was simply to enable him to express the logarithms, with great accuracy, in whole numbers. These changes had been suggested by Napier in an Appendix to the *Constructio* headed: "On the Construction of another and better kind of Logarithms, namely one in which the Logarithm of unity is 0." Napier continues, "Among the various improvements of Logarithms the more important is that which adopts a cypher as the Logarithm of unity, and 10,000,000,000 as the Logarithm of either one-tenth of unity or ten times unity." They had also been more vaguely hinted at in "An Admonition" printed in Wright's translation of the *Descriptio* in which Napier says, "But because the addition and subtraction of these former numbers may seeme somewhat painfull, I intend (if it shall please God) in a second Edition to set out such Logarithmes as shal make those numbers aboue written to fall upon decimal numbers such as 100,000,000; 200,000,000; 300,000,000, etc."

In this way, a system of logarithms to base 10 was developed, the system today known as *Common Logarithms*, to distinguish them from *Naperian Logarithms* or *Natural Log-*

*arithms*, which are not the same as those first proposed by Napier, despite their title.

In 1617 Briggs published a pamphlet containing the logarithms to base 10 of the first thousand numbers. In 1620 Edmund Gunter, Professor of Astronomy at Gresham College, London, published the first table of logarithmic sines to base 10. Then in 1624 appeared Briggs' *Arithmetica Logarithmica* giving the logarithms of numbers from 1 to 20,000 and from 90,000 to 100,000. Four years later, a Dutch mathematician, Adrian Vlacq, published at Gouda, in Holland a table that completed the gap left in Briggs' work between 20,000 and 90,000. Since he had to calculate 70,000 logarithms and only made use of 30,000 calculated by Briggs, Vlacq would have been justified in calling this a new work. Instead, he modestly described it as a second edition of Briggs' *Arithmetica Logarithmica*. Briggs himself had been busily filling in the gap in his tables. He wrote to a friend, "My desire was to have those chiliades [thousands] that are wantinge betwixt 20 and 90 calculated and printed, and I had done them all almost by my selfe, and by some frendes whom my rules had sufficiently informed, and by agreement the busines was conveniently parted amongst us; but I am eased of that charge and care by one Adrian Vlacque, an Hollander, who hathe done all the whole hundred chiliades and printed them in Latin, Dutche, and Frenche, 1000 bookes in these 3 languages, and hathe sould them almost all." Until some sixty years ago, the hundreds of tables of logarithms that had appeared were all based on the work done by Briggs and Vlacq in the thirteen years between 1615 and 1628. In addition to giving the logarithms of numbers from 1 to 100,000, Vlacq gave a table of logarithms of "Sinus" (sine), "Sin.Compl." (cosine), "Tang." (tangent), "Tang. Compl." (cotangent), "Secan." (secant), and "Sec.Compl." (cosecant), calculated to 10 figures and based on the values of these trigonometric functions given in the tables drawn up by Rheticus.

We have mentioned the logarithmic table drawn up by Edmund Gunter. He was also responsible for the idea that led to the modern slide rule. He drew a number of lines whose lengths were proportional to the logarithms of various numbers. By measuring various such lengths on a pair of compasses he was able to work multiplications and divisions. Figure 62 shows nine lines. The line at the top represents 1 unit and so may be regarded as representing log 10 and as being a yardstick by which other logarithms may be here represented.

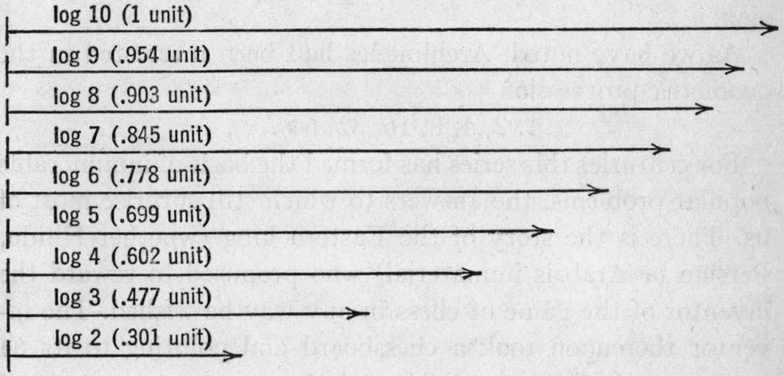

log 10 (1 unit)
log 9 (.954 unit)
log 8 (.903 unit)
log 7 (.845 unit)
log 6 (.778 unit)
log 5 (.699 unit)
log 4 (.602 unit)
log 3 (.477 unit)
log 2 (.301 unit)

FIG. 62

From logarithmic tables we know that log 9 = .954, so the second line has been made .954 units long, and therefore represents log 9. Similarly, the other lines represent log 8, log 7, log 6, log 5, log 4, log 3, and log 2. The logarithm of 1 now being zero, can have no length assigned to it.

To multiply 4 by 2, place the lengths representing their logarithms end to end. The resulting length will be .903 units, which represents log 8. By drawing a larger number of lines, the possibility of multiplication by this method will be indefinitely increased.

In 1636, a well-known mathematician, the Reverend William Oughtred (who is said to have expired in a transport of joy on hearing that the House of Commons had voted for the return of Charles II and an end of Puritan rule) placed two of Gunter's scales side by side so that one of them could slide along the other. This is the principle of the modern slide rule, another debt we owe to Napier.

At the same time that Napier was working out his invention, a Swiss watchmaker, Jobst Bürgi, was working on a similar project, but by an entirely different line of approach. While Napier's reasoning was geometric, Bürgi's was algebraic. It was definitely based on the structure of a geometric progression.

As we have noted, Archimedes had been interested in the geometric progression

$$1, 2, 4, 8, 16, 32, 64 \ldots$$

For centuries this series has formed the basis of innumerable popular problems, the answers to which still surprise most of us. There is the story of the Eastern king (whether Hindu, Persian or Arab is immaterial) who promised to reward the inventor of the game of chess in any way he wished. The inventor thereupon took a chessboard and pointing to its 64 squares made the apparently modest request for one grain of wheat for the first square, two grains for the next, four grains for the next, and so on. The really industrious reader will now take pencil and paper and discover whether it is a fact that if 10,000 tons of this wheat were loaded into *each* of 131,762,457 ships, (allowing 7,000 grains to 1 pound), 93,709,551,615 grains would still remain to be handled.

A similar type of problem concerns the blacksmith who charged a penny for the first nail in a horseshoe, two pence for the next, four pence for the third nail, and so on for twenty-four nails. A modern version is that of the applicant for a job who suggests a salary of 1 cent for the first day, 2 cents for the next, 4 cents for the third, and so on, generously agreeing to start again from scratch at the commencement of each month.

It was not, however, this type of problem that interested Archimedes and later mathematicians in this geometric progression. As we have seen, they were interested in trying to discover the connection that existed between it and the arithmetic progression 0, 1, 2, 3, 4, 5 . . .

Here was a real problem, whose solution was eventually to lead to the discovery of the laws concerning exponents, concepts which were to lead to great simplification and extension of algebraic ideas. Early in the sixteenth century it had been realized that addition of any two terms in the above arithmetic progression had some connection with multiplication of the correspondingly placed terms in the geometric progression. Nowadays, as we have seen, we have only to write the series

$$2^0, 2^1, 2^2, 2^3, 2^4, 2^5 \ldots$$

to see at a glance the connection between them, but in 1600 this symbolism had yet to be developed. The idea behind it, however, enabled Jobst Bürgi to produce a table of antilogarithms (to base 1.0001). Since, to use our modern base of 10, $10^2 = 100$, 2 is said to be the logarithm of 100 to base 10, *and 100 is said to be the antilogarithm of 2 to base 10.* In Bürgi's tables, the logarithms were printed in red, the antilogarithms in black, so he called his tables *Die Rothe Zahl.* They were published in 1620, but by that time the much simpler logarithms of Napier and Briggs, based on 10, were already firmly established and accepted by mathematicians everywhere. Although in England today tables of antilogarithms (to base 10) are in use, they are unnecessary, since the number corresponding to any given logarithm can easily be found from modern tables of logarithms.

The invention of logarithms may be regarded as marking the end of the renaissance period of mathematical development. From this point we shall enter the period of modern mathematics.

# CHAPTER VI

# Preparing the Ground for Newton and Leibniz

W HEN Napier was a boy of fourteen, Galileo Galilei, who was to become the father of dynamics—the branch of science that deals with the action of force in producing motion —was born in Pisa, the Italian city famous for its leaning tower.

For nearly two thousand years, the inadequate and often incorrect notions of Aristotle had held undisputed sway in all branches of science. The solitary intellectual revolt, that of Aristarchus, which we discussed in Chapter IV, had been quickly forgotten, and had lain in the faded manuscripts of Archimedes, unknown and inaccessible to European students throughout the Middle Ages.

Galileo was the son of an impoverished Florentine nobleman who was himself interested in mathematics, and also in music. When seventeen years old, Galileo was sent to the University of Pisa to study medicine. One day, while attending a service in the cathedral, his mind wandered from the contemplation of heaven to that of a great bronze lamp suspended from the ceiling. He watched its oscillations to and fro, and, using the beat of his pulse for a time-keeper, was surprised to find that the lamp took as long to make a tiny oscillation as it had taken to make a great one. [Later, in 1656, Huygens, the great Dutch scientist, showed that the time required for one complete vibration, or oscillation of a pendulum was always $2\pi\sqrt{\dfrac{l}{g}}$, where l

stands for the length of the pendulum in feet, and g stands for the acceleration due to gravity, about 32 feet per second every second. Thus, if a pendulum is 2 feet long, it will always take about 1.57 seconds to go to and fro.]

Galileo's interest in science was aroused by this problem, and was further stimulated by a chance attendance at a lecture on mathematics, his first encounter with this subject. So great was his interest in science that he was led to abandon his medical studies, and, on leaving the university when twenty-one years of age, to commence to investigate the subject of dynamics.

When twenty-five years old, he was appointed a professor of mathematics at Pisa, and while holding this appointment, he made his famous experiments with falling bodies, using for this purpose the leaning tower of Pisa. Before a crowd of students, professors and priests he dropped two pieces of metal, one of them ten times the weight of the other, from the top of the tower. They struck the ground at practically the same moment. Even this did not shake the faith of the other professors in the teaching of Aristotle, who had said that a heavy body fell faster than a light one. Indeed, when the youthful professor had the temerity to announce that Aristotle had been wrong, the authorities at Pisa were so horrified at such sacrilegious insolence they made things so unpleasant for Galileo that he was forced to resign his professorship.

He was, however, able to obtain a professorship of mathematics at Padua, where no doubt he was to hear many stories of famous alumni such as Cardan and Copernicus, who had studied in his department there. Padua was a city of the Venetian Republic, where freedom of thought was encouraged. So at Padua Galileo was able to continue his experiments and teaching in a friendly atmosphere. So successful was he that scholars

from all over Europe—some of them princes—flocked to his
lectures. Eventually, he had to be given a lecture hall that
would accommodate 2000 people. He remained at Padua for
nearly eighteen years, and so highly were his lectures and his
scientific researches valued that his salary rose from 180 florins
for 1592 to 1000 florins for 1610.

Archimedes had built up the science of equilibrium, or
"balance"; it was left to Galileo to lay the foundations of the
science of *motion*. Without his work in this field it is doubtful
whether even Newton would have solved the problem of the
motion of the planets.

Starting with the assumption that if a body falls freely from
rest toward the earth, there are equal increases in velocity in
equal times (that is, it moves with uniform acceleration, as we
now should say) he deduced the extremely important law that
*the distance covered is proportional to the square of the time taken.*

The automobile has familiarized the modern world with the
idea of "acceleration," or increase in velocity during a unit
period of time. It will therefore be obvious that if $a$ (feet per
second per second) represents the uniform acceleration of a
body falling from rest, and $v$ (feet per second) its final velocity
after $t$ (seconds), $v$ must equal $at$.

Now suppose another body falls for $t_1$ seconds and acquires a
final velocity of $v_1$ feet per second. Since its acceleration remains the same as in the former case, $v_1$ must equal $at_1$.

Comparing these two results, we see that the same "$a$" is
equal to both $\dfrac{v}{t}$ and to $\dfrac{v_1}{t_1}$. So $\dfrac{v}{t} = \dfrac{v_1}{t_1}$, or $\dfrac{v}{v_1} = \dfrac{t}{t_1}$.

Now suppose that $v$ and $t$ have the same meanings as before,
and that $d$ (feet) represents the distance through which the
body falls freely. The velocity steadily increases from 0 to $v$,
so, since the acceleration, or increase in velocity, is uniform
throughout the falling movement, the *average* velocity will be

$\dfrac{0 + v}{2}$, or $\frac{1}{2}v$. Since the time occupied is $t$ seconds, the distance covered will be $\frac{1}{2}vt$. So

$$d = \tfrac{1}{2}vt.$$

This result may be represented (as Galileo represented it) by the area of a right triangle having its shorter sides respectively equal to $v$ units and $t$ units (since the area of a triangle equals $\frac{1}{2}$ base times height), thus:

FIG. 63

Now compare the distances $d$ ft. and $d_1$ ft. covered by two bodies that fall from rest. Suppose one of them falls for $t$ seconds, acquiring a final velocity of $v$ ft. per sec., and that the other falls for $t_1$ seconds, acquiring thereby a final velocity of $v_1$ ft. per sec. These distances will respectively be represented by the areas of the triangles shown in Figure 64.

By Euclid's geometry we know that the areas of similar triangles bear the same proportion to each other as do the squares of their bases. So, from Figure 64,

$$\frac{d}{d_1} = \frac{t^2}{t_1^2}.$$

Here we have a geometric proof of the law discovered by Galileo.

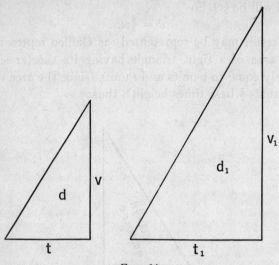

By observing the times of descent of bodies rolling down inclined planes, Galileo illustrated the truth of this law. Shortly before he died he was able to prove that the velocity acquired by a body in descending a long inclined plane was the same as that acquired in descending a short one *of equal height*.

In 1607, or thereabouts, a young apprentice to a spectacle maker, named Hans Lippershay, of Middleburg, Holland, was playing with his master's spectacle lenses. He found that by holding two of them in a certain position, objects became enlarged. He pointed this out to his master, who placed two lenses in a tube and displayed it as a toy in his shop window. Here it was seen by a government official, who bought it and gave it to Prince Maurice of Nassau, the stadtholder of Holland, who saw the possibilities of the "toy" as a spy-glass for military use. By 1609, news of this invention reached Galileo,

who soon made a spy-glass that greatly surpassed the one made
by Lippershay. He was summoned to Venice to demonstrate
his instrument, and many of the Venetian senators, though of
an advanced age, climbed to the top of the highest church
tower in Venice and were able to see the sails of an approaching
ship two hours before they were visible to the naked eye. The
Doge of Venice saw the immense possibilities of the instrument in naval and military operations, and was delighted when
Galileo presented his model to him. It was on this occasion
that his salary was raised to 1000 florins a year. Galileo then
made four other telescopes, as his instruments were named
(from the Greek *tele*, "far," *skopos*, "watcher"), each of them
more powerful than the last. With the fifth, which made objects appear more than thirty times as large as they were when
viewed by the naked eye, he noticed that on January 7, 1610,
there were two small stars to the east of the planet Jupiter and
one to the west. The next night, to his amazement, all three
were to the west of the planet. Three nights later he found
there was another small star revolving around Jupiter. Here
he had discovered a striking confirmation of the Copernican
theory that the planets themselves revolved around the sun.
Once more he aroused the frenzied opposition of Churchmen
who preferred the teaching of Aristotle, which considered the
earth—and consequently man—the center of the universe.
One of them even declared that Galileo had put these four new
satellites (revolving around Jupiter) in his telescope! However, the Grand Duke of Tuscany was delighted when Galileo
named these four satellites "the Medicean stars" after the
family name of the ruler of Tuscany, and offered him the
well-paid sinecure of being the Duke's official "Philosopher
and Mathematician." Soon afterwards, Galileo accepted the
offer (which included the title "First Mathematician to the
University of Pisa" though no duties at Pisa were involved)
and was unwise enough to leave the freedom-loving atmos-

phere of Venetia, whose rulers were jealous of the power of the Pope, and return to Tuscany, where he should have known his unorthodox views would receive bitter opposition. At Florence, by the aid of his telescope, he made further discoveries that confirmed the truth of the Copernican system, and he also discovered the existence of sun-spots—another cause of deep offense to the followers of Aristotle, who accepted his view that the sun was without spot or blemish. Despite the violent uproar of the more ignorant churchmen, certain ecclesiastics of that day, such as the Pope himself and Cardinal Barberini, who later became Pope, did not oppose his views. Cardinal Barberini actually confirmed Galileo's discoveries by looking at the stars through his telescope. Nevertheless, the forces of reaction gained the upper hand, and Copernicus' book was placed on the Index of prohibited books (where it remained for two hundred years). Galileo was advised to cease supporting the system proposed by Copernicus, but nevertheless in 1630 he published a book which indirectly supported that system. By that time his friend Barberini had become Pope under the title of Urban VIII, but he now listened to the reactionaries who suggested that a character in Galileo's book called Simplicio ("the simpleton") represented him, as the supporter of the system of Ptolemy, which was based on that of Aristotle. The sale of the book was prohibited, and a commission was appointed, which reported unfavorably on Galileo. The report condemned him for "maintaining that the earth moves and that the sun is stationary." Soon Galileo was summoned to appear before the Inquisition. On June 22, 1633, Galileo was forced, under threat of torture, to declare, "I abjure, curse, and detest the said errors and heresies and generally every error and sect contrary to the said Holy Church; and I swear that I will nevermore in future say or assert anything verbally or in writing which may give rise to a similar suspicion of me; but that if I know any heretic, or any one suspected of heresy, I will denounce him to this Holy Office or to the Inquisitor and Ordinary [bishop] of the place in which I may be."

It is easy to condemn Galileo—as many of his biographers have condemned him—for lacking the courage to face martyrdom, but only those who in similar circumstances have displayed that courage have the right to criticize the old man who thus perjured his conscience. His life was now broken, and although he still continued to do scientific work (on which much of Newton's work on the laws of motion was to be based) he became blind and died in January, 1642, still under the outrageous supervision of the Inquisition, and to all intents and purposes a prisoner in his own home.

Apart from his actual discoveries in connection with astronomy and dynamics, Galileo's work laid the foundations of the modern scientific method which regards the collection of experimental evidence as the essential prelude to the formulation of scientific laws and theories.

Strange to say, Galileo ignored three great laws concerning the movements of the planets that were empirically discovered by his great contemporary Johann Kepler, and which form one of the landmarks in the story of mathematical science. They were to provide Newton with the basis of much of his work on universal gravitation.

Johann Kepler, whose "laws" have placed him among the foremost astronomers of all time, was born in 1571 at Weil der Stadt near Stuttgart. His father was the drunken son of a former burgomaster of the town who, having run through the fortune left him by his father, became a mercenary soldier. His mother was unable to read or write, and was suspected of dabbling in witchcraft. When his father returned to civil life he opened an inn, and presumably made a little money, for he saw to it that Johann received a sufficiently good education to enable him to enter the school maintained by the Duke of

Würtemberg for promising boys. From this school he passed on to the University of Tübingen, his original intention being to become a minister of the Lutheran Church. He became interested in astronomy, however, and strongly supported the Copernican theory. In 1594 he was appointed to a lectureship at the University of Grätz, in Austria. There he had the misfortune to meet a moderately wealthy widow, and the still greater misfortune to marry her, since the marriage proved to be a constant source of unhappiness. Another misfortune fell on him when Grätz fell under Catholic control and Kepler, being a Protestant, was expelled from the university. In the long run, this misfortune bore rich scientific fruit, for it brought Kepler into association with Tycho Brahe, and this association in turn was to give him access to the tremendous collection of astronomical data brought together by the Danish-Swedish astronomer.

Tycho Brahe was born in Sweden some twenty years after that country had finally secured its independence from Denmark. He was a member of a wealthy, aristocratic family that had branches in both Sweden and Denmark. An eclipse of the sun in 1560 led him to study astronomy at the University of Copenhagen, and later at the University of Rostock, the Baltic town that had once been a prosperous member of the Hanseatic League. While there he quarreled with a Danish nobleman, fought a duel, and had the misfortune to lose part of his nose, the missing portion being replaced by a piece of material composed of wax, gold and silver. Some time later he incurred the violent opposition of his aristocratic family by marrying a peasant girl, an action he apparently never had reason to regret.

In 1576, Frederick II, King of Denmark and Norway, gave him the island of Hveen, in the Sound that separates Sweden and Denmark. Here he erected an observatory, by the aid of considerable financial assistance from Frederick II, which was

given the name of Uraniburg—"the Castle of the Heavens."
Tycho Brahe remained at Uraniburg for more than twenty
years and made the greatest and most accurate collection of
astronomical data that existed before the invention of the telescope. When James VI of Scotland—"the wisest fool in Chris-
tendom," who later became James I of England—went to Denmark to marry the Danish Princess Anne, he visited Brahe at
Uraniburg and wrote some verses in praise of the astronomer.

After the death of Frederick II, Denmark withheld financial
assistance from Brahe, so the astronomer, always a man of
violent temper, went to live in Germany. Here he received an
invitation from the Emperor Rudolph II to become his "Imperial Mathematician" at the castle of Benatky, near Prague,
with a salary of 3000 crowns a year. Brahe's removal to
Benatky coincided with Kepler's removal from the University
of Grätz. Wanting an assistant, Brahe approached Kepler,
and the latter accepted the invitation and went to live at
Prague, where Brahe had gone to live at the request of the
Emperor. The next year—1601—Brahe unexpectedly died at
the age of 55 and on his death-bed asked Kepler to finish some
tables on planetary motions on which he had been engaged for
some time. In this way the finest collection of astronomical observations ever made up to that time passed into the keeping
of Johann Kepler, who shortly succeeded Brahe as the Emperor Rudolph's astronomer. His royal master had an unfortunate habit of omitting to pay him his salary; so he was
forced to earn money by casting horoscopes—a perfectly re-
spectable undertaking in his day. More domestic troubles
crowded in on him: his favorite child died of small pox: his
wife became insane and died; he had to spend many months in
defending his mother against a charge of witchcraft; the arrears
of his salary accumulated more and more.

Despite all these distressing events, Kepler concentrated
his mind on the task of finding the laws that lay behind

planetary motion, basing his work on the mass of observations taken by Tycho Brahe. After eight years of work he was able to publish a book on the motions of the planet Mars. For years, misled by the opinion of Copernicus, who had believed that each planet moved around the sun in a circle, Kepler had struggled in vain to account for the irregular movements of this planet, as recorded by Brahe's observations. At last, after making tremendous computations, he found that the movements of Mars could only be accounted for if its orbit were an ellipse which had the sun at one of its foci.* Kepler's first law dealt with this elliptical movement of planets.

By studying the great mass of observations at his disposal he concluded that, contrary to all belief, the planet Mars did not move with uniform, unchanging speed. He found, however, that if an imaginary line were drawn from the planet to the sun, this line would sweep through equal areas in equal times, no matter what might be the position of Mars on its elliptical orbit when the observations commenced. From this, it follows that Mars moves fastest when nearest the sun, slowest when furthest away from the sun. After reaching similar conclusions regarding the orbit and movement of the earth, he extended them by analogy to the other planets. These two laws were published in 1609 in the book already mentioned, entitled *De motibus stellae Martis*, "Concerning the movements of the star Mars." In this same book he touched on the subject of gravity and suggested that the "pull" of the moon was responsible for tides on the earth.

Ten years later, he published a book called *Harmonices*

* An ellipse is traced out when a point moves in such a way that the sum of its distances from two fixed points is constant. Each of these fixed points is called a *focus* of the ellipse. Those who are not mathematically-minded can easily grasp the meaning of this statement if they will mark two points, F and $F_1$ on a piece of paper, then fasten the ends of a piece of tape that is longer than $FF_1$ by thumb-tacks at these points. If the tape is now stretched taut with a pencil point and the latter is allowed to trace out a curve, this curve will be an ellipse whose *foci* will be the points F and $F_1$.

*Mundi*, in which he attempted to establish a theory that the planets, as they rushed through the heavens with varying speeds, set up a celestial harmony which was audible to the "sentient soul" behind the universe. In the midst of these flights of fancy Kepler laid down his third and greatest law, that the square of the time of one complete revolution of any planet is proportional to the cube of its mean distance from the sun. We can picture the joy and satisfaction Kepler must have felt when, after having pored over his vast accumulation of measurements, and having vainly tried in countless ways to find some numerical connection between the distances of planets from the sun and their times of revolution around the sun, he suddenly discovered that the ratio between the second power of the time and the third power of the distance was always the same. If we make use of modern figures and express the distance from the sun in astronomical units (an astronomical unit, A.U., is the average distance of the earth from the sun) we get the following results:

|         | Time in years (T) | Distance (D) | $T^2$ | $D^3$ |
|---------|-------------------|--------------|-------|-------|
| Mercury | .24  | .387 A.U.  | .058  | .058  |
| Venus   | .61  | .723 A.U.  | .378  | .378  |
| Earth   | 1.00 | 1.00  A.U. | 1.00  | 1.00  |
| Mars    | 1.98 | 1.524 A.U. | 3.54  | 3.54  |
| Jupiter | 11.86 | 5.202 A.U. | 140.7 | 140.8 |
| Saturn  | 29.46 | 9.539 A.U. | 867.9 | 868.0 |

Although Kepler's work lay almost exclusively in the realm of mathematical astronomy, he made important contributions to pure mathematics. He was largely responsible for the introduction of logarithms in Germany, while he was the first of the seventeenth-century mathematicians to make use of methods that involved the idea of "infinity" that had been banished from mathematics ever since the time of Zeno. In 1613 the vintage was especially good, and Kepler was led to consider the best method for gauging the contents of a wine cask. Basing his method on the work of Archimedes, he took a short cut by making use of what subsequently became known as "infinitesimals" (which we shall consider shortly). Although his methods aroused much adverse criticism, since they employed illogical statements regarding "infinitesimals," they achieved the required results and prepared the way for the method of *indivisibles*, which we shall meet when we come to discuss Cavalieri, and for the calculus of Newton and Leibniz.

Despite the worldly misfortunes that dogged his footsteps, Kepler remarried in 1612, and apparently found real happiness this time.

His books show a strange blend of mystical speculation, of a highly fanciful nature, combined with a sure grasp of scientific truth. His three great laws reduced the solar system to simplicity: they showed that the sun was situated at the common focus of the elliptical orbits of all the planets, and they enabled astronomers to calculate the exact position which any planet would occupy at any given moment. Kepler died in 1630, when 59 years old, while on a journey undertaken to try to obtain some of the arrears of salary due to him.

The story of Napier, Galileo and Kepler has taken us into the seventeenth century. That century was to see tremendous and brilliant achievements in mathematics in many countries of Europe.

In 1596, the year when Napier started out on his twenty-year search that was to lead to such surprising simplifications in computation, a boy was born near Tours, in France, who was to revolutionize mathematical concepts, and usher in modern mathematics. René Descartes, like Napier, was the son of a wealthy landowner. He was sent at the age of eight to a Jesuit boarding school, where, on account of ill-health—or maybe by virtue of possessing an influential father—he was allowed to lie in bed as late each morning as he pleased, a habit he retained all his comparatively short life of fifty-four years.

Despite being an apt pupil, he later declared that his studies had done nothing for him but to give him a conviction of his complete ignorance. In this he was like the great Isaac Newton, who declared, toward the end of his brilliant life, that he had always felt like a boy playing by the seashore, while the great ocean of truth lay all undiscovered before him.

Descartes could find no mental satisfaction in any of the prevailing systems of philosophy taught him by the Jesuits. "And this is why," he says, "as soon as my age permitted me to quit my preceptors, resolving to seek no other science but that which I could find in myself or else in the great book of the world, I employed the remainder of my youth in travel, in seeing courts and camps, in frequenting people of diverse humors and conditions." In these words Descartes gives us the key to his strange, unsettled life of intermittent intercourse with others and periods of solitude. This little man with a large head, prominent nose and projecting forehead over which thick black hair fell almost to his eyebrows, and who nearly always dressed in somber black, had a cold and selfish disposition. He never married, though he had an illegitimate daughter who died in infancy. His main object in life was to establish a new school of philosophy; his great mathematical invention only saw the light of day incidentally, as an appendix to a work on philosophy. For a time, his philosophical followers, the "Cartesians," as they were called, flourished in certain European countries, despite bitter opposition. Their tenets have long since been abandoned; the mathematical matter that was relegated to an appendix has won undying fame for its author.

On leaving school, Descartes followed the usual procedure for a young man of wealth in the France where Cardinal Richelieu was rising to power under the youthful Louis XIII. He joined in the trivialities of the world of fashion in Paris and later entered the army, in the service of Prince Maurice of Orange, in Holland. While in Paris, however, he came in contact with a French mathematician, Claude Mydorge, who aroused his interest in mathematics. It has been suggested that Descartes joined the army in order to break away from the distractions of fashionable Paris, but it was the normal thing in his day for the son of a wealthy man to enter either the army or the church.

Descartes' arrival in Holland coincided with a lull in the fighting there, and he made use of the leisure time thus afforded him by applying himself to the study of mathematics. After spending two years in Holland without seeing any fighting, he joined the Bavarian army that was then taking part in the disastrous Thirty Years' War that was soon to sweep like a tempest through Germany. He tells us that during this campaign, in the winter of 1619, while in winter quarters on the Danube, he "was filled with enthusiasm and discovered the foundations of a marvellous science." These words are usually supposed to refer to his discovery of analytic geometry, but they may refer to the general philosophical methods he was later to employ.

Descartes took part in the battle of Prague in September, 1620, while Briggs in England was busy preparing tables of logarithms for his *Arithmetica Logarithmica*, and the following year he saw service in Hungary. This was the end of his soldiering, for he took to traveling widely through Europe. The death of his mother gave him an independent income which enabled him to follow his own inclinations. He settled in Paris, where he became interested in the theory of the refraction of light and in the grinding of lenses for optical instruments. Scientists everywhere were at this time excited by the new instrument called a telescope that was laying the foundations of modern astronomy.

Before long, Descartes found the visits of his fashionable friends more than he could bear; they distracted his meditations—one of them actually disturbed him in bed as early as eleven in the morning! Disgusted at such intolerable interruptions in a student's life he eventually left Paris and settled in Holland in order to be able to spend his days in meditation and the search for truth. For the next twenty years he moved from place to place in Holland, changing his home no fewer than twenty-four times. At last, he was free from intruders. "I sleep ten hours every night," he wrote from Amsterdam, "and no care ever shortens my slumber." Here he studied physics, mathematics and music, in which he was deeply interested. He was never a strenuous worker. He himself wrote, "The principle which I have always observed in my studies, and which I believe has helped me most to gain what knowledge I have, has been never to spend beyond a few hours daily in thoughts which occupy the imagination, and a very few hours yearly in those which occupy the understanding, and to give myself all the rest of my time to the relaxation of the senses and the repose of the mind." Descartes' background may be unusual and not particularly attractive; his genius, on the other hand, places him among the greatest mathematicians of all time.

In 1637 he published a book outlining his views on philosophy and entitled *A Discourse on the Method of rightly controlling the Reason and seeking Truth in the Sciences*. He had been working on it intermittently for eighteen years. There were three appendices to the book, the third being on geometry. This third appendix is the one on which Descartes' fame rests. It first deals with problems that can be solved by constructions which employ only ruler and compasses, and

then passes on to consider various types of curves. Euclidean
geometry, which Descartes had studied as a young man, consists of a large number of separate theorems, each of which,
to all outward appearance, stands alone. Descartes perceived
that certain general truths lay behind geometric figures. "But
it did not seem to me," he said "that they told my mind with
sufficient clearness why the things were as I was shown and by
what means their discovery was attained."

Descartes' genius showed itself in the method he found
whereby any curve may be represented by means of some relationship or other that can be shown to exist between the
lengths of two straight lines, "than which I could find no objects more simple or capable of being more distinctly represented to my imagination and senses," as he puts it.

The lengths of these two straight lines are known as co-
ordinates, though Descartes did not use this term, its invention
being due to Leibniz, whom we shall meet later. In Figure 65,
in addition to a given curve, two straight lines called *axes of co-
ordinates* have been drawn at right angles to each other. These
axes are usually drawn in this way, but this is not an essential
requisite.

To illustrate the meaning of "coördinates," four points, A,
B, C and D have been taken on the curve. They lie respectively
in what are known as the 1st., 2nd., 3rd., and 4th. *quadrants*, or
"quarters" made by the two axes.

The coördinates of A are the distances YA (or OX) and XA
(or OY). Each of these is *positive*, since measurements to the
right of the vertical axis, and measurements upward from the
horizontal axis are considered positive.

The coördinates of B are the distances $Y_1B$ (or $OX_1$) and
$X_1B$ (or $OY_1$). The first of these is *negative*, since measurements to the left of the vertical axis are negative; the second,
being measured upward from the horizontal axis, is *positive*.

The coördinates of C are the distances $Y_2C$ (or $OX_2$) and

$X_2C$ (or $OY_2$). Each is negative, measurements downward from the horizontal axis being negative, as well as distances to the left of the vertical axis.

The coördinates of D are the distances $Y_3D$ (or $OX_3$) and $X_3D$ (or $OY_3$). It will be seen that the first of these is positive, the second negative.

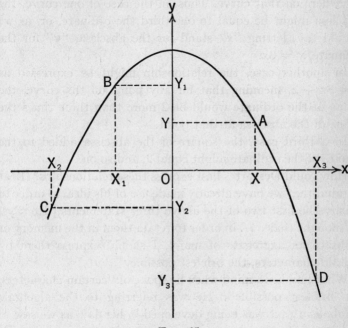

Fig. 65

Fifty-five years after the *Discourse* was published, Leibniz called a measurement to the right or left of the vertical axis the *abscissa* of the point; that upward or downward from the horizontal axis, the *ordinate* of the point. Both these words had been used by mathematicians in ancient times, though, of course, in different connections. The word *abscissa* (*ab*, "from," *sciss-*, "cut") originally meant the same thing as our modern "line segment," or part "cut off" from a line which has unlimited length; as such it was used by Apollonius in conic sections. Our word "scissors" comes from the same root as *abscissa*.

Descartes then showed that for every curve, some relationship could be shown to exist between the coördinates of a point anywhere on that curve. Thus, in the case of one curve, the abscissa might be equal to one-third the ordinate, or, as we should say, letting "x" stand for the abscissa, "y" for the ordinate, $y = 3x$.

In another case, the relationship might be expressed as $y = 3x + 2$, meaning that for any point on the curve, the value of the ordinate would be 2 more than three times the value of the abscissa at that point.

In a third case, the square of the abscissa added to the square of the ordinate might equal 9, and so on.

How could Descartes best express these relationships? [Bear in mind that we have already made use of his idea, in order to clarify the first two of the above three statements.] He says, "I thought that . . . in order to retain them in the memory or embrace an aggregate of many, I should express them by certain characters, the briefest possible."

What had he in mind when he spoke of "certain characters, the briefest possible"? He was referring to the algebraic symbolism that was being developed in his day, as we saw in Chapter III. By letting x represent an abscissa and y an ordinate, he could express relationships such as $y = x$, or $y = 2x$, or $y = 2x + 3$. The reader who has forgotten his analytic geometry can discover for himself that each of these equations represents a straight line, if he will take a piece of squared paper, draw two axes at right angles, choose two values for x for each equation, calculate the related values for y, then mark these points and draw a line through them. The first two lines, $y = x$, and $y = 2x$ will pass through the

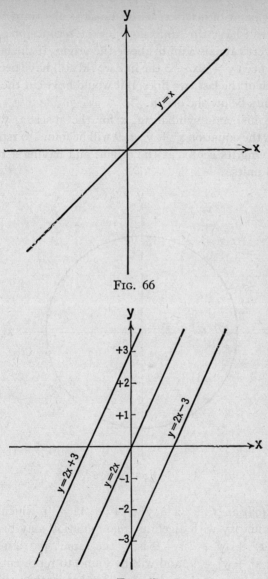

FIG. 66

FIG. 67

origin, or point of intersection of the axes; the third line, $y = 2x + 3$, will have the same slope as the second line, but will cut the vertical axis 3 units above the origin. If the last equation had been $y = 2x - 3$ the line would still have been parallel to each of the last two lines, but would have cut the vertical axis 3 units below the origin.

Using this same symbolism, x for the abscissa, y for the ordinate, the equation $x^2 + y^2 = 9$ will be found to represent a circle having its center at the origin, and having a radius of $\sqrt{9}$, or 3 units.

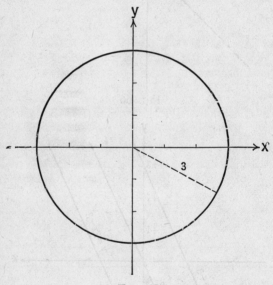

FIG. 68

The equation $x^2 - 8x + y^2 + 4y + 11 = 0$, which, with a little familiarity with algebraic manipulation may be written as $(x - 4)^2 + (y + 2)^2 = 9$ is of the same "pattern" as the equation $x^2 + y^2 = 9$, and will be found to represent a circle having its center at the point $(4, -2)$, that is, the point whose abscissa is +4, and whose ordinate is −2, and having a radius of $\sqrt{9}$, or 3 units.

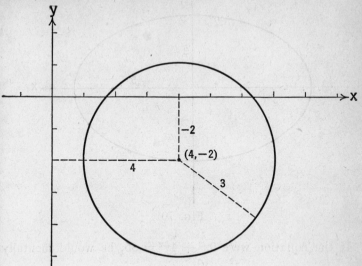

Fig. 69

Nowadays, when a mathematician sees the equation $\frac{x^2}{25} + \frac{y^2}{9} = 1$, (which would most probably be given in the form of $9x^2 + 25y^2 = 225$) he knows, without making a drawing, that it represents an ellipse whose center is at the origin, whose semi-major axis equals $\sqrt{25}$, or 5 units, semi-minor axis equals $\sqrt{9}$, or 3 units, and whose major axis is horizontal. [The equation also tells him certain other facts, but we will not complicate the issue by including them.] The ellipse representing this equation is shown in Figure 70, page 216.

If given the equation $x^2 + 4y^2 = 16$, he would turn this into the equivalent equation $\frac{x^2}{16} + \frac{y^2}{4} = 1$ [Ellipse; semi-major axis $= \sqrt{16}$; semi-minor axis $= \sqrt{4}$.]

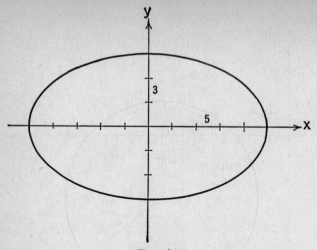

Fig. 70

If the equation were $9x^2 + 4y^2 = 36$, he would mentally turn it into the form $\dfrac{x^2}{4} + \dfrac{y^2}{9} = 1$, and would then know, with-

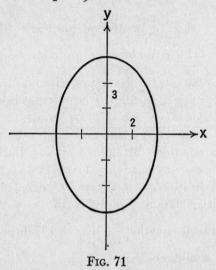

Fig. 71

out making a drawing, that it represented an ellipse whose center is at the origin, whose semi-major axis equals $\sqrt{9}$, or 3 units *and is vertical*, and whose semi-minor axis equals $\sqrt{4}$, or 2 units.

If he were given the equation $9x^2 + 54x + 4y^2 - 32y + 1 = 0$ he would turn it into the equivalent form

$$\frac{(x+3)^2}{16} + \frac{(y-4)^2}{36} = 1$$

and could then at once say that this must be the equation of

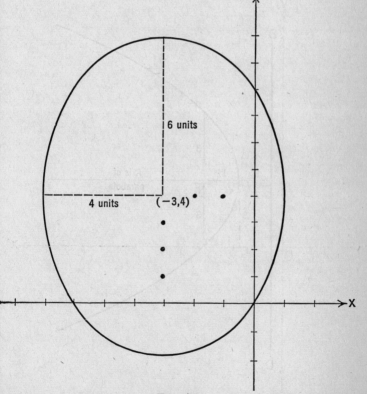

FIG. 72

an ellipse whose major axis is vertical, whose center is at the point $(-3, +4)$, whose semi-major axis is 6 units long (that is, $\sqrt{36}$, and whose semi-minor axis is $\sqrt{16}$, or 4 units long.

In similar fashion he would know that the equation $y^2 - 6y - 6x + 21 = 0$, which may be written as $(y - 3)^2 = 6(x - 2)$, represented a parabola opening out toward the right, having its *vertex*\* at the point whose abscissa is $+2$ and ordinate $+3$; its *focus*\* one-quarter of 6 units from its vertex (measured along the axis), and its *latus rectum*, or line through the focus perpendicular to the *axis*,\* equal to 6 units.

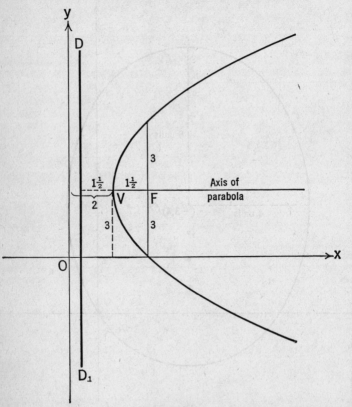

Fig. 73

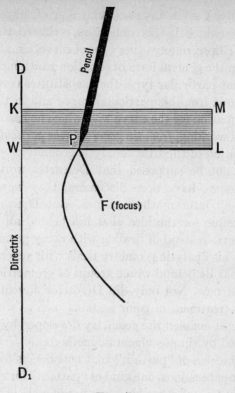

Fig. 74

* *A parabola is the path traced out by a point that moves in such a way that its distance from a fixed line is always the same as its distance from a fixed point not on that line.* To understand what this means, draw a line DD₁. Mark a point F, say ½ inch from the line. Take a rectangular block of wood (KWLM in Figure 74) and place its shorter edge along DD₁. Fasten a piece of tape the same length as WL at corner L and fasten the other end of the tape at F. Now slide the block along DD₁, at the same time keeping the tape taut alongside WL by means of a pencil, whose point touches the paper.

Since the length of tape equals WL (which may be written as WP + PL), and since that length of tape is FP + PL, it follows that WP must equal PF no matter where the pencil point makes its mark. The path traced out by the pencil point will be a *parabola;* every point on this path will be the same distance from DD₁ as it is from F. The line DD₁ is called the *directrix*, and the point F the *focus* of the parabola. A line through F perpendicular to the directrix is called the *axis* of the parabola. Its *vertex* lies on this axis.

Conversely, if given any particular type of curve, whether a straight line (which, in this connection, is classed as a "curve"), a circle, an ellipse, or any other type of curve, a mathematician writes down the general form of equation which includes every curve of that particular type, then substitutes certain dimensions obtained from his particular curve and in this way obtains the equation for the curve with which he has to deal. It is this kind of working, *from the general to the particular*, that led to the adoption of the title "analytic geometry."

It must not be supposed that Descartes worked out all these things we have been discussing; they were gradually developed by later mathematicians. But Descartes' genius was responsible for the idea that lies behind all subsequent developments. Instead of dealing with every geometric figure separately, his analytic geometry deals with general, abstract qualities that lie behind whole groups of geometric figures, as we saw just now. Not only did Descartes' invention revolutionize the treatment of conic sections such as we have been considering, it enabled the geometry developed by the Greeks to be treated by simple, algebraic methods.

Notice the idea of "pattern" that now begins to show itself in algebraic expressions, one kind of "pattern" for the equation of a straight line, another kind for that of a circle, another for that of an ellipse, and so on. This "pattern" in numbers (or their equivalent algebraic representations) plays an important part in higher branches of mathematics. It has led many people to believe that mathematics is not just a man-made invention, but that it forms part of the eternal make-up of the universe.

Descartes did not apply his methods to solid figures: this branch of the subject was developed by various mathematicians, among them being Euler (1707–1783). In this kind of analytic geometry, three coördinates, and the equations of surfaces have to be employed, since three dimensions are involved.

Ten years after the publication of the *Discourse*, Descartes was granted a pension by the French king, on the suggestion of Cardinal Mazarin, in recognition of his early work. He was to enjoy it for two years only. In 1649 he was invited by Queen Christina of Sweden, the daughter of Gustavus Adolphus, to become a member of her court. Christina had aroused great discontent by her wayward and irresponsible behavior and was anxious to retrieve her reputation by inviting writers like Grotius and philosophers like Descartes to her court. The energetic Christina wished to follow the example of the French nobility and "enjoy" the learned discussions of great philosophers. After much hesitation, Descartes, always susceptible to royal personages, accepted the invitation and in September, 1649, sailed for the cold land of Sweden in a man-of-war specially sent for him. Little did he know what was in store for him; his royal patroness insisted on receiving instruction in philosophy at 5 o'clock in the morning! Soon Descartes fell a victim to inflammation of the lungs and in ten days was dead. Sixteen years later, in 1666, his ashes were taken to France and interred in Paris.

In 1636, the year before Descartes published his *Discours*, G. P. de Roberval, professor of mathematics at the University of Paris, received a letter from a distinguished contemporary of Descartes which shows that the idea of analytic geometry was developed simultaneously in the minds of two great French mathematicians. A coincidence like this has frequently occurred in both mathematics and science, two individuals, each unaware of the work being done by the other, making almost identical discoveries. We saw this happen in the case of Napier and Bürgi; we shall see it happen again in the case of Newton and Leibniz.

While Descartes was working out his analytic geometry, a quiet, hard-working lawyer in the South of France was thinking out the same principles.

Pierre de Fermat, although busily occupied for thirty-four years as councillor in the local parliament at Toulouse, nevertheless ranks as one of the greatest mathematicians of the seventeenth century, when great mathematicians abounded. Whatever leisure he could find from his legal duties, he devoted to the study of mathematics and languages. Unlike Descartes and his other contemporary, Pascal, he was not interested in abstruse philosophical arguments; apart from his love of Greek and Latin and his interest in Spanish poetry, his one great and absorbing passion and hobby was pure mathematics.

We shall see in due course the importance of his work on tangents to a curve, which anticipated Newton's more general work on the calculus some dozen years before Newton's birth. In this connection Fermat was led into a dispute with Descartes, the only unpleasant incident that is recorded in the life of this hard-working, scholarly lawyer.

Like many another amateur mathematician, Fermat found unfailing fascination in the apparently valueless study of the theory of numbers, one of the chief topics in the *arithmētikē* of the ancient Greeks. Far from being valueless, these researches into the properties of numbers have led to the development of many important methods in more "practical" branches of mathematics. The kind of problem that fascinated Fermat was to discover whether an odd prime number n (that is, an odd number, n, which can be divided without remainder *only by itself and 1*) can be expressed as the difference of the squares of two integers in more than one way. Fermat found that there was *only one way* of doing this, namely, when the values of the integers are $\dfrac{n+1}{2}$ and $\dfrac{n-1}{2}$. [For example: can the number *eleven* be expressed as the difference of two squares in any other way than $6^2 - 5^2$?].

Another among the many problems he solved was that of

showing that if a, b, and c are integers such that $a^2 + b^2 = c^2$, then ab cannot be a square. One of his own theorems was that if n is any integer and p any prime number, then $(n^p - n)$ can be divided exactly by p.

When speaking of Diophantus in Chapter III we saw that his *Arithmetica* was studied by Fermat. The French lawyer had a habit of scribbling notes in the margin of his copy. Consequently, since there was so little space available, his custom was to note down some conclusion he had reached, and omit the steps by which he reached that conclusion. One problem he noted down in this way has never been solved, though some of the world's greatest mathematicians have puzzled over it for centuries. The problem is to show that if n stands for any integer *greater than 2*, it is impossible to find whole numbers a, b, c, such that $a^n + b^n = c^n$. Fermat added "I have found for this a truly wonderful proof, but the margin is too small to hold it."

In conjunction with Pascal, as we shall shortly see, Fermat helped to build the foundations of the *theory of probability*.

In 1623, when Descartes was twenty-seven years old, Blaise Pascal was born at Clermont Ferrand, in France. He was the son of a local judge who moved to Paris seven years later. Pascal's mother had died when he was four, and his father, fearing that his only son might be overworked, kept him at home, to be educated by tutors under his supervision. Since the boy displayed great promise, his father, fearing lest his brain should be overtaxed, gave orders that his studies should be limited to languages and should not include any mathematics. This naturally aroused the child's curiosity, and when, at the age of twelve, he heard that geometry was the science of constructing figures and finding the proportions between their various parts, he discovered many geometrical facts for himself, including the fact that the sum of the angles of a triangle is two right angles. It is said that he discovered this last fact by cutting out a triangle and folding over its angular points so that they all met at a point on the longest side of the triangle. Though not a mathematical proof, this shows considerable intelligence and ability, and, on hearing of it, his father gave him a copy of Euclid's *Elements*. Pascal, then twelve years of age, devoured the book and quickly mastered it. Two years later, he was allowed to attend weekly meetings held by Professor Roberval, to whom Fermat had communicated his discovery of analytic geometry. He also came to know Professor Mydorge, who had first interested Descartes in mathematics, and other distinguished mathematicians. This weekly meeting was eventually, in 1666, to grow into the French Academy of Sciences, which was formed six years after Charles II had approved of the formation of the Royal Society of London, to which science owes so much.

Young Pascal's amazing precosity is shown in the fact that, by the time he was sixteen, he had written a book on conic sections which showed such genius that Descartes refused to believe that it had been written by a boy of that age. It was never published, and now is lost, but Leibniz saw it and spoke about its contents. Pascal published a book on conics in 1640. His treatment of the subject, in which practically no progress had been made since the days of Apollonius, was based on the "projective geometry" which had been introduced some years previously by Gérard Desargues, an engineer and architect whose ideas greatly influenced Descartes, as well as Pascal. The general reader can get an idea of the underlying principle of this kind of geometry if he makes a paper cone (leaving a small hole at the point) and places in it any conic section (say an ellipse or parabola, cut out in paper) in its normal position. If he looks at that section through the hole at the point of the cone he will apparently see a circle. Hence, Desargues and Pascal treated conic sections as projections of circles.

Pascal is said to have deduced four hundred propositions on

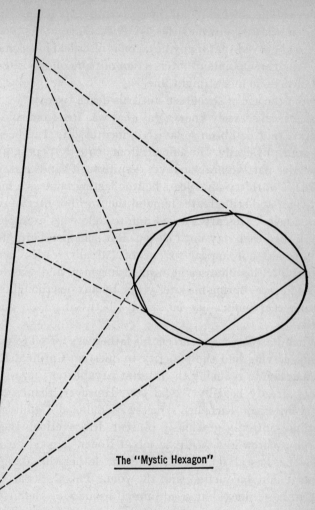

The "Mystic Hexagon"

FIG. 75

conic sections, including all those given by Apollonius, from a theorem that is known as the "Mystic hexagon."

Pascal proved that if any hexagon is inscribed in a conic section, the three points of intersection of pairs of opposite sides will always lie in a straight line.

From the age of seventeen until his death twenty-two years later, Pascal scarcely knew a day that was free from suffering. Nature, that had been so lavish in mental gifts, had been less generous physically. He suffered from acute dyspepsia, and at times was partly paralyzed; yet despite such handicaps, in his short life of thirty-nine years he won lasting fame as a mathematician, and still greater fame in the world of literature. On one occasion, Descartes urged him to follow his example and stay in bed each day until eleven. But such pandering to the flesh would not appeal to one of Pascal's restless nature. Through all his illnesses he worked furiously and ceaselessly, his mind torn, during his later years, by anxious thoughts concerning the conflict—as he saw it—between reason and religion.

When Pascal was seventeen, his father was forced to go into hiding, having had the temerity to question Cardinal Richelieu's action in reducing the interest payable on City of Paris bonds already held by Pascal *père*. However, thanks to the intervention of Richelieu's niece, Madame d'Aiguillon, the Cardinal not only graciously consented to overlook the outrage, but threw in a well-paid job at Rouen as good measure.

So the Pascal family, Étienne the father, his daughters Gilberte and Jacqueline, and the young Pascal, departed for Rouen. Here, Pascal amused himself by making the first calculating machine, while soon afterwards an event took place that was eventually to have an enormous influence on the lives of at least Jacqueline and Blaise Pascal: the whole of the Pascal family came under the influence of the Jansenites, or followers of Jansen, the former bishop of Ypres, in Belgium.

In 1640, two years after Jansen's death, a great work this bishop had written on Saint Augustine was published, which had taken him twenty years to write. In this book he attacked the Jesuits, who retaliated by their bitter opposition to his followers. The Jansenites remained members of the Roman Catholic Church, although, later, they denied the infallibility of the Pope. For eight years, Pascal's attitude towards religion, as interpreted by the Jansenites, seems to have been somewhat lukewarm. He became deeply interested in scientific experiments, especially those connected with the barometer, and began to take an interest in *mathematical probability*, the branch of mathematics to which he was to make his greatest contribution.

The family returned to Paris in 1647 but left the following year, returning to Clermont. During the two years they remained at Clermont, Pascal is believed to have had a mild love affair with a "belle savante" in whose company he was frequently seen, but nothing is heard of her after 1650, when the restless family returned to Paris once more. The following year Étienne Pascal died, and Jacqueline entered the convent of Port Royal, a nunnery in Paris connected with its more famous namesake some eight miles outside Versailles.

Meanwhile, Pascal and Fermat had laid the foundations of a new branch of mathematics. It arose from a gambling problem sent to Pascal by a gamester, the Chevalier de Méré. Pascal worked out his solution of the problem, then asked Fermat to work it. Both agreed as to the answer, but gave different proofs. As a result of the discussion that took place between Fermat and Pascal on this subject, the idea of *mathematical probability* emerged. Today, the child born on a gambling table has grown into a dignified and important member of the family of mathematics. It is essential in actuarial and insurance work and in all branches of mathematical statistics and some branches of modern physics. In working problems of probability, Pascal made use of arrangements, or combinations. In mathematics, a *combination* of a set of things is a group of all or of any part of them, without regard to the order in which the things in the group are arranged. Today we have a simple formula which enables us to find the number of combinations of, say 10 different things taken 4 at a time, but Pascal had no such assistance. He found out, almost uncannily, that a "pattern" of numbers known as an *arithmetic triangle* would tell him at a glance the number of combinations he required. This "triangle" is now generally known as *Pascal's triangle*, although he did not invent the "triangle" itself. Certain numbers are written down as shown in Figure 76.

Having set down the 1's in the top line and the left-hand column, the number to fill any empty space is obtained by finding the sum of the number above that space and the number on the left of that space. Thus, the number that would go on the right of the 7 in the second row would be 8, the number under that 7 would be 28.

Pascal's remarkable feat was to discover that by making use of *diagonals* and *columns*, he could obtain the answers to problems involving these groups, or combinations. Thus, the number of combinations of *4* things taken *2* at a time is found in the *4th*. diagonal and *3rd*. column, namely, 6. The number of combinations of *5* things taken *3* at a time is found in the *5th*. diagonal and *4th*. column, namely, 10. The number of combinations or groupings of *7* things taken *4* at a time is found in the *7th*. diagonal and *5th*. column, namely, 35.

[Pascal also used this "triangle" for working out expansions such as $(a + b)^2$, $(a + b)^3$, and so on. If a binomial, or expression containing two terms, is to be raised to the *2nd*. power, the numerical coefficients in the answer will be found on diagonal *2;* if to the *3rd*. power, on diagonal *3*, and so on. Thus:

$$(a + b)^2 = (1)a^2 + 2ab + (1)b^2;$$
$$(a + b)^3 = (1)a^3 + 3a^2b + 3ab^2 + (1)b^3;$$

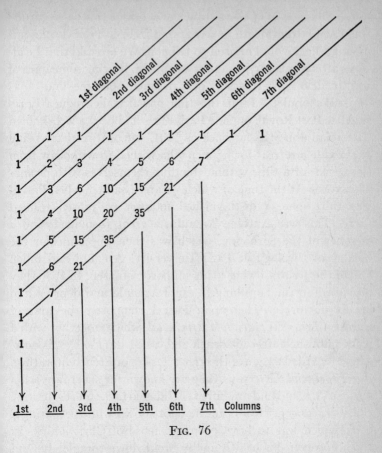

FIG. 76

$(a + b)^4 = (1)a^4 + 4a^3b + 6a^2b^2 + 4ab^3 + (1)b^4;$
$(a + b)^5 = (1)a^5 + 5a^4b + 10a^3b^2 + 10a^2b^3 + 5ab^4 + (1)b^5.$]

Soon after Pascal had worked out the foundations of the theory of probability, a great change came over his life. Except for one brief mathematical interlude, he turned his creative genius into new channels. On November 23, 1654, while driving to Neuilly, his horses bolted; had not the traces snapped, he would have been hurled into the river when the horses plunged over the parapet of a bridge. Pascal regarded this escape from death as a warning from heaven. From this moment he devoted himself to religion. We are told that he always afterwards carried a parchment slip bearing some lines of mystic devotion; this slip of parchment became known as "Pascal's amulet." From this time onwards, he frequently resided at Port Royal, outside Paris. This had been a well-known Cistercian abbey as far back as 1204, one of its objects being to provide a retreat for laymen who wished to withdraw from the world for a time without binding themselves with permanent vows. At the time of which we are speaking, when Pascal was thirty-one, a distinguished follower of Jansen resided there. This was Antoine Arnauld, a great theologian and a member of the Sorbonne, which was then the name for the faculty of theology at Paris University. Arnauld had fallen foul of the Jesuits, owing to his support of Jansen. In 1656 they prevailed on the Sorbonne to expel Arnauld and deprive him of his doctorate. Thereupon Pascal composed the first of eighteen *Letters Written to a Provincial*, which, together with a work published after his death and called the *Pensées*, is nowadays regarded as one of the great classics of French literature. *The Provincial Letters*, as they are known for short, are a defense of Arnauld and are full of scathing attacks on the Jesuits. The *Pensées* consist of notes he wrote down while preparing a book which was to have been a defense of Christianity. In 1658, however, his health finally broke down completely, and after some years of suffering he died in 1662 at the age of thirty-nine, before the book was finished.

The only mathematical work he did after his "conversion" at Neuilly was in connection with the *cycloid*. If a circle rolls along a straight line, any point on that circle traces out a curve that consists of a series of "arches" like the one shown in Figure 77. Such series of "arches" is called a *cycloid*.

Pascal was lying in bed sleepless and tortured by toothache.

His mind, so long concentrated on religious topics, turned to mathematics, and he began to think of this most interesting of all curves, the cycloid. After a time he suddenly realized that his toothache had ceased. Taking this as a sign from heaven that he was not committing a sin by thinking of mathematics instead of what he felt to be higher matters, he returned to his

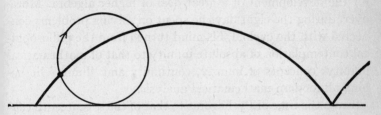

FIG. 77

old love for eight strenuous days, during that time solving many problems connected with this curve and with the surface and volume of the solid that is generated if it is revolved about its axis, or about its base, or about the tangent at its vertex. In doing this, he made use of Cavalieri's *indivisibles*, which we shall shortly consider. Some of the strange facts connected with the cycloid are that the area under each "arch" is exactly three times that of the circle; the length of curve in each "arch" is exactly four times the diameter of the circle; if an "arch" of a cycloid is inverted, like a bowl, an object will always take the same time to slide down to the lowest point on the curve. For this reason, the cycloid is known as the *tautochrone* (line of "the same time"). This last fact was not discovered until 1673, when the great Dutch scientist, Christiaan Huygens, showed how this property of the cycloid could be applied to his invention of pendulum clocks.

It is idle to speculate as to what Pascal's amazing brilliance might have achieved had he been granted normal health, and devoted his life to mathematics and science. As it was, during the few years he gave to mathematics, he contributed so much to the subject that he won a lasting place among the great mathematicians of the seventeenth century. Not only did he lay the foundations of mathematical probability, but by perceiving the "pattern" that exists in certain groups of numbers and in certain mathematical expressions, he pointed the way for the development of a great deal of higher algebra. Moreover, during the eight days he spent on solving problems connected with the cycloid, his mind turned from the philosophical contemplation of absolute infinity to that of mathematical infinity; concepts of infinity, continuity and "limits" lie behind all modern mathematical analysis.

From the time of Pythagoras to that of the seventeenth century, mathematicians went to great lengths to avoid the use of the idea of infinity. The Greeks of Euclid's day restricted their work to investigating the finite properties of geometric figures. Archimedes, more daring, approached the idea of infinity, but with great skill avoided its actual use by adopting complicated and roundabout expedients. Not until the seventeenth century did a mathematician, Kepler, boldly make use of the idea, apparently ignoring and certainly brushing aside the many intellectual difficulties with which it bristles. His example was followed by Cavalieri, Pascal, Wallis, Newton (who, in one of his later writings suggested a more logical process) and Leibniz. The storm of protest that arose from their use of concepts of infinity caused Maclaurin (1698–1746) to develop Newton's later approach to the subject, by which the use of illogical statements was avoided by the concept of a *limit*. All these matters will be dealt with in due course; we will first trace, in as simple a manner as the subject permits, the roots from which these various ideas and methods sprang. Only by doing this can we understand the processes involved and the violent controversies aroused by the manner in which they were first presented.

Mathematicians first ran into the puzzling problem of infinity when the Pythagoreans found themselves baffled by the apparently simple and guileless problem of finding a number by which the length of the diagonal of a square could be expressed. The best they and all subsequent mathematicians could do was to find an *approximate* value for such a length.

The Pythagoreans invented a very neat and interesting method for finding successive approximations for $\sqrt{2}$, a glance at which will help us appreciate some of the difficulties connected with "infinity." Their actual method is given in Heath's *History of Greek Mathematics*, Volume I. Simplified and translated into modern notation, it is substantially as follows:

Build up two columns of numbers, each headed by "1." Each succeeding number in the left-hand column is equal to the sum of the numbers last written in the two columns; each succeeding number in the right-hand column is equal to the sum of its corresponding number in the left-hand column and the number previously written in that left-hand column. Thus:

| | |
|---|---|
| 1 | 1 |
| 2 | 3 |
| 5 | 7 |
| 12 | 17 |
| 29 | 41 |
| 70 | 99 |
| etc. | etc. |

If we now successively divide each number in the right-hand column by its corresponding number in the left-hand column, and group these answers in pairs, it will be seen that the first answer in each pair is *less* than any answer that follows it; the second answer in each pair is *greater* than any answer that follows it; *the square root of 2 lies between each pair of answers*, and the farther we go down the list, the closer does each pair close in on the value of $\sqrt{2}$, although no matter how far the process is continued, the two answers concerned never close in on it completely, by coinciding. No matter how far we carry the process, all we can say is that $\sqrt{2}$ is "a little more than this, a little less than that." Using modern notation, we see that the decimal never "repeats," as does that for $\frac{1}{7}$, which, of course, has a definite and known place on the number-scale.

We will mark with an L the answers which are less than all those that follow them; those that are greater than all that follow them will be marked with a G.

$\sqrt{2}$ *lies between each of the following pairs of answers:*

$$\begin{cases} 1 & \text{(L)} \\ 1.5 & \text{(G)} \end{cases}$$
$$\begin{cases} 1.4 & \text{(L)} \\ 1.416 & \text{(G)} \end{cases}$$
$$\begin{cases} 1.413 & \text{(L)} \\ 1.41428 & \text{(G)} \end{cases}$$

etc. *ad infinitum.*

Highly ingenious and interesting though all this may be, it does not explain the mystery of $\sqrt{2}$. As an Irishman might say, its value lies at the bottom of a bottomless well.

Obviously, the "value" of $\sqrt{2}$ (if it exists at all) lies somewhere on the number-scale between the definite points on that scale marking the positions of 1.413 and 1.41428, though we could insert an infinite number of closer points between 1.413 and $\sqrt{2}$, and between $\sqrt{2}$ and 1.41428, as we saw just now. As was noted in Chapter III, the impossibility of expressing $\sqrt{2}$ exactly as a number upset the Pythagorean view that any two lengths must have some common measure. If a line AB is 8 inches long, and a line CD is 22 inches long, AB can be divided exactly into four portions, each 2 inches long, while CD can be divided exactly into eleven of those portions. The lengths AB and CD are in this case said to be "commensurable." But no matter how far the process of subdivision is carried, it is not possible to find a unit small enough to provide a common measure for the diagonal PR and the side PQ of a square PQRS. In this case, PR and PQ would be said to be *incommensurable*.

The Pythagoreans were thus forced to abandon their original conception of a line or number-scale as being made up of points like tiny beads, each "bead" being of finite size and just like all the others.

They were now led to conceive of a line as being made up of an infinite number of dimensionless points. But here again, they ran into difficulties. They found themselves drawn into the metaphysics of Parmenides, whom we met on page 110, and who expounded the view that matter (for instance, a line) was indivisible.

The "Theory of Numbers" sounds simple enough; in reality, as we shall now see, it can be exceedingly abstruse. It merges into philosophical concepts before we realize where we are heading, especially at the present day. The one subject blends into the other very much in the way that Archimedes' polygons (page 61) would blend into a circle if the number of their sides were indefinitely increased. (Archimedes was careful not to say this, however.)

The question as to whether a line could be regarded as being made up of an infinite number of points came to a head when a pupil of Parmenides, Zeno of Elea, thought up certain paradoxes, eight of which still survive in the writings of Aristotle and Simplicius, but four of which were sufficient to frighten mathematicians away from using the idea of "infinity" until the seventeenth century, when mathematicians had become so deeply interested in the application of mathematics to the realities of time and space that they ignored logical difficulties and developed the "infinitesimal calculus." We must bear in mind that until the time of the Renaissance, mathematicians, with the partial exception of Archimedes, regarded their subject as a purely intellectual form of reasoning based on certain

rigid principles. Antiphon (page 60) had aroused bitter opposition when he had tried to "square the circle" by the
"method of exhaustion." The objection seems to have been
that the mind had to jump across the final steps in this process
and could only *imagine* them as happening. So philosophers
like Aristotle, who lived just before the time of Euclid, declared that Antiphon's method violated "geometrical principles." Aristotle does not appear to have objected to the notion that a line consists of an infinite number of points, since
he declared that Zeno's paradoxes, one of which we are now
going to consider, were fallacies (though he could not refute
them). Greek mathematicians, however, saw quite clearly
that Zeno's arguments were fatal to "infinitesimals." Consequently they avoided using the idea of "infinity" as they
avoided the plague. Even Archimedes was careful to avoid the
notion (except, as we shall see, in his own private "method"
for getting a rough idea of what to aim at in a rigorous geometrical proof which would follow his preliminary investigations) and in his formal proofs contented himself by saying
that the difference between two areas could be made "as small
as we pleased."

To come to one of Zeno's paradoxes, which will be sufficient
for our purpose. A *paradox* is a statement that seems absurd
at first sight, but which is actually well founded. To show that
a line could not (in his opinion) consist of an infinite number of
points, he declared that if it *did* so consist, it would be impossible for a body moving swiftly to overtake a body moving
slowly. He pictured a race between Achilles and a tortoise.
Let us suppose that Achilles can run 10 times as fast as the
tortoise, and let him give the tortoise 1000 yards start. By the
time Achilles has covered the 1000 yards, the tortoise will be
100 yards ahead; by the time Achilles has covered that 100
yards, the tortoise will be 10 yards ahead; by the time Achilles
has covered that 10 yards, the tortoise will be 1 yard ahead;

by the time Achilles has covered that yard, the tortoise will be $\frac{1}{10}$ yard ahead; by the time . . . etc., *ad infinitum*. Therefore, said Zeno, Achilles never catches up with the tortoise; he is constantly getting nearer to it, but never actually reaches it. This paradox still perplexes even those who know that it is possible to find the sum of an infinite series of numbers forming a geometric progression whose common ratio (page 176) is less than 1, and whose terms consequently become smaller and smaller and thus "converge" on some limiting value. The sum of such an "infinite convergent series" is given by the formula $\frac{a}{1 - r}$, where a stands for the first term in the series, r for the common ratio (which must be less than 1). So the distance Achilles runs is represented by the infinite convergent series $1000 + 100 + 10 + 1 + \ldots$ and its sum will be $\frac{1000}{1 - \frac{1}{10}}$, or $\frac{1000}{\frac{9}{10}}$, or $\frac{10000}{9}$, or $1111\frac{1}{9}$ yards. Similarly, the distance run by the tortoise will be the sum of the infinite convergent series $100 + 10 + 1 + \ldots$, which, by the same formula, will be found to be $111\frac{1}{9}$ yards. So even although we have had to deal with an infinite number of subdivisions, we have been able to arrive at their sum. The paradox, however, which worried the Greeks exceedingly, has not been *explained*, even though we have shown that we can arrive at a solution that agrees with the facts of experience that we classify under the vague and often misleading heading of "common sense." If we keep on adding diminishing quantities of sand to a pile of sand, we can eventually reach a point when the operation comes to a stop with the addition of 1 grain of sand to the pile. Similarly, if we hang a weight by a piece of string and allow it to swing to and fro, the "pendulum" eventually comes to rest. In the case of the pile of sand, we came to an end of the operation of addition when we reached the number 1; in the case of the pendulum, we could, up to a point, express the lengths of successive swings by employing fractional parts of a unit of length. Our concept of "numbers," however, permits us to *conceive* of *unending* additions of ever-diminishing fractions of a whole. Unlike the final grain of sand, we can go on adding $\frac{1}{10}$ of a unit, $\frac{1}{100}$ of a unit, $\frac{1}{1000}$ of a unit . . ., or any other series of diminishing fractions of a unit. Is it that our number-system is inadequate to interpret the realities that lie in time and space, or is it, as some would say with Plato, that what we imagine to be realities are really only shadows of reality? Is mathematics merely an imperfect invention of man, devised for the interpretation of what most of us regard as "reality"? Or should mathematics be classed with such phenomena as gravitation and light, which existed before man appeared on the earth? In other words, did man "discover" mathematics or "invent" mathematics?

Bertrand Russell, one of the most profound philosopher-mathematicians of the present day, has admitted that the "immeasurably subtle and profound" arguments of Zeno still "tease out of thought" the average man. Even the abstruse arguments put forward by Dedekind (1831–1916), Cantor (1845–1918) and Russell (1872–    ) in their mighty efforts to straighten out the paradoxical problems of infinity into which we are led by our concept of "numbers," have resulted in the creation of still further paradoxes. These discussions are too profound and abstruse to be dealt with in non-technical language. The reader who is unfamiliar with them and who wishes to pursue them should start by reading J. W. A. Young's *Fundamental Concepts of Algebra and Geometry* and follow this up with Dedekind's *Essays on the Theory of Num-*

*bers*, an English translation of which work is published by the Court Publishing Co. He may then be able to tackle Cantor's *Contributions to the Foundation of the Theory of Transfinite Numbers* (an English translation is published by the same company), and finally, Russell and Whitehead's profound and abstruse *Principia Mathematica*.

Fortunately for modern science and astronomy, mathematicians in the seventeenth century paid no attention to Zeno's paradoxes. Ignoring logical imperfections in their use of infinitesimal quantities, they developed methods whereby whenever a quantity changed in value according to some continuous law (as most things in nature change) the rate of increase or decrease in such change could be measured. Later, as we shall see, when these logical imperfections were avoided, mathematicians, scientists, engineers and countless others were given a mathematical machine tool called the infinitesimal calculus, which enabled them to pry open secrets of nature that had been a closed book to their predecessors. These problems involved, in the main, continuous growth or continuous motion, and thus embraced vast new fields of science and astronomy. Again, by an inverse process, the original changing quantity could be found from its rate of increase or decrease. Moreover, the application of a single rule took the place of elaborate individual calculations in finding such things as the lengths of curves, the areas enclosed by them, the surfaces of solid bodies, the volumes of solids, and many other problems.

The "infinitesimal calculus" includes the "differential calculus," or (originally) the method of calculating the infinitesimal difference between consecutive values of quantities that continuously vary, and the "integral calculus," whereby a changing quantity can be found from its rate of change.

We shall have to go back to Archimedes in order to trace the roots from which the "integral calculus" grew; then we shall see how the "differential calculus" arose, and finally, how "integration" was shown to be the inverse of "differentiation."

One of the first seventeenth-century mathematicians who stepped in where even Archimedes had feared to tread was Bonaventura Cavalieri. As was to be expected, he was promptly classified by most of his contemporaries with those who depart from the well-trodden pathway followed by those who, taking no risks, reputedly join the angelic band.

This brilliant Jesuit was born at Milan in 1598, two years after the birth of Descartes, and studied under Galileo. When thirty-one years old he was appointed a professor of mathematics at Bologna, which appointment he retained until his death in 1647. When we come to glance at his work, it will be clear to those who have seen the difficulties raised in Zeno's paradoxes that he deliberately ignored obvious inconsistencies in his own arguments. It would be interesting to know what led this acutely minded man to lay himself open to certain attack. It may well have been that so strong was his intuitive certainty that for the correct interpretation of most natural phenomena one thing must be regarded as "merging" into another, that he used arguments he must have known to be illogical but which he found led to correct results.

The mathematical *principle of continuity* which had been stressed by Kepler lies at the root of Cavalieri's thought. This principle recognizes the way in which one thing "merges" into another, even though we cannot say exactly when or how the "one thing" ceases to be and the other thing comes into being. Imagine, for instance, a section of a cone whose outline is an ellipse (Figure 25, page 54) slowly swinging over until its outline becomes the circle in Figure 26. How does it change? By a sudden "jerk"? Or does one outline blend imperceptibly into the other? Is there a continuous change in all movement and growth, or are these processes a vast aggregation of minute jerks? Unquestionably, when Cavalieri had studied Archimedes' method of calculating the circumference of a circle

(page 61) he must have sensed the steady growth of the inscribed polygon's perimeter and the steady shrinking of that of
the circumscribed polygon as both these perimeters approached the length of the circumference. Instead of adopting
the highly ingenious, though complicated and roundabout
methods used by Archimedes, he found he could get similar
results by making use of the idea of infinitely small values.
So he used those values.

Two wonderfully ingenious solutions made by Archimedes
made a deep impression on Cavalieri. These were two different
methods he had used for effecting the quadrature of a parabolic segment. "Effecting a quadrature" meant finding the
area of a square that would be exactly equal to that of some
figure bounded by a curve. Frequently, this was done by finding the area of an equivalent triangle; once this was done, the
problem was as good as solved, since it is a simple matter to
construct a square equal in area to a triangle.

We will first consider a purely geometric method used by
Archimedes for finding the area of a parabolic segment. He
inscribed a triangle (ABC in Figure 78) with the same base
as the parabolic segment, the vertex of the triangle being
the point of contact of the tangent (not drawn below) parallel
to AC.

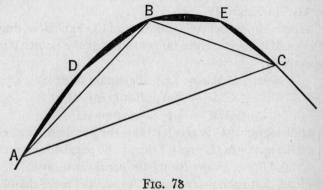

Fig. 78

He then showed that the area of the parabolic segment was $\frac{4}{3}$ that of the triangle ABC. To do this, he employed the "method of exhaustion," though, unlike the example of this method we discussed on page 61, he "exhausted" the area in this case from the "inside" only.

First, he drew triangles ADB and BEC "in the recognized manner," that is, placing vertex D at the point of contact of the tangent to the parabola parallel to AB; vertex E at the point of contact of the tangent parallel to BC. Thus, each of these smaller parabolic segments was treated on the same lines as had been followed for the original segment.

Archimedes then showed by Euclidean geometry that $\triangle ADB + \triangle BEC = \frac{1}{4}\triangle ABC$.

Now he repeated the last process, drawing triangles "in the recognized manner" in each of the shaded segments shown in Figure 78. He showed that the sum of their areas was $\frac{1}{4}(\triangle ADB + \triangle BEC)$, or $\frac{1}{16}(\triangle ABC)$, that is to say, using modern symbolism, $(\frac{1}{4})^2\triangle ABC$.

He argued that by repeating this process indefinitely (in imagination) the parabolic segment would approach "as near as one wished" to "exhaustion," since, with each step taken, more than half of the remaining segment(s) would be exhausted. For instance, take the first step, involving the triangle ABC in Figure 79.

M is the mid-point of AC, and AP and CQ have been drawn parallel to MB, meeting the tangent at B at the points P and Q respectively.

$$\text{Now, } \triangle AMB = \frac{1}{2} \text{ parallelogram MP;}$$
$$\triangle CMB = \frac{1}{2} \text{ parallelogram MQ,}$$
$$\therefore \triangle ABC = \frac{1}{2} \text{ parallelogram AQ.}$$

But parallelogram AQ is greater than the parabolic segment;
$\therefore \frac{1}{2}$ parallelogram AQ is greater than $\frac{1}{2}$ the parabolic segment;
$$\therefore \triangle ABC \text{ is greater than } \frac{1}{2} \text{ the parabolic segment.}$$

It follows that each new triangle "exhausts" more than half

the segment in which it is drawn. So Archimedes argued that by continuing this process of exhaustion indefinitely, the difference between the area of the parabolic segment and the sum of all the triangles could be made as small as desired. But

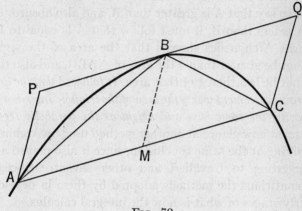

FIG. 79

was it possible to find the sum of such triangles? Here we meet yet further evidence of the genius of Archimedes, for he proved geometrically that the sum of an indefinitely long series of areas, in which any area was one-quarter of the area preceding it in the series, was equal to $\frac{4}{3}$ the first area in the series. In this way Archimedes again made mathematical history, for he had found the sum (as we should say) of the infinite convergent series

$$1 + \tfrac{1}{4} + (\tfrac{1}{4})^2 + (\tfrac{1}{4})^3 + \ldots$$

which, as we saw on page 237, can be found by the formula $\dfrac{a}{1-r}$, where $a = 1$, $r = \tfrac{1}{4}$.

Archimedes was therefore able to say that the sum of $\triangle ABC, \tfrac{1}{4}\triangle ABC, (\tfrac{1}{4})^2\triangle ABC, (\tfrac{1}{4})^3\triangle ABC, \ldots$ [or $\triangle ABC(1 + \tfrac{1}{4} + (\tfrac{1}{4})^2 + (\tfrac{1}{4})^3 + \ldots)$] was $\tfrac{4}{3}\triangle ABC$.

To avoid the use of the concept of an infinite number of tri-angles being inserted "in the recognized manner," Archimedes made use of *reductio ad absurdum*, a method frequently used by Greek mathematicians to prove that two things were equal. They argued that if, for example, it can be shown that it is absurd to say that A is greater than B, and also absurd to say that A is less than B, it must follow that A is equal to B. In this case, Archimedes showed that the area of the segment could not be greater than $\frac{4}{3}$ the area of $\triangle ABC$, and also that it could not be less than $\frac{4}{3}$ of that area. *It followed that the area of the parabolic segment was $\frac{4}{3}$ the area of the triangle inscribed in it, and having the same base and height as the parabolic segment.*

We must now glance at another method used by Archimedes for arriving at the same conclusion, since it also played a part in suggesting to Cavalieri and other seventeenth-century mathematicians the methods adopted by them in developing the early stages of what is now the integral calculus.

In 1906, Dr. Heiberg discovered in Constantinople a letter written by Archimedes to his friend the librarian Eratosthenes (page 49). In this letter, Archimedes tells his friend the method of inquiry, or analysis, he used when tackling certain problems connected with area and volume. He made use of his great knowledge of mechanics in order to get an idea of the solution at which to aim in a subsequent rigorous geometrical proof. To quote his own words, as translated in Heath's *History of Greek Mathematics:* "Certain things first became clear to me by a mechanical method, although they had to be demonstrated by geometry afterwards because their investigation by the said method did not furnish an actual demonstration. But it is of course easier, when we have previously acquired, by the method, some knowledge of the questions, to supply the proof than it is to find it without any previous knowledge."

The underlying principle of this method can be understood by anyone who has balanced another person on a seesaw. If a man weighing 150 lb. wants to balance a boy weighing 50 lb. and seated 6 ft. from the point on which the seesaw balances, he must sit 2 ft. from the point of balance. In other words, the ratio between the weights of boy and man $\left(\frac{50}{150}, \text{ or } \frac{1}{3}\right)$ must equal the ratio between the distances of man and boy respectively from the point of balance $\left(\frac{2}{6}, \text{ or } \frac{1}{3}\right)$.

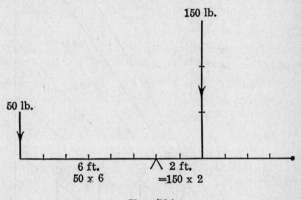

FIG. 79A

Using this principle, Archimedes was able to discover the truth he later proved geometrically (as we have seen), about the area of a parabolic segment. He drew diagrams in which he pictured an unknown area, such as that of the triangle QER in Figure 80, balancing a figure of known area, each being suspended from a balance, from points vertically above their respective centers of gravity. [Figure 80 has been drawn upside down so far as this balancing process is concerned; our interest lies in matters which can more easily be grasped if the figure is drawn as shown here.]

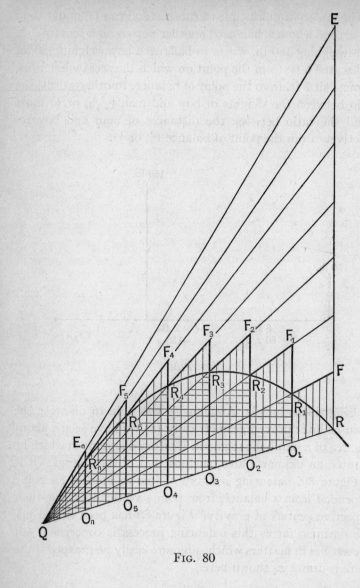

FIG. 80

By a wonderful and elaborate application of the mechanics connected with a balance, Archimedes showed that

(1) the area of $\triangle QER$ was 3 times that of a known area, as suspended from a certain point on his imaginary balance;

(2) the sum of the areas which are horizontally shaded in Figure 80 (namely, trapezia $R_1O_2$, $R_2O_3$, $R_3O_4$, $R_4O_5$, $R_5O_n$, and triangle $R_nO_nQ$) was *less* than the known area in (1);

(3) the sum of the areas which are vertically shaded in Figure 80 (namely, trapezia $FO_1$, $F_1O_2$, $F_2O_3$, $F_3O_4$, $F_4O_5$, $F_5O_n$, and triangle $E_nO_nQ$) was *greater* than the known area in (1).

It followed that the horizontally shaded areas were together *less* than $\frac{1}{3}$ the area of $\triangle QER$; the vertically shaded areas were together *greater* than $\frac{1}{3}$ the area of $\triangle QER$.

Archimedes then showed that by increasing the number of parts into which QR and RE are divided, the difference between the vertically shaded and the horizontally shaded areas can be made as small as desired, since it can be shown that this difference in the areas is equal to triangle FQR, which gets smaller and smaller as the number of divisions is increased.

By this process of exhaustion, Archimedes shows that the area of the segment must be equal to the known area in (1) above; in other words, he finds by this method that the area of the parabolic segment is $\frac{1}{3}$ that of the triangle QER, and he easily proves geometrically that this triangle is 4 times as large as a triangle with the same base and the same height as the segment. So once more it follows that the area of the parabolic segment is $\frac{4}{3}$ the area of such triangle.

Archimedes does not use *reductio ad absurdum* in this mechanical method used by him for discovering results which later he would prove geometrically by the method of exhaustion, coupled with its double *reductio ad absurdum*.

More than eighteen centuries were to pass before the seeds thus sown some 250 years before Christ were to spring into life. Fortunately, they were not lost, but were stored away all those years in a few manuscripts. In the third century A.D. some Alexandrian mathematicians quoted from Archimedes' works, and in the ninth century all the then-known works were collected together and copied in Greek for the University of Constantinople, which city, fortunately, had not fallen into the hands of the barbarian ancestors of many of us. This manuscript came into the possession of the Norman kings of Sicily in the twelfth century, from whom it passed to Manfred, King of the Two Sicilies, in the thirteenth century. This ruler fell foul of Pope Urban IV, who persuaded Charles of Anjou to come to his assistance against Manfred, who had overrun the papal states in Tuscany. In 1266 Charles defeated the Sicilians at the battle of Benevento. Manfred was killed in the battle, and part of the spoils of war was this ninth-century copy of the works of Archimedes, which Charles sent to the Pope. It remained in the papal library until the end of the fifteenth century, when it passed into private possession, and has since been completely lost. Fortunately, however, while still in papal hands it had been translated into Latin (this translation, made in 1269, is still in Rome) while at least four Greek copies are known to have been made. The first edition of the works of Archimedes to be printed was based on one of these Greek copies. It was published at Basel in 1544. Fourteen years later, a Latin translation was published, and there can be little doubt that it was through this edition that the genius and inspiration of Archimedes became fully known to the brilliant mathematicians of the seventeenth century. This Latin translation contains the *Measurement of a Circle*, *On Spirals*, the *Quadrature of the Parabola*, *On Conoids and Spheroids*, and the *Sand Reckoner*. [In addition to these works of Archimedes, other manuscripts have preserved his books *On the Sphere and Cylinder*, *On Plane Equilibriums*, and *On Floating Bodies*. As already stated, in 1906 another Greek manuscript was discovered in Constantinople that included the *Method*.]

At last the seed that had lain so long in dusty manuscripts fell on fertile soil and sprang to life in the minds of Kepler, Cavalieri, Pascal and subsequent mathematicians.

We saw that Kepler, in 1613, had become interested in the problem of gauging the contents of a wine cask. He conceived of a circle as being composed of an infinite number of tiny triangles having their vertices at the center and their infinitesimally small bases in the circumference. By a similar train of thought he regarded solids as composed of an infinite number of infinitely small cones (or disks). His method for finding the volume of a solid was to imagine the figure that would be generated by a curve that revolved about some axis.

Kepler's idea of infinitesimally small parts, combined with the principle of mathematical continuity mentioned on page 240 prepared the way for Cavalieri's method of *indivisibles*. Although Cavalieri did not say exactly what he had in mind when using this term, it is evident that he was making use of a concept discussed by Aristotle and medieval philosophers like Thomas Aquinas, with whose works Cavalieri, being a Jesuit, would be very familiar. To them, a point was the "indivisible" of a line; a line the "indivisible" of a surface; a surface the "indivisible" of a solid. In Cavalieri's final treatment, each "indivisible," by moving, could generate the next higher "continuum" (a term *now* used by mathematical philosophers like Russell for the infinite number of points on a line). Thus, a moving point generated a line; a moving line generated a surface; a moving surface generated a solid.

Cavalieri never gave the area of a figure as being "so many" square units; he compared the size of one figure with the size of another. In other words, he found the ratio between the required area and that of some other easily calculated area, thus following the method adopted by the ancient Greeks. It was John Wallis (1616–1703) who introduced our present method of expressing area, as we shall see.

The next three figures will explain in a simplified way the general idea that lay behind Cavalieri's use of "indivisibles."

Figure 81 shows, on the left, a rectangle that has been divided into five small rectangles, each having the same area. The number of units of area in each is immaterial, since we are going to find a *ratio*.

The shaded figure in the center consists of a series of rectangles having areas which increase uniformly in size, the lowest rectangle having the same area as each of the small rectangles in the left-hand figure. The reader must imagine a "rectangle" having no area at the top of these "steps."

The figure on the right shows the center figure placed on top of the left-hand figure. Let us now compare the area of the shaded part of this figure with the area of the whole large rectangle.

$$\frac{\text{Shaded part}}{\text{Whole rectangle}} = \frac{0 + 1 + 2 + 3 + 4}{4 + 4 + 4 + 4 + 4} = \frac{10}{20} = \frac{1}{2}.$$

[If we remember the formula $S = \dfrac{n(a + 1)}{2}$ given on page 70, we can find the sum of the numbers in the numerator by finding the value of $\dfrac{5(0 + 4)}{2}$, or $\dfrac{5(4)}{2}$, or $\dfrac{20}{2}$, or 10. This method will save time in later computations.]

Now repeat all this process for the figures shown in Figure 82.

The ratio is now

$$\frac{\text{Shaded part}}{\text{Whole rectangle}} = \frac{0 + 1 + 2 + \ldots + 8 + 9}{10(9)} = \frac{45}{90} = \frac{1}{2}.$$

Now repeat the whole process for the figures shown in Figure 83.

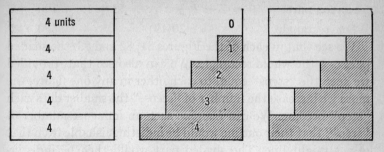

Fig. 81

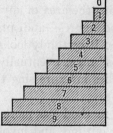

Fig. 82

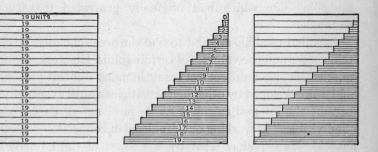

Fig. 83

$$\frac{\text{Shaded part}}{\text{Whole rectangle}} = \frac{0 + 1 + 2 + \ldots + 18 + 19}{20(19)} = \frac{190}{380} = \frac{1}{2}.$$

We see that in each of the Figures 81, 82 and 83, the shaded part is $\frac{1}{2}$ the whole rectangle. We can also see that, provided we keep the "steps" equal to each other in any one figure, the more we increase the number of "steps," the smaller does each "step" become. We can *imagine* such an immense number of "steps" that their outline would be indistinguishable from that of a straight line. The shaded part would then be indistinguishable from a triangle. Now we know from geometry that the area of a triangle is $\frac{1}{2}$ the area of the rectangle on the same base and having the same height, which result, as we have seen, corresponds with the area of any of the shaded parts in the above right-hand figures—and, presumably, in those we imagined to exist. So it certainly looks as though the jagged outline of the "steps" must eventually merge into a straight line. The difficulty lies in expressing this idea in logical language.

Cavalieri's actual method was more complicated than that shown in the above outline, and involved illogical concepts. For instance, he imagined each small rectangle to be compressed to such an extent that eventually it became the "indivisible" line which had originally generated that small rectangle.

Cavalieri used his method to find the areas enclosed by certain curves and the volumes of certain solids. His work, though unscientific, gave the correct result in many difficult problems and was developed by other mathematicians until eventually it became the integral calculus. As we have noted, Pascal used "indivisibles" in working out problems in connection with the cycloid. He explained that by the "sum of right lines" he meant the "sum of infinitely small rectangles."

The scene now changes to England, to Oxford, that city of spires, of quiet quadrangles and gardens in which generation after generation of dons and undergraduates had calmly strolled and meditated. The restful peace of this fairest English city had been rudely broken when Charles I had made it his headquarters during the civil war between Royalists and Parliamentarians. In May, 1646, Charles was forced to flee from the city in disguise. In 1649, the year in which he was beheaded on a scaffold outside Whitehall, a young clergyman aged thirty-three was appointed to the Savilian chair of geometry at Oxford, despite the fact that he had signed a protest, known as the Remonstrance, against the king's execution. His name was John Wallis, a Cambridge graduate in medicine, who became a clergyman and supported Cromwell's Parliamentarians in the civil war by deciphering Royalist papers that had been captured. He was rewarded by being appointed to a parish in London. While there, he grew more and more interested in mathematics, attending meetings of scientists which a few years later grew into the Royal Society of London. So great was his mathematical ability that he was appointed to the Oxford professorship and remained at Oxford until his death at the age of eighty-seven. He wrote many books on a variety of subjects, including logic, philosophy and mathematics. One of the many mathematical books dealt with Descartes' geometry, and for the first time set it forth in a clear and simple manner. His most famous book, however, was called *Arithmetica Infinitorum*, "The Arithmetic of Infinites," which was published in 1656. In it, he made use of, and extended, the methods employed by Descartes and Cavalieri, while he found a meaning for fractional and negative exponents, although he did not write them as we write them today; Newton was the first to employ our modern method. Wallis showed that (as we now write them) $a^0$, $a^{-1}$, $a^{-2}$, $a^{-3}$ . . . respectively represent $1, \dfrac{1}{a}, \dfrac{1}{a^2}, \dfrac{1}{a^3}$ . . . ; that $x^{\frac{1}{2}}$ stands for the square root of x, $x^{\frac{2}{3}}$ for the cube root of $x^2$, and so forth.

Both Cavalieri and French mathematicians had been able
to find the area lying between part of a parabola, the x-axis
and a y-ordinate such as is shown in the shaded part of Figure
84.

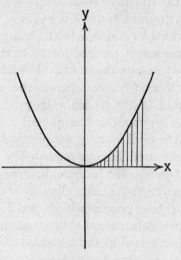

Fig. 84

They imagined the shaded portion as being made up of an
infinite number of infinitely small rectangular strips, whose
sum gave the required area. We shall shortly see how Wallis
used this method, but made a great advance by introducing an
arithmetical concept of what is nowadays called a *limit*.

Before we consider his actual method, we shall observe how
he calculated the value of the ratio between the area of his
shaded figure and that of the rectangle on the same base as
that shaded figure and having its maximum height. As we shall
see, he found the ratio to be

$$\frac{1^2 + 2^2 + 3^2 + 4^2 + \ldots + m^2}{(m + 1)m^2}$$

where m stood for the number of rectangles into which he divided the shaded figure.

Thus, if m = 1, the ratio would be $\frac{1^2}{2}$, or $\frac{1}{2}$, or $\frac{3}{6}$.

If m = 2, the ratio would be $\frac{1+4}{3(4)}$, or $\frac{5}{12}$.

If m = 3, the ratio would be $\frac{1+4+9}{4(9)}$, or $\frac{7}{18}$.

If m = 4, the ratio would be $\frac{1+4+9+16}{5(16)}$, or $\frac{9}{24}$.

Continuing in this way, it will be found that successive values for m = 5, 6, 7 . . . are $\frac{11}{30}$, $\frac{13}{36}$, $\frac{15}{42}$, $\frac{17}{48}$, $\frac{19}{54}$, $\frac{21}{60}$, and so on. [It will be seen that the numerators of all these fractions form an arithmetic progression whose first term is 3, and whose common difference is 2; their denominators, another arithmetic progression whose first term is 6, and whose common difference is 6.]

Now we can re-write these successive values of the ratio between the two areas, as follows:

When m = 1, ratio = $\frac{3}{6}$ = $\frac{1}{3} + \frac{1}{6}$

When m = 2, ratio = $\frac{5}{12}$ = $\frac{1}{3} + \frac{1}{12}$

When m = 3, ratio = $\frac{7}{18}$ = $\frac{1}{3} + \frac{1}{18}$

When m = 4, ratio = $\frac{9}{24}$ = $\frac{1}{3} + \frac{1}{24}$

When m = 5, ratio = $\frac{11}{30}$ = $\frac{1}{3} + \frac{1}{30}$

. . . . . . . . . . . . . . . . . . . . . . . . . . . . . . . . . . . . . . .

When m = 100, ratio = $\frac{201}{600}$ = $\frac{1}{3} + \frac{1}{600}$

. . . . . . . . . . . . . . . . . . . . . . . . . . . . . . . . . . . . . . .

When m = 10000, ratio = $\frac{20001}{60000}$ = $\frac{1}{3} + \frac{1}{60000}$

and so on.

In each case, the ratio is equal to $\frac{1}{3}$ plus some fraction. The successive fractional additions to this $\frac{1}{3}$ will be seen to have 1 for numerator and successive terms of the arithmetic progression 6, 12, 18, 24 . . . for denominator. *So the greater the value taken for m, the smaller will be the value of the fractional addition to* $\frac{1}{3}$. By taking m sufficiently large, we can make the difference between the ratio and $\frac{1}{3}$ smaller than any small quantity any-one may mention. Thus, if one asks, "Can you make the difference between the value of the ratio and $\frac{1}{3}$ less than $\dfrac{1}{10,000,000}$ ?" the answer is "Certainly; by taking m = 1,666,-667." "Can you make it less than $\dfrac{1}{100,000,000,000}$ ?" The answer is "Certainly; by taking m = 16,666,666,667," and so on, indefinitely.

Wallis saw that by increasing the value of m enormously, he could say that the value of

$$\frac{1^2 + 2^2 + 3^2 + 4^2 + \ldots + m^2}{(m + 1)m^2}$$

was as near to $\frac{1}{3}$ as he wished. Nowadays we say that $\frac{1}{3}$ is the *limit* to which the value of this ratio approaches as m approaches an infinite value.

Bearing in mind the idea suggested by Figures 83, 84 and 85, we can now easily follow Wallis' method for finding the shaded area in Figure 85.

Imagine that the shaded rectangles have been placed on top of unshaded rectangles, each of which is as large as the largest shaded rectangle. The shaded rectangles represent areas of $1^2, 2^2, 3^2, 4^2, 5^2, 6^2$ square units respectively. The actual kind of units employed is immaterial, since we are going to find a ratio, but the areas must be in the above proportions and all the rectangles must have the same width, or x-value, so far as the graph is concerned. The number of shaded rectangles must be one less than the number of unshaded rectangles.

It will be seen that the ratio between the sum of the shaded rectangles and that of the unshaded in Figure 85 is

$$\frac{1 + 4 + 9 + 16 + 25 + 36}{7(36)} = \frac{91}{252} = \frac{13}{36}, \text{ or} \left(\frac{1}{3} + \frac{1}{36}\right),$$

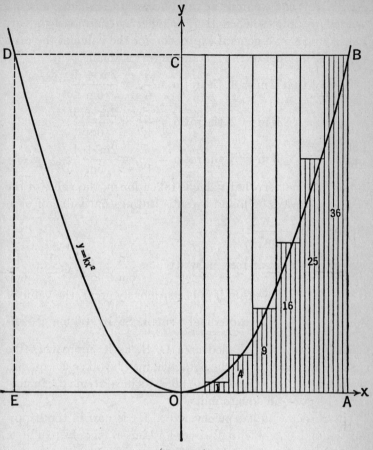

FIG. 85.

$$\text{or } \frac{1^2 + 2^2 + 3^2 + \ldots + m^2}{(m+1)m^2}$$

If we now successively increase the number of rectangles, not only will this smaller fraction, $\frac{1}{36}$, be whittled down by each successive increase, but the "steps" in the shaded portion will approach more and more closely to the outline of the

curve. How can we find the ratio between the shaded and unshaded rectangles when their number is enormously great?
Let us first find a general expression for the value of the ratio
when the number of the rectangles (m) is small.

We saw that if m = 1, the ratio = $\dfrac{3}{6}$ , or $\dfrac{2m+1}{6m}$;

if m = 2, the ratio = $\dfrac{5}{12}$, or $\dfrac{2m+1}{6m}$;

if m = 3, the ratio = $\dfrac{7}{18}$, or $\dfrac{2m+1}{6m}$;

in fact, no matter what value is taken for m, the value of the
ratio can always be found by substituting that value of m in
the formula $\dfrac{2m+1}{6m}$.

Now this formula may be written as $\dfrac{2m}{6m} + \dfrac{1}{6m}$, or $\dfrac{1}{3} + \dfrac{1}{6m}$.
It therefore follows that if m is enormously great, the value of
the fraction $\dfrac{1}{6m}$ is exceedingly small. So by taking m sufficiently large, the shaded area OAB, as it approaches the
shape of the area under the parabola, may be taken as equal to
*one-third the area of rectangle OABC*. Its measurement can now
easily be given in square units.*

The reader who has persevered so far is now in the happy
position of being able to discover for himself (thanks to a little

* Notice how this result enables us to obtain the same result as that obtained
by Archimedes for the area of the parabolic segment DOB. The area OBA = ⅓
rectangle OABC. ∴ the area COB = ⅔ rectangle OABC. Now, the parabola
is symmetrical, or "balanced" with respect to the axis OC, so area DOC = area
COB. So the area of the parabolic segment DOB is twice area COB, or ⁴⁄₃
rectangle OABC. If triangle DOB were drawn, its area would be equal to ½
rectangle EABD (compare Figure 79, page 243). In other words, triangle
DOB = rectangle OABC. It follows that the area of the parabolic segment
DOB = ⅔ the area of triangle DOB.

aid from Archimedes, Kepler, Cavalieri, Descartes and Wallis!) an essential step in the integral calculus.

The shaded part of Figure 86 shows the area covered by the graph of $y = 4$ (which we might write as $y = 4x^0$, since $x^0$, as we have just seen, is equal to 1) between the origin and an ordinate erected $x$ units from that origin.

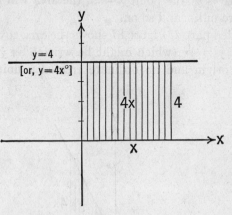

FIG. 86

In this particular instance, the value of *any* ordinate (y) will be 4. Now, in *any* graph, the value of any particular ordinate is always connected with the value of the point where it cuts the x-axis. *The connection is given in the equation of the graph*. In order to show this connection in this particular case, we will write $y = 4x^0$ instead of just $y = 4$. No matter what value x may have, $x^0$ is always equal to 1, so the value of any ordinate, y, will in this case always be 4 times 1, or 4. We will call "$4x^0$ the *ordinate-function of x*. Readers who are not familiar with the term "function" may want to look it up again on page 167.

Since the shaded figure is a rectangle, its area will be length times breadth, or x times 4, or 4x square units. This area we will write in the somewhat peculiar form $\frac{1}{1}$ 4x¹, for reasons which will shortly become apparent. We will call this peculiar-looking expression the *area-function of x*. By means of this area-function we can find the area covered by the "curve" between the origin and any given point on the x-axis. Thus, if the ordinate is at the point x = 5, the area will be $\frac{1}{1}$ (4)(5), or 20 square units, and so on.

The shaded part of Figure 87 shows the area covered by the "curve" of y = 4x (which might be written as y = 4x¹) between the origin and an ordinate erected x units from the origin.

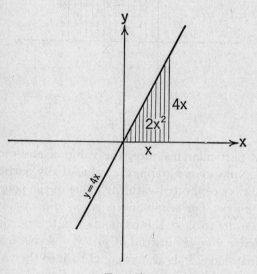

Fig. 87

Here, the *ordinate-function* is 4x¹. We want to find the *area-function*. It will be seen that the shaded area is no longer a rectangle, but is a triangle. Now, the area of a triangle is half its base times its height, so its area is $\frac{1}{2}$x times y, which we may write as $\frac{1}{2}$x times 4x, since no matter where the ordinate is situated, the value of y is always 4 times that of the x-value of the point where that ordinate cuts the horizontal axis. So the area is $\frac{1}{2}$ 4x², which will be the *area-function* in this case. So the area covered from x = 0 to x = 5 will be $\frac{1}{2}$(4)(5)(5), or 50 square units; the area covered between x = 0 and x = 9 will be 162 square units, and so on.

The shaded part of Figure 88 shows the area covered by the graph of y = 4x² from the origin to the ordinate erected x units from the origin. Here, the *ordinate-function* is 4x².

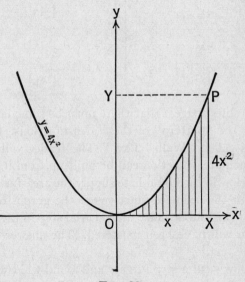

Fig. 88

We saw just now how Wallis found that this area could be regarded as $\frac{1}{3}$ that of the rectangle OXPY. Now, the area of this rectangle is xy, but we can put 4x² in place of y, since the ordinate-function here tells us that any ordinate in this figure is always equal to 4x², x being the value of the point (here marked X) where the ordinate under consideration cuts the x-axis. So the area of the rectangle is $4x^3$, consequently the *area-function* of the shaded figure will be $\frac{1}{3} 4x^3$. If we want to find the shaded area up to the point x = 5, for instance, this area-function tells us that it is $\frac{1}{3}$ (4)(5)(5)(5), or $166\frac{2}{3}$ square units.

Let us collect together the facts we have just discovered:

| When the ordinate-function was | The area-function was |
|---|---|
| $4x^0$ | $\frac{1}{1} 4x^1$ |
| $4x^1$ | $\frac{1}{2} 4x^2$ |
| $4x^2$ | $\frac{1}{3} 4x^3$ |

These results suggest that there must be some law that accounts for the "pattern" of these area-functions. This law is sometimes called "Wallis' Law." The reader will doubtless see how each area-function can be built up from its ordinate-function. He will then be able to supply the area-functions connected with the ordinate-functions of the graphs of $y = 4x^3$, $y = 4x^4$. If this can be done, an essential step in the process of integration will have been mastered. [The answers are given later in the text.]

Wallis now went a step further and found what we now call the area-function connected with the ordinate-function of the graph of $y = p\sqrt{x}$, where p stands for some constant. [Wallis did not use the word "function"; it was first used by Leibniz in 1694, though not in its modern sense. It was first used as we use it today by John Bernoulli in 1718.]

The reader may care to see whether he can reach the same conclusions as those reached by Wallis when searching for the area-function connected with the ordinate function of $y = 5x^{\frac{1}{2}}$, which is equivalent to $y = 5\sqrt{x}$. [If he is a stranger to the calculus, he may care to know that the two area-functions he was asked to supply just now were $\frac{1}{4}\,4x^4$ and $\frac{1}{5}\,4x^5$.] After trying his hand at finding the area-function connected with $y = 5x^{\frac{1}{2}}$ he can check his result from what follows.

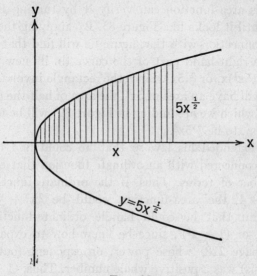

FIG. 89

The shaded portion of Figure 89 shows the area covered by the graph of $y = 5x^{\frac{1}{2}}$ from the origin to the ordinate erected $x$ units from the origin.

By Wallis' Law it will be seen that the area-function will be found as follows:

The fraction in the answer will be obtained by inverting the improper fraction representing 1 more than the exponent of $x$ in the given ordinate-function. (Compare the three examples given in the table above.)

The new exponent of x will be 1 more than the exponent of x in the ordinate-function.

So the area-function will be $\frac{2}{3}$ $5x^{\frac{3}{2}}$. This means that if the area is bounded on the right by an ordinate at the point x = 4, the area will be $\frac{2}{3}(5)(8)$, since $4^{\frac{3}{2}} = (2^2)^{\frac{3}{2}} = 2^3 = 8$. So the area would then be $26\frac{2}{3}$ square units. If x = 9, the area will be found to be 90 square units. The reader who feels doubtful about this area-function can verify it by turning Figure 89 around until it looks like Figure 85. By applying the method used in connection with that figure he will find that the area under the right-hand part of the curve (in its new position) will be $\frac{1}{3}$ $(5x^{\frac{3}{2}})x$, or $\frac{1}{3}$ $5x^{\frac{3}{2}}$. Since the rectangle involved in this solution will have an area of $5x^{\frac{3}{2}}$, the area of half the parabolic segment (which we are finding in Figure 89) will be found, by subtraction, to be $\frac{2}{3}$ $5x^{\frac{3}{2}}$.

Wallis extended his law so that he could find the area-function connected with an ordinate-function that contained any number of terms. Thus, if the ordinate function were $x^2 + 3x - 4$, the area-function would be $\frac{1}{3}x^3 + \frac{3}{2}x^2 - 4x$. This meant that he could handle ordinate-functions like $(1 - x^2)^2$, or $(1 - x^2)^3$, since he knew how to expand a binomial (page 228) whose power, or exponent (outside the parenthesis) was a positive whole number. Thus, $(1 - x^2)^2 = 1 - 2x^2 + x^4$; $(1 - x^2)^3 = 1 - 3x^2 + 3x^4 - x^6$, and so on.

By applying his law, he could easily find the areas bounded by the x-axis, the ordinate at the point x = 1 and the graphs of

$$y = (1 - x^2)^0 \text{ [That is, } y = 1]$$
$$y = (1 - x^2)^1 \text{ [That is, } y = 1 - x^2]$$
$$y = (1 - x^2)^2$$
$$y = (1 - x^2)^3$$

and so on.

Now we saw on page 213 that the equation of a circle is $x^2 + y^2 = r^2$, where r is the radius. If r = 1, this equation becomes $x^2 + y^2 = 1$, which may be written as $y^2 = 1 - x^2$, or as $y = (1 - x^2)^{\frac{1}{2}}$.

Wallis saw that if he could find the area-function connection with the ordinate-function $(1 - x^2)^{\frac{1}{2}}$, he would be able to find the area of a circle from his answer. Now, the area of a circle $= \pi r^2$, so if $r = 1$, this area becomes $\pi$, while the area of a semi-circle will be $\dfrac{\pi}{2}$.

But here Wallis ran into a difficulty. We have seen that binomials which had a positive whole number for their power, or exponent, could be expanded. But nobody knew how to expand a binomial which had a fraction for its exponent. [This problem we are considering led Newton to discover how to expand certain binomials having fractional exponents.] Wallis thought he could get his desired answer by calculating the area-functions of a series of curves such as the four we have listed above. If the reader will apply Wallis' Law to the various ordinate functions in that list and find the areas for values from $x = 0$ to $x = 1$, he will get the following results:

| Equation | Area |
|---|---|
| $y = (1 - x^2)^0$ | $1$ |
| $y = (1 - x^2)^1$ | $\frac{2}{3}$ |
| $y = (1 - x^2)^2$ | $\frac{8}{15}$ |
| $y = (1 - x^2)^3$ | $\frac{48}{105}$ |

Now Wallis argued that since the ordinate-function $(1 - x^2)^{\frac{1}{2}}$ lies between the ordinate-functions $(1 - x^2)^0$ and $(1 - x^2)^1$, he ought to be able to interpolate a value for its area-function somewhere in between the areas $1$ and $\frac{2}{3}$, basing his calculations on the "steps" in the series of areas $1$, $\frac{2}{3}$, $\frac{8}{15}$, $\frac{48}{105}$ etc. He did not of course succeed in doing this exactly, but his attempt shows a remarkable "number-pattern." Here it is:

$$\frac{\pi}{2} = \frac{2 \cdot 2 \cdot 4 \cdot 4 \cdot 6 \cdot 6 \cdot 8 \cdot 8 \cdot \ldots \ldots}{1 \cdot 3 \cdot 3 \cdot 5 \cdot 5 \cdot 7 \cdot 7 \cdot 9 \cdot \ldots \ldots}$$

Now twice the right-hand side gives successive values which "close in" on the value of $\pi$. As it stands above, it only gives 2.9 . . . which is too small. If we place one more term (10) on the numerator, and one more term (9) on the denominator, we get 3.3 . . . , which is too large. If we now place another 10 on the numerator and 11 on the denominator, we get 3.0, which is still too small, but better than 2.9 . . . ; while if we place another pair of numbers in the fraction we get 3.2 . . . which is still too large. Compare this very interesting "pattern" of numbers with the Greek pattern given on page 234. Wallis had found an entirely new way of "closing in" on the value of $\pi$, which, like $\sqrt{2}$ etc. is "incommensurable." He asked a friend of his, Lord Brouncker, who later became the first President of the Royal Society, to see whether he could find an exact value for $\pi$. Naturally, Lord Brouncker failed to do this, but he produced the following extraordinary continued fraction:

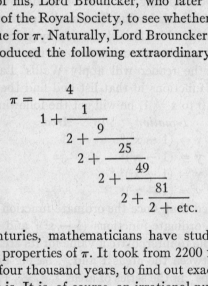

$$\pi = \cfrac{4}{1 + \cfrac{1}{2 + \cfrac{9}{2 + \cfrac{25}{2 + \cfrac{49}{2 + \cfrac{81}{2 + \text{etc.}}}}}}}$$

For centuries, mathematicians have studied and investigated the properties of $\pi$. It took from 2200 B.C. to A.D. 1882, just over four thousand years, to find out exactly what kind of number it is. It is, of course, an irrational number, but it differs from irrationals like $\sqrt{2}$ in that it can never be the root of an equation such as $7x^5 - 2x^4 + 3x^2 + 9x + 8 = 0$. For this reason, $\pi$ is called a *transcendental* number. Among the great mathematicians who have studied the properties of $\pi$ were

Archimedes, Ptolemy, Fibonacci, Vieta, Fermat, Huygens (around 1670), Wallis, Newton, Leibniz, the Bernoullis (around 1700), Euler (around 1750), Lambert (a German mathematician, around 1750), Lagrange (around 1775) and Lindemann (of the University of Munich, around 1875). Not until 1882 did Lindemann prove beyond all doubt that $\pi$ was transcendental; thus he showed once and for all that no circle can be "squared"—no circle can have its area found *exactly*. The reader who wishes to pursue the subject of *transcendentals* should read "The Transcendence of $\pi$," in J. W. A. Young's *Monographs on Topics of Modern Mathematics*.

We shall now temporarily leave the story of the development of the integral calculus, to return to it as soon as we have seen how the *differential* calculus was developed.

Before we discuss this latter development it will help those who are not familiar with the calculus if we digress for a moment and consider another aspect of the *ordinate-functions* of graphs, while they are fresh in our minds. If the very simple arguments developed in the next few paragraphs are grasped, the underlying idea of both the differential and the integral calculus will become clear.

Suppose water is flowing steadily into a rectangular tank, and that we measure the depth of the water at regular time-intervals from the moment the water is turned on. Since these time-intervals are equal to each other, we can picture them as marked by equal lengths on a straight line. We will use the x-axis for these equal time-intervals. If at the end of the first time-interval (that is, at the point x = 1) we erect a perpendicular line representing the depth of the water at the end of the first interval, another perpendicular at the point x = 2, representing the depth at the end of the second time-interval, and so on, we can draw a line touching the top of each perpendicular. This line will be a graph indicating the depth of water at any time during the period under observation. The perpendiculars will be a few of the innumerable *ordinates* of this graph.

It is obvious that since the graph slopes upward from left to right, it indicates ever-increasing values of the function.

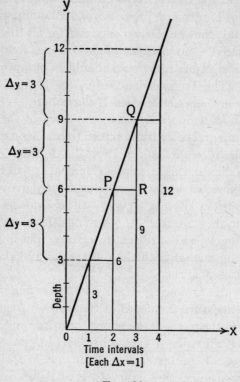

FIG. 90

Further, since in this case the depth of water added during each time-interval is the same, the *rate* at which the depth increases will remain unchanged throughout the operation. This is indicated by the fact that the difference between the lengths of any two successive and equally spaced ordinates is always the same.

[To avoid the constant repetition of the phrase "the difference between the lengths of any two successive ordinates" we will use the shorthand sign $\Delta y$, the Greek letter D (delta) standing for all but the last word in this phrase, the y indicating "ordinates." We shall also make use of the shorthand $\Delta x$ to indicate "the difference between the lengths of any two successive x-values measured along the x-axis."]

We see that in Figure 90, each $\Delta y$ has the same value. Since the $\Delta x$ values are equal to each other, it follows that the figure may be likened to a flight of steps in which not only are the "treads" all equal to each other, but the "risers" are also all equal to each other. Consequently a straight plank could be placed on the steps so as to touch the edge of each step. So, whenever the graph of a function is a straight line, it indicates an unchanging slope reflecting an unchanging rate of increase (or decrease) in the value of the function (a decrease would, of course, be indicated by a *downward* slope from left to right). There is no need to draw a graph in order to find whether the $\Delta y$ values are equal to each other. This can easily be discovered algebraically. Thus, to take the equation of the graph in Figure 90, $y = 3x$:

| Values of x: | 0 | 1 | 2 | 3 | 4 |
|---|---|---|---|---|---|
| Related values of y: | 0 | 3 | 6 | 9 | 12 |
| Values of $\Delta y$: | | 3 | 3 | 3 | 3 |

Now consider a mathematical flight of steps which is not quite so easy to negotiate, since, although all the "treads" are the same width ($\Delta x$), the "risers" do not all have the same $\Delta y$ value.

Although it is quicker to work algebraically, we shall in this case draw the graph of $y = x^2$. To make the example realistic, we shall suppose that a ball rolls down a rather rough incline from rest, and that the number of feet it has rolled at the end of x seconds is given by the equation $y = x^2$. Our own observation has told us that provided there are no serious obstacles in its path, the ball will gather speed as it rolls. Thus, in 1 second it rolls 1², or 1 foot; in 2 seconds, 2², or 4 feet; in 3 seconds, 3², or 9 feet, and so on.

No longer can we imagine a plank so placed that it touches each step. The graph is part of a parabola. Since the Δy values

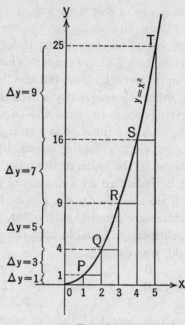

FIG. 91

are not equal to each other, the *rate* by which the distance y increases is not constant. If, however, another graph were drawn having equally-spaced ordinates representing the Δy values 1, 3, 5, 7, and 9, "the difference between the lengths of any two successive Δy values" (which impressive phrase we will indicate in future by the symbol $\Delta_2 y$, or "second difference-of-ordinate-values") will always be the same. In other words, this last graph will look like a flight of steps sloping upward from left to right, on which we can imagine a plank so placed as to touch each step. So this will indicate that the *rate* at which the ball rolls down the slope increases uniformly. In other words, it has the same constant *acceleration*. So *speed* is connected with $\Delta y$ in some way, *acceleration* with $\Delta_2 y$, as we shall see later.

All this can be seen quickly if the problem is treated algebraically. Thus, since $y = x^2$,

| Values of x: | 0 | 1 | 2 | 3 | 4 | 5 |
|---|---|---|---|---|---|---|
| Related values of y: | 0 | 1 | 4 | 9 | 16 | 25 |
| Values of $\Delta y$: | | 1 | 3 | 5 | 7 | 9 |
| Values of $\Delta_2 y$: | | | 2 | 2 | 2 | 2 |

In this digression about ordinate values we have jumped out of the seventeenth century and made use of modern symbolism so that the non-mathematical reader may become accustomed to thinking about "differences in values of successive ordinates" of a curve. This lies at the root of the differential calculus, whose object is to find out facts connected with the rate with which a quantity changes in value. Provided we know—or can find out—how far an object moves in a given time, we can find not merely its *average* rate or speed for any given period of time, which is a very simple matter, but also its speed at any given instant, which is apparently not so simple a matter. Consider, for instance, the rolling ball in our last example. During the first second it rolled 1 foot. So its average speed during this period of time was 1 foot per second. But to begin with, its speed was less than this, since it started from rest. So at the end of the first second, its speed must have been greater than 1 foot per second, otherwise it would not have *averaged* this speed. If we take 2 hours to drive 60 miles, our average speed would be found by dividing the distance by the time taken. Thus, average speed $= \dfrac{\text{distance}}{\text{time taken}}$.

Obviously, our average speed would be 30 m.p.h., or $\frac{60}{2}$. This does not mean we were traveling at 30 m.p.h. from the instant we started until we finished our journey. If we imagine a journey of 60 miles over a perfectly straight level road with no obstacles in our way such as traffic lights or other vehicles, we can picture ourselves starting from rest and gently and uniformly accelerating throughout the whole journey so that we complete it in 2 hours. Clearly, our speed would slowly rise from 0 m.p.h. to 30 m.p.h. and would be considerably more than 30 m.p.h. at the end of the journey, if we were to average 30 m.p.h. throughout.

In Figure 90, the *average* rate of increase in the depth of the water between the depths indicated at the points P and Q will be $\dfrac{\text{increase in depth between P and Q}}{\text{time taken for this increase}}$. Now, the increase in depth between P and Q is $\Delta y$, the time taken is $\Delta x$. So the *average* rate of increase in depth between P and Q will be $\dfrac{\Delta y}{\Delta x}$. It is clear from Figure 90 that in this particular problem, $\dfrac{\Delta y}{\Delta x}$ is the same during each of the first, second, third and fourth seconds. Thus, the rate of increase in the depth of the water does not change throughout the operation depicted in this graph.

In Figure 91, however, it will be seen that $\dfrac{\Delta y}{\Delta x}$ is successively greater and greater during the first, second, third, fourth and fifth seconds of the ball's path down the incline. The fact that the ball travels a greater distance during each successive second is another way of saying that its *average speed* during successive periods of time becomes greater and greater. Thus, between O and P its average speed was 1 foot per second, between P and Q it was 3 feet per second, between Q and R it was 5 feet per second, between R and S it was 7 feet per second, between S and T it was 9 feet per second. But at P its speed was greater than 1 foot per second, at Q it was greater than 3 feet per second, . . . at T it was greater than 9 feet per second. The problem of finding the speed at points like these can be solved with absurd ease by means of the differential calculus. We shall see how Newton solved this, and many other problems, by its aid.

In our story of Wallis' work we have been careful to avoid speaking, as he did, of a figure "as if" made up of "an infinite number of parallel lines in arithmetic proportion." Here, he was following the example of Cavalieri. Wallis' great contributions to the development of the calculus were his development of the arithmetic concept of a *limit*, and his application of analysis which enabled an area-function to be found from an ordinate function by the application of a general algebraic law.

The seeds sown by Archimedes were at last springing up; to some, the new growths seemed like dangerous weeds. But by the skill and genius of two men, and the assistance of a few others, they were to be cultivated and developed into the finest and most valuable crop that mathematicians have ever harvested.

# CHAPTER VII

# *Newton*

"I do not know what I may appear to the world; but to myself I seem to have been only like a boy playing on the seashore, and diverting myself in now and then finding a smoother pebble or a prettier shell than ordinary, whilst the great ocean of truth lay all undiscovered before me."

*Brewster's Memoirs of Newton.*

IN OCTOBER, 1661, a youth between eighteen and nineteen years of age traveled to Cambridge and found his way to Trinity College. The previous June, the Master of Trinity had admitted him as a member of the great college founded more than a century previously by Henry VIII. On July 8th he had been admitted as a student-member of the University of Cambridge. Now he had "come up" for the October term and was about to commence his life there as an unknown undergraduate.

As he walked through the King's Gateway, with its statue of the royal founder of the college, he can little have dreamed that there were rooms on one side of that gateway which, centuries later, would proudly be shown to visitors as having been occupied by him.

As he entered the courtyard with its statue that he was to find was in memory of Thomas Neville, the Master of Trinity from 1593 to 1613, and saw for the first time the college chapel built in Queen Mary's reign, he little could have dreamed that

one day his own statue would be placed in that chapel, and that
one of the world's greatest poets would describe that statue as

"The marble index of a mind forever
Voyaging through strange seas of thought alone."

He would undoubtedly have been annoyed and embarrassed
had he known that Pope was to rhapsodize extravagantly

"Nature and Nature's laws lay hid in night:
God said 'Let Newton be!' and all was light."

Never having read a book on mathematics, he most definitely could not have conceived the possibility that within
eight years of that October day he would be appointed a professor of mathematics in the University of Cambridge, and
that he would write a book on science and applied mathematics
which, more than a century later, was to be described by the
profound French mathematician Laplace (usually very sparing
in his tributes to others) as assured of "a pre-eminence above
all other productions of human genius."

Had he been able to look into the future, it would have
seemed strange that a man who had been appointed Savilian
Professor of Astronomy in the University of Oxford the
previous year should be about to change his profession and
become the best-known of all English architects; it would
have seemed unlikely that Christopher Wren, while busy de-
signing a new St. Paul's cathedral that was to take the place
of the old one, to be destroyed in 1666 in the Great Fire of
London, should find time to design a great new library for
Trinity College; it would have seemed still more unlikely than
any of these apparently fantastic visions that in 1948 one of
that library's most treasured possessions would be his own
manuscripts on mathematics and science, subjects of which,
in October, 1661, he was entirely ignorant.

Isaac Newton was born on Christmas day 1642 (the year
of Galileo's death, and the year when civil war broke out between Charles I and the English Parliament) in the little vil-

lage of Woolsthorpe, Lincolnshire, some six miles from the town of Grantham. He never knew his father, for the latter, a small farmer with a reputation for extravagance, had died before his son was born. The boy was so frail at birth that he was not expected to live. Thus he was given his first of many opportunities of astonishing others. As in the case of all these other opportunities, he seized on this first one to the full, living to his eighty-fifth year, when he still had perfect vision and a thick head of silvery hair—his hair turned prematurely gray when he was thirty.

His childhood's frailty prevented him from joining in the rough and tumble of village schoolchildren. Instead, he amused himself by making mechanical toys: little working models of such things as waterwheels and windmills, a tiny carriage moved by its rider, and ingeniously constructed kites. The mechanical skill and ingenuity he thus developed were to be very useful to him later in life, when making practical experiments in connection with lenses and the study of the properties of light. The joy of creating things thus tasted early in life never deserted him; he passed from the creation of mechanical objects to that of intellectual concepts. Thus it came about that he never felt the need to have others "amuse" and "entertain" him. He provided his own recreation in probing into the mysteries of the universe: the only matters of lasting and absorbing interest for an intellect such as his. In his search to find an answer to the riddle of the universe he became absorbed in philosophy and theology to such an extent that he would turn to the certainties of mathematics

". . . that held acquaintance with the stars
And wedded soul to soul in purest bond
Of reason, undisturbed by space or time,"

and find relief and recreation in them.

His interests were overwhelmingly intellectual; he never married; he cared nothing for dress; meals would be prepared for him and would be left untouched when his mind was wrestling with the intricacies of some problem.

Fortunately, as we have seen, he was unlike Pascal in that he outgrew his childhood's weakness, and until the last few years of his long life he was able to endure the intense mental and physical strain involved in writing on the most profound subjects for as many as eighteen or nineteen hours on end. Like Archimedes, he possessed the power of concentration to a remarkable degree. His mind would close on a problem like a steel trap, and nothing was allowed to divert it from its goal. Meals would be ignored, and, on getting up in the morning he would forget to dress and would be found hours later sitting in his bedroom oblivious to everything save the problem in which he was absorbed. Although Nature had been so lavish in her mental equipment, he once came near to ruining her gifts by his neglect of food and his reluctance to spend precious hours in sleep. In the Michaelmas Term 1684 he had given a course of lectures at Cambridge on the laws of motion. By 1685 he had incorporated these lectures into what was to be the first of three books which were to constitute his world-famous masterpiece the *Principia*. This book gave the world his law of universal gravitation, which, as Dr. F. J. Cajori said in his *History of Mathematics* "envelops the name of Newton in a halo of perpetual glory."

The second book was completed in the summer of 1685, and the third in the incredibly short time (in view of its contents) of nine months. The years of intense concentration and labor involved in the production of these great works undermined his strength and some years later brought on what would now be described as a near nervous breakdown. Fortunately he made a complete recovery and the very next year after his illness he showed that his powers were unimpaired by solving the problem of the *brachistochrone* (*brachistos*, "shortest," *chronos*, "time") or curve of quickest descent. This problem had been

issued as a challenge to other mathematicians by Johann
Bernoulli, who had coined the Greek word *brachistochrone*.
Newton received the problem on January 29, 1697, and gave
the solution (a cycloid) on January 30, 1697. Again, in 1716,
Leibniz issued an extremely difficult problem. Newton, aged
seventy-four, solved it in five hours. Nevertheless, after com-
pleting the *Principia* that was assured of "a pre-eminence
above all other productions of human genius" a distinct change
took place in Newton. He produced very little original mathematical or scientific work, while, as we shall see, his nature
seems to have changed. He allowed the cordial relationship
that had existed between himself and Leibniz, for example, to
degenerate into a shamefully distressing state of animosity
during all the years when, as President of the Royal Society, a
word from him would have saved the situation. Possibly his
illness had deeper effects than those that appeared on the
surface.

It is not surprising to learn that during the years when he
was exercising intense concentration on mathematical and
scientific matters he was at times forgetful of everyday things.
On one occasion, it is said, while leading his horse up a steep
hill, he turned his mind to some problem. Some considerable
time later he was puzzled to find the bridle still in his hand, but
no horse attached to it. On another occasion—one of the few
occasions when he entertained friends—he went from the room
to fetch more wine for his guests. After a long and trying interval, his thirsty guests were driven to investigate their host's
prolonged absence. They found him absorbed in some problem
or other. Without doubt, the thought of wine would bring to
Newton's mind Kepler's use of infinitesimals rather than the
qualities usually associated with the "vinous beverage."

At the very beginning of his career he discovered that mathematicians and scientists were quick to question and criticize
any departure from habitual practices. At first Newton took

great pains to answer their criticisms with patience and courtesy, and to try to clear up their misunderstandings of his work. But as their criticisms continued, he became hypersensitive on the subject, and bitterly resented the hours—wasted hours, in his opinion—that were consumed in replying to his critics. On November 18, 1676, he wrote to Henry Oldenburg, the Secretary of the Royal Society, with reference to a fresh batch of criticisms that had been sent to him by a Mr. Lucas, Professor of Mathematics at Liége, Belgium. In the course of his letter, Newton said, "I promised to send you an answer to Mr. Lucas this next Tuesday, but I find I shall scarce finish what I have designed, so as to get a copy taken of it by that time, and therefore I beg your patience a week longer. I see I have made myself a slave to philosophy [science], but if I get free of Mr. Lucas's business, I will resolutely bid adieu to it eternally, excepting what I do for my private satisfaction, or leave to come out after me; for I see a man must either resolve to put out nothing new, or to become a slave to defend it." Twelve years later, he reiterated his detestation of the disputes aroused by new scientific discoveries. "Philosophy [science] is such an impertinently litigious lady," he remarked in a letter to his good friend, the eminent astronomer Edmund Halley, "that a man has as good be engaged in lawsuits, as have to do with her." Halley's reply, dated June 29th, shows the tact and patience with which he handled the sensitive genius. He said, "I am heartily sorry that in this matter, wherein all mankind ought to acknowledge their obligations to you, you should meet with anything that should give you unquiet. . . . I am sure that the Society [Royal Society] have a very great satisfaction, in the honour you do them, by the dedication of so worthy a treatise [the first two books of the *Principia*]. Sir, I must again beg you, not to let your resentments run so high as to deprive us of your third book." The world has to thank Halley, not only for bearing the cost of printing the *Principia* and for correcting all the proofs, but also for so gently and tact-fully urging Newton to complete his great work.

This reluctance on Newton's part to publish his discoveries led to a regrettable and acrimonious dispute as to whether he or Leibniz invented the calculus. As we shall see, Newton actually used his methods as early as 1665–6; in 1669 he com-municated an outline of them privately to Isaac Barrow, his predecessor as Lucasian Professor of Mathematics at Cam-bridge, but they were not made available to scholars generally until 1693. Thus, nearly thirty years elapsed before the world outside Cambridge learned of his work in this connection. As we shall see, this led to most unfortunate misunderstandings on the part of the followers of Leibniz.

Newton's life falls into three distinct sections: the first covers his boyhood in Lincolnshire; the second, his life at Cambridge from 1661 to 1696; the third, his work as a highly paid government official from 1696 to his death in 1729.

After attending two small schools in hamlets close to Woolsthorpe, he was sent, at the age of twelve, to the grammar school at Grantham. In the sixteenth century, "grammar schools" had been founded in England with the object of pro-viding an inexpensive education based on the study of Latin and the classics. Mathematics was seldom if ever taught in them. The grammar school at Grantham was not a boarding school; so arrangements were made for young Newton to lodge with a local druggist, or, as he would then be termed, apothecary, named Clark. Newton later admitted that his early days at Grantham school were far from industrious. He stood low in his class, and, doubtless owing to his physical frailty, he seems to have suffered from an inferiority complex until the day when he was goaded into a fight with a bully. Newton's biographer, Sir David Brewster, says that Newton got the better of the fight, and, dragging the bully by the ears, pushed his face against the wall. This story seems a little too good to be true, but there is no question that from this time onward Newton's work showed great and rapid improvement. Brewster attributes this sudden development of mental concentration to Newton's determination to vanquish the bully in class. Not only was Newton eventually successful in doing this, but he rose to be head of the school.

When he was fifteen, however, his mother, who had remarried in 1645 and had become a widow for the second time in 1656, withdrew him from the school, feeling that it was time he began to learn how to cultivate his father's small farm, and thus become a farmer. Farming, however, did not appeal to the boy. Whenever his mother sent her servant to Grantham to shop for her, Newton contrived to accompany the servant, and, as soon as he reached the town, go to Mr. Clark's house and spend the precious hours thus snatched from farming in reading Mr. Clark's books. It would be very interesting and instructive if we could know the titles of some of Mr. Clark's books. Unfortunately, we can only surmise that some of them must have been of a scientific nature and thus have aroused the boy's interest in subjects he would not have met at school. Without this surmise it is difficult to imagine what led him to take up the study of mathematics and science when he went to Cambridge.

When on the farm, he preferred to sit under a tree reading a book or carving a model to preventing the sheep and cattle from straying, while in later years he told a friend that on Friday, September 3, 1658, when a great tempest swept over England as Oliver Cromwell passed away, he occupied himself in trying to measure the force of the gale by leaping, first with the wind and then against it, and then comparing these measurements with the distance he could jump on a calm day. It was activities such as these (when a farmer's mind ought to be occupied in protecting his stock and equipment) that caused his mother to realize that he was unfitted for farming. For-

tunately for mankind, she had the good sense to send him back
to Grantham Grammar School, where he was prepared for
entrance to Cambridge University on the advice of his uncle,
the Reverend W. Ayscough, the rector of a neighboring parish,
who not only persuaded his sister to let him arrange for her
son's entry into the college at Cambridge which he himself
had attended, but also lent him books, such as Sanderson's
*Logic*, which would have to be studied when he went into residence there. Thus it came about that, thanks to the good
offices of a graduate of Trinity College, Newton was granted a
sizarship there, which meant that his mother would pay reduced fees.

Very few details have come down to us of his undergraduate
days at Cambridge. The best we can do is to try and piece together some notes made by him many years later.

In his first term, that is, between October and Christmas
1661, he went to the little village of Stourbridge, near Cambridge, in order to visit the fair that was held there every year,
at one time, the greatest fair in England. Here he bought a
book on the stars, but found he was unable to understand it on
account of his ignorance of geometry. So he bought an English
edition of Euclid's *Elements*. He found the contents so "self-
evident" (to quote his own words) that he put aside the *Elements* as a "trifling book"! He therefore got hold of a copy of
Descartes' *Geometry* and, after a hard struggle, managed to
master it. It was unfortunate that he had no one to guide him
by advising him to read Wallis' book on Descartes' *Geometry*,
which set forth the subject much more clearly than had the
original. However, Descartes' book was sufficient to open up
the fascination of mathematics to him, and we find references
in his notes to his having read some of Vieta's works and also
Wallis' *Arithmetica Infinitorum* and thus making the acquaintance of infinite series during the years 1663 and 1664.

In 1664 he sat for a scholarship at Trinity, to which he was elected on April 28th of that year, despite the fact that one of his examiners, Dr. Barrow, the first occupant of the Lucasian Chair of Mathematics, reported adversely on his knowledge of Euclid's *Elements*, a verdict which is not surprising, in view of the extent of his acquaintance with the "trifling book." This led Newton to study the *Elements* with care, and thus come to realize that the book was no trifling matter, as he had supposed. He was later to make a masterly use of Euclid's geometry in order to give to the world his mathematical explanation of universal gravitation. He had himself reached his conclusions by means of his own invention, the calculus; since, however, he knew that other mathematicians were ignorant of his invention—and would doubtless raise objections to it and thus deny the truth of conclusions based on it—he re-cast his arguments in geometric form, as we shall see. Thus, Barrow's criticism of the young candidate for a Trinity scholarship was to bear good fruit in the end.

Since Isaac Barrow was to play an important part in Newton's life, we will digress for a moment and glance at this first occupant, in 1663, of the mathematical professorship endowed by Mr. Lucas in his will.

Barrow's father was a London linen draper who sent his boy to Charterhouse School. There he was so troublesome and so fond of fighting that his father is reported to have said that if it pleased God to take any of his children, he could best spare Isaac.

After leaving Charterhouse, however, he applied himself so well to the study of literature and science at Trinity College, Cambridge, that he became a Fellow of the college.

Then followed several years of travel and adventure. While on a voyage from Italy to Turkey his ship was attacked by pirates. Barrow then found that his entirely unofficial activities at Charterhouse stood him in good stead, for he gave a very good account of himself in the fight that ensued and that resulted in driving off the intruders.

He remained in Constantinople some time, and became interested in reading the works of the early Church Fathers. On his return to England he was ordained, and in 1660 was appointed to the Greek professorship at Cambridge. Two years later, he was chosen as Professor of Geometry at Gresham College, London, whose first Professor of Geometry had been Henry Briggs, the friend and helper of Napier.

In 1663 Barrow received two great honors: he was the first Fellow to be chosen by the newly formed Royal Society [Today, "F.R.S." after a scientist's name is an indication of the highest distinction attainable by a scientist in England, namely "Fellow of the Royal Society."]; and he was chosen as the first Lucasian Professor of Mathematics at Cambridge.

Thus it came about that one of Newton's examiners for his scholarship in 1664 was Isaac Barrow, who thereby unknowingly played a part in securing for his lectures a student who was to become the greatest mathematician England, if not the world, has ever produced. By 1669 Barrow fully realized the "unparalleled genius" of his pupil, to quote his own words, and, on deciding to devote himself to the study of theology, resigned his mathematical professorship and was instrumental in securing the appointment of Newton as his successor. In 1672 Barrow became Master of Trinity College, and in 1675 Vice-chancellor of the University.

To return to Newton's undergraduate days. Before the study of mathematics was commenced, it was then customary at Cambridge to read Sanderson's *Logic* as a preliminary training for the mind. We have seen how Newton's uncle had given him a copy of this work; so well had Newton studied and grasped its contents that Benjamin Pulleyn, his tutor at Trinity, excused his attendance at lectures on the book. While still an undergraduate, Newton began to make careful observations of the heavenly bodies. He himself remarks in his *Optics* that "in the beginning of the year 1664, February 19th, at night, I saw two such crowns [about the moon]." In January, 1665, he took the degree of bachelor of arts but was later in that year forced to leave Cambridge owing to the plague. In December, 1664, "the Plague of London" had commenced. The diarist Samuel Pepys (1633–1703) who was Secretary to the Navy, or to give him his actual title, "Clerk of the Acts of the Navy," tells us that on June 7, 1665, he saw for the first time houses marked with the—then—dread red cross and the words "Lord, have mercy upon us." On September 4th, Pepys wrote, "I have stayed in the city till above 7400 died in one week and of them about 6000 of the plague, and little noise heard day or night but tolling of bells." As a precautionary measure Trinity College was closed during part of 1665 and part of 1666, by which year the Great Fire of London had destroyed not only the city but also the germs of the disease. While the college was closed, Newton went to Woolsthorpe, and there it was that he began to think about the fundamental principles of his theory of gravitation.

It was here, at Woolsthorpe, in 1666 that the well-known legend of Newton and the apple arose. Tradition holds that the idea of gravitation was suggested to Newton by the fall of an apple. Certainly, the supposed tree from which it fell was kept standing until a gale destroyed it in 1820. But the *earth's* gravitation was an accepted scientific fact long before Newton's time; his genius lay in developing the law of *universal* gravitation. The most probable explanation of the rise of the legend is that given by Professor S. Brodetsky in his book *Sir Isaac Newton:*

"The fall of the apple—if it was really responsible for initiating in Newton's mind the train of thought that culminated in the discovery of the law of gravitation—did it in the following manner, if one may venture to put into feeble words the flash of Newton's genius:

'Why do the planets go round the sun? Why do they not move in straight lines? Evidently there is a force pulling them out of the straight-line path at every moment, and clearly this force is due to the sun. The moon goes round the earth and does not go off on a straight line. This must be due to the earth. Ah! An apple has just fallen to the ground: the earth has pulled it down. How far up does the earth's influence extend? . . .' " *

Living in the peaceful countryside where he had once feared he would have to spend his life as a farmer, he invented his "fluxional calculus" which was to enable him to build up his law of universal gravitation, and was to give mathematicians and scientists their most powerful weapon. In order that we may follow the steps that led to this epoch-marking invention, we must go back and accompany him in imagination to the lecture room of Isaac Barrow. Barrow's contribution to the development of the calculus lay in his extension and simplification of Fermat's method of drawing a tangent to a curve. Fermat had explained this method in a letter to Roberval in 1629. It had been published in Herigone's *Cursus Mathematicus* in 1644.

To understand this method, we must first glance at Fermat's method for finding the maximum or minimum values of certain functions. Suppose $y = 3x - x^2$ is the equation of the curve shown in Figure 92.

The value of the function "$3x - x^2$" will, of course, change as the value of x changes. For some value of x, this particular function will have either a maximum or minimum value. How could this be found? Fermat's method was as follows:

Suppose the ordinate at A is x units from the origin. Then the length of this ordinate, in terms of x, will be $3x - x^2$.

---

* Reprinted by courtesy of Methuen & Co. Ltd.

Now suppose there is another ordinate, at B, that is the same length as the ordinate at A. We will suppose the ordinate at B is h units further from the origin than the ordinate at A. In other words, B will be $(x + h)$ units from the origin. Now, the equation of this curve, $y = 3x - x^2$, tells us that the length

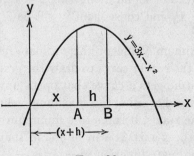

Fig. 92

of any ordinate is "3 times its x-value, minus the square of that x-value." So the length of the ordinate at B will be given by the function $3(x + h) - (x + h)^2$, which can be simplified to $3x + 3h - x^2 - 2xh - h^2$. Now these two ordinates are assumed to be equal. So

$$3x - x^2 = 3x + 3h - x^2 - 2xh - h^2$$
$$\therefore 3h - 2xh - h^2 = 0$$

Now divide throughout by h:

$$\therefore 3 - 2x - h = 0$$

Now suppose the two equal ordinates are moved so close together that "h" approaches zero [Fermat said "let the added quantity be taken as zero," which doesn't make sense].

Fermat would then say that $3 - 2x = 0$

$$\therefore 3 = 2x$$
$$\therefore x = 1\tfrac{1}{2}$$

[We should say that as h approaches zero, $3 - 2x$ approaches zero, and x approaches its limit, $1\tfrac{1}{2}$]

Now a glance at Figure 92 will make it clear that as h becomes smaller and smaller, the two equal ordinates come closer and closer together. Each approaches the same "limiting" value when $x = 1\frac{1}{2}$. Also, each becomes greater and greater as it approaches its limiting value. So the greatest ordinate in Figure 92 would be one drawn at the point where $x = 1\frac{1}{2}$, and its length can be found by putting $x = 1\frac{1}{2}$ in the ordinate-function $3x - x^2$, and consequently will be $3(1\frac{1}{2}) - (1\frac{1}{2})^2$, or $4\frac{1}{2} - 2\frac{1}{4}$, or $2\frac{1}{4}$.

So the maximum value of the ordinate-function $3x - x^2$ will be $2\frac{1}{4}$. [If the reader cares to draw the graph of $y = x^2 - 3x$, he will find he gets a curve that opens upward instead of downward; instead of rising to a maximum value and then falling back to the x-axis, it sinks to a minimum value and then rises back to the x-axis. It will be found that the minimum value of the ordinate-function $x^2 - 3x$ is $-2\frac{1}{4}$, and that this occurs when $x = 1\frac{1}{2}$.]

Fermat now applied part of his method of "maxima and minima" to the problem of drawing a tangent at any given point on a curve. He did this by calculating the length of the *subtangent*, or the length TS in Figure 93.

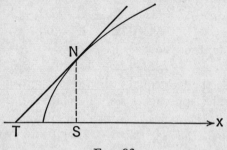

Fig. 93

We will not spend time discussing Fermat's method but will go straight to that used by Barrow, since the only difference between these methods was that Barrow not only made use of an increase, or increment, in the x-value, but also of an increment in the y-value. Let us draw the graph of y = 3x — x² and then take two ordinates, AP and BQ. We will suppose that the length of BQ is j units greater than the length of AP, and that BQ is h units further from the origin than is AP.

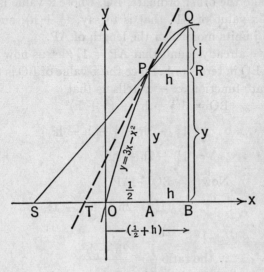

FIG. 94

[Triangle PQR is known as "Barrow's differential triangle"]

Suppose we wish to draw the tangent at P, and that we know that the ordinate AP is ½ unit from the origin O.

Join QP and extend this line to meet the x-axis at S. It is clear that triangle SPA is similar to triangle PQR,

$$\therefore \frac{RQ}{PR} = \frac{AP}{SA}$$

We must always bear in mind that the length of any ordinate can be found provided we know its *function* (in terms of x, where x indicates any horizontal distance from the origin), and also its actual horizontal distance from that origin. Thus, since, in this problem, the ordinate-function is $3x - x^2$, the length of the ordinate AP (whose x-value is $\frac{1}{2}$) will be

$$AP = 3(\tfrac{1}{2}) - (\tfrac{1}{2})^2$$
$$= 1\tfrac{1}{2} \quad - \tfrac{1}{4}$$
$$= 1\tfrac{1}{4}$$

Now take the other ordinate, BQ, whose x-value is h more than the x-value of AP, that is to say, $(\frac{1}{2} + h)$, and whose length is j units more than the length of AP.

We have already found that $AP = 1\frac{1}{4}$; let us now find the length of BQ in terms of h. Since the x-value of BQ is $(\frac{1}{2} + h)$, the ordinate-function $3x - x^2$ tells us that

$$BQ = 3(\tfrac{1}{2} + h) - (\tfrac{1}{2} + h)^2$$
$$= 1\tfrac{1}{2} + 3h - \tfrac{1}{4} - h - h^2$$
$$= 1\tfrac{1}{4} + 2h - h^2$$

Now $j = BQ - AP$

$$= (1\tfrac{1}{4} + 2h - h^2) - 1\tfrac{1}{4}$$
$$= 2h - h^2$$

$\therefore$ the ratio $\dfrac{j}{h} = \dfrac{2h - h^2}{h}$

$$= 2 - h$$

[At this point we shall depart from the language used by Barrow and other seventeenth-century mathematicians, in order to avoid certain illogical statements made by them.]

It will be seen that the closer to the point P we take the point Q, the smaller does h become. Moreover, as Q approaches P, the ratio $\dfrac{j}{h}$ gets (in this figure) larger and larger in value, approaching 2 but never actually reaching 2. Again, as Q approaches P, the secant SPQ approaches nearer and nearer to the position of the tangent at P. The secant never "becomes" the tangent at P though it approaches it as closely as we wish.

The position of the tangent at P has been indicated in the figure by a dotted line. While the secant is approaching the tangent, the ratio $\dfrac{AP}{SA}$ (which we saw was equal to $\dfrac{RQ}{PR}$, or $\dfrac{j}{h}$) is at the same time approaching nearer and nearer to the value of the ratio $\dfrac{AP}{TA}$. Here we have a geometric illustration of the algebraic process that showed us that the ratio $\dfrac{j}{h}$ approaches but never reaches 2 in value as h is made smaller and smaller. The value of the ratio $\dfrac{AP}{TA}$ is the *exact* (not approximate) value of the limit which the ratio $\dfrac{j}{h}$ approaches, namely, 2. So $\dfrac{AP}{TA} = 2$. In other words, the subtangent TA is, in this example, half the length of the (known) ordinate AP. It is now a simple matter to find the point T and draw the tangent TP.

The importance of this method of Barrow's, so far as Newton's work was concerned, did not lie so much in its usefulness in drawing the tangent, as in the method employed for finding [as we now should say] the limit to which the ratio $\dfrac{RQ}{PR}\left(\text{or } \dfrac{j}{h}\right)$ approached as PR (or h) approached zero. This lies at the very root of the method of *differentiation*, so we will work a similar problem in more general terms, by which is meant that instead of taking the distance of the ordinate AP from the origin as $\frac{1}{2}$ unit, we shall call that distance "x," which can stand for any definite value. [Again, we shall use modern language and concepts, but the *method* is, in its essentials, that used by Newton in building up his "fluxional calculus."]

Using Figure 94, but calling OA "x units" instead of $\frac{1}{2}$ unit, we get, from the ordinate-function $3x - x^2$,

$$AP = 3x - x^2$$
$$BQ = 3(x + h) - (x + h)^2$$
$$= 3x + 3h - x^2 - 2xh - h^2$$
$$\therefore j\,[= BQ - AP] = \qquad 3h \qquad - 2xh - h^2$$
$$\therefore \frac{j}{h} = \frac{3h - 2xh - h^2}{h}$$
$$= \qquad 3 - 2x - h$$

It follows that as h approaches zero, the ratio $\frac{j}{h}$ approaches $3 - 2x$.

We have now "differentiated" the function $3x - x^2$ and have obtained its "derived function," or "derivative" $3 - 2x$. Let us see if we can find a meaning for this "derivative" of the original ordinate function $3x - x^2$.

If the reader will glance back at Figure 90 on page 268 he will see four triangles, each of which is exactly the same shape and size as the one marked PQR. Attaching the meanings we have just connected with j and h, we can label PR as h, and RQ as j.

Now what exactly would $\frac{j}{h}$ signify in Figure 90 (reproduced in Figure 95)?

FIG. 95

"j" represents the increase in the depth of water in a tank during a time-interval h. As we have seen, an average rate of speed is found by dividing the distance gone by the time taken. So $\frac{j}{h}$ gives the *average rate* at which the depth of water was increasing during the time-interval h. We saw, however, on page 271 that the *average* rate of increase during any interval was not the same as the rate at the beginning or end of that interval, *unless no change in rate occurred*. Whenever the *rate* of growth increases, $\frac{j}{h}$ represents the *average* rate of growth. This cannot in such a case be equal to the rate at which an ordinate is growing at the beginning or end of any interval of time (or whatever the x-axis may represent). It is true that $\frac{j}{h}$ will be *approximately* equal to such instantaneous rate if both j and h are very small (not "infinitesimals"). The *exact* instantaneous rate of growth, however, is not the value of the ratio $\frac{j}{h}$; it is the limit which the value of that ratio approaches. *This "limiting value" is not an approximate value; it is an exact value*, giving the rate of growth of the ordinate situated x-units from the origin at the instant that x-value began to increase to $(x + h)$.

This "instantaneous rate" of increase in the length of an ordinate can also be represented geometrically as the exact *slope* of the tangent at the point where the curve is cut by the ordinate which is x-units from the origin.

Let us see what mathematicians mean by "slope."

In mathematics, the slope of a straight line is measured by the ratio $\frac{\text{perpendicular rise}}{\text{horizontal length}}$, or $\frac{j}{h}$ in any of the triangles in Figure 96.

In the case of a straight line, the slope never changes, so there can be no "rate of increase in slope." The greater the slope of a line, the more upright will that line be; the smaller the slope of a line, the more it approaches the horizontal, as

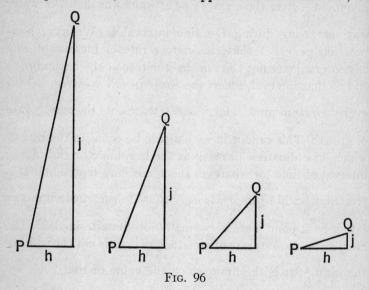

FIG. 96

will be seen in Figure 96. The nearer a line is to the horizontal, the smaller is the value of $\frac{j}{h}$. When a line is horizontal, its slope is 0.

In the case of a curve, the slope continually changes. We saw that the *average* rate of increase between P and Q in Figure 94 was $\frac{j}{h}$; we have now seen that $\frac{j}{h}$ is also the measure of the *slope* of PQ. We also saw that the limit which $\frac{j}{h}$ approached was the ratio $\frac{AP}{TA}$, which we now see is the *slope* of the tangent at P.

So the instantaneous rate at P is shown by the slope of the tangent at that point. It follows that the slope of a curve at any point on that curve is shown by the slope of the tangent at that point; the *average slope* between any two points on the curve by the slope of the line joining those two points. There is no need to draw the tangent to find the instantaneous rate, or the chord to find the average rate. Both of these, as we have seen, can easily be calculated algebraically.

Thus, in the problem illustrated in Figure 91, page 270, the equation was $y = x^2$. We need not draw any figure, but can suppose that AP is an ordinate which is x-units from the origin, BQ an ordinate which is $(x + h)$ units from the origin, and that $BQ - AP = j$ units.

$$AP = x^2$$
$$BQ = (x + h)^2$$
$$= x^2 + 2xh + h^2$$
$$\therefore j\,[= BQ - AP] = 2xh + h^2$$
$$\therefore \frac{j}{h} = \frac{2xh^2 + h^2}{h}$$
$$= 2x + h$$

So as h approaches zero, $\frac{j}{h}$ approaches 2x. In other words, although the rate with which the ball rolls down the incline is constantly changing, we can find exactly what that rate was at any moment. Thus, at the end of 3 seconds, the rate was $2(3)$, or 6 feet per second; at the end of 4 seconds it was 8 feet per second, and so on.

We found (page 292) that the derivative of the ordinate function $3x - x^2$ was $3 - 2x$. This tells us that the rate with which the function $3x - x^2$ increases at any point (that is to say, the rate with which the length of the original ordinate at any point increases) is given by the derivative $3 - 2x$. So from this derivative we can say that after $\frac{1}{4}$ seconds, the value of the function was growing at $3 - 2(\frac{1}{4})$, or $2\frac{1}{2}$ units of length per unit of time; at the end of $\frac{1}{2}$ second, at $3 - 2(\frac{1}{2})$, or 2 such units.

Since a clear grasp of the meaning of a *derivative* is essential for an understanding of the calculus, we will consider yet another example. Suppose a ball is thrown vertically into the air so that its height above the thrower's hand, y feet, is given by the equation $y = 40x - 16x^2$, where x stands for the number of seconds that have elapsed since it left the thrower's hand. Suppose we wish to find the speed of the ball at any instant during its flight up and down.

Suppose AP is an ordinate of the curve that would result if we drew the graph of $y = 40x - 16x^2$, and let AP be x-units from the origin. Let BQ be another ordinate, $(x + h)$ units from the origin. Since the ordinate-function is $40x - 16x^2$,

$$AP = 40x - 16x^2$$
$$BQ = 40(x + h) - 16(x + h)^2$$
$$= 40x + 40h - 16x^2 - 32xh - 16h^2$$
$$\therefore j[= BQ - AP] = \phantom{40x +} 40h \phantom{- 16x^2} - 32xh - 16h^2$$
$$\therefore \frac{j}{h} = \frac{40h - 32xh - 16h^2}{h}$$
$$= 40 - 32x - 16h$$

$\therefore$ as h approaches zero, $\dfrac{j}{h}$ approaches $40 - 32x$. So the derivative of $40x - 16x^2$ is $40 - 32x$. [The stranger to the calculus will find it now pays to pause a moment and see whether he can find any apparent inverse connection here with the law discovered by Wallis, discussed on page 262.]

We shall see more clearly the connection between a derivative and its original function if we draw up a table, showing various values of each, at the end of $0, \frac{1}{4}, \frac{1}{2}$ . . . seconds.

The meaning of the values of the ordinate-function will be obvious; they tell us that the ball's height above the thrower's hand increased for $1\frac{1}{4}$ seconds, at which moment the ball

| Values of x, in seconds: | Values of ordinate-function $40x - 16x^2$: | Values of derivative, $40 - 32x$: |
|:---:|:---:|:---:|
| 0 | 0 | 40 |
| $\frac{1}{4}$ | 9 | 32 |
| $\frac{1}{2}$ | 16 | 24 |
| $\frac{3}{4}$ | 21 | 16 |
| 1 | 24 | 8 |
| $1\frac{1}{4}$ | 25 | 0 |
| $1\frac{1}{2}$ | 24 | $-8$ |
| $1\frac{3}{4}$ | 21 | $-16$ |
| 2 | 16 | $-24$ |
| $2\frac{1}{4}$ | 9 | $-32$ |
| $2\frac{1}{2}$ | 0 | $-40$ |

reached its greatest height, 25 feet. The height above the thrower's hand then began to decrease until, $2\frac{1}{2}$ seconds after it was thrown into the air, it arrived back at its starting point.

Knowing that a derivative tells us the *rate of increase* in the values of the ordinates at any moment, we see that the thrower imparted a speed, or rate, of 40 feet per second to the ball. At the end of $\frac{1}{4}$ second, this speed had been reduced to 32 feet per second; at the end of $\frac{1}{2}$ second, to 24 feet per second, and so on. At the instant when the ball had attained its greatest height, namely, after $1\frac{1}{4}$ seconds, there was no speed at all. The ball having lost its upward speed now began to return toward the earth, so the speed is marked with negative signs.

*If a derivative is positive, it indicates that the value of the ordinate of the original function at that point is increasing; whenever a derivative is negative, it indicates that the value of the original ordinate at that point is decreasing.* So by observing the sign of the derivative at any point, we may tell whether the value of the original function is increasing or decreasing at that point. This procedure is of great importance, since it enables us to find whether certain values of a function are maximum or minimum values. Let us draw the graph of $y = 40x - 16x^2$, and also that of its derivative, which we will call $y_1 = 40 - 32x$. [See Figure 97.]

Notice the following points:

(1) In Graph A, *the y values increase* during the period 0 sec. to $1\frac{1}{4}$ sec; they *decrease* from $1\frac{1}{4}$ sec. to $2\frac{1}{2}$ sec.

(2) In Graph B, $y_1$ values are *positive* (above the x-axis) from 0 sec. to $1\frac{1}{4}$ sec.; *negative* (below the x-axis) from $1\frac{1}{4}$ sec. to $2\frac{1}{2}$ sec.

(3) In Graph A, the maximum value of y is reached when $x = 1\frac{1}{4}$. In Graph B, the value of $y_1$ is zero when $x = 1\frac{1}{4}$.

(4) If the tangent were drawn at the maximum point on Graph A, it would be horizontal. In other words, when $x = 1\frac{1}{4}$, its slope would be 0, as we saw on page 294. Notice how this fits in with Graph B, the graph of the "rate" (= slope of tangent at any point on Graph A). When $x = 1\frac{1}{4}$, $y_1 = 0$.

The above suggests the following procedure for finding maximum and minimum values of a function of x. Suppose the function is $y = x^3 - x$.

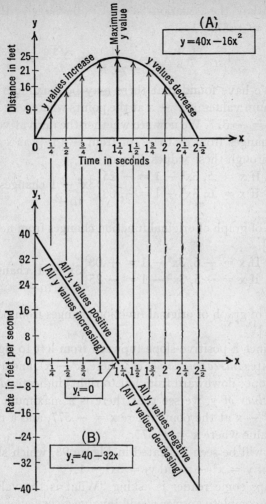

FIG. 97

(1) Find the derivative of $x^3 - x$. This will be found to be $3x^2 - 1$. Let us call this derivative "$y_1$." We have seen that if $y_1 = 0$, the original function $x^3 - x$ may have a maximum or a minimum value at whatever values of x

satisfy the equation $3x^2 - 1 = 0$, namely, the values $x = \pm.577$ *

* Since $3x^2 = 1$ ∴ $x^2 = \dfrac{1}{3}$ ∴ $x = \pm\dfrac{1}{\sqrt{3}} = \pm\dfrac{\sqrt{3}}{3} = \pm\dfrac{1.732}{3} = \pm.577$

(2) We have found that there may be maximum or minimum values of $x^3 - x$ at the points where $x = +.577$ or $x = -.577$. We now see whether the derivative $3x^2 - 1$ changes from $+$ to $-$, or from $-$ to $+$ as x increases through these values. Thus:

If $x = .5$, $3x^2 - 1 = -.25$ ⎫
if $x = .6$, $3x^2 - 1 = +.08$ ⎬ $3x^2 - 1$ changes from $-$ to $+$

[slope of graph of original function changes from negative to positive]

If $x = -.6$, $3x^2 - 1 = +.08$ ⎫
if $x = -.5$, $3x^2 - 1 = -.25$ ⎬ $3x^2 - 1$ changes from $+$ to $-$

[slope of graph of original function changes from positive to negative]

Since a positive slope (upward from left to right) indicates *increasing values of y* (here, $x^3 - x$), and a negative slope (downward from left to right) indicates *decreasing values of y*, we see that there is a maximum value of $x^3 - x$ at the point where $x = -.577$, and a minimum value where $x = +.577$.

All this will be seen indicated in Figure 98, which shows the graphs of $y = x^3 - x$ and $y_1 = 3x^2 - 1$.

Perhaps some reader is asking "What is the value of all this?" A complete answer would involve a survey of countless problems connected with science, engineering and everyday life. Even the mere nodding acquaintance we have made with the calculus will enable us to solve many problems such, for example, as one raised by the Post Office regulation regarding the size of parcels that may be sent through the post. "What

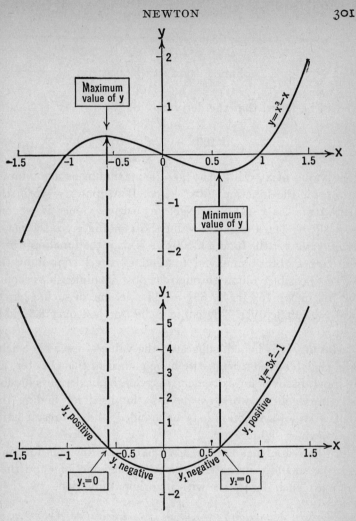

FIG. 98

are the dimensions of a box with a square end which will contain the largest possible volume and still comply with the regulation that 'The size of parcels must not exceed 100 inches in
length and girth combined'?"

Suppose each edge of the square end is x inches long.

$$\therefore \text{ length of box } = 100 - 4x$$
$$\therefore \text{ volume of box } = x^2(100 - 4x)$$
$$= 100x^2 - 4x^3$$

It will be found that the derivative of $100x^2 - 4x^3$ is $200x - 12x^2$.

$$\text{If } 200x - 12x^2 = 0$$
$$\therefore x = 16\tfrac{2}{3}$$

The value of $x = 16\tfrac{2}{3}$ may give a maximum or a minimum value for the function $100x^2 - 4x^3$. If we put $x = 16$ in the derivative $200x - 12x^2$ we get a positive value; if we put $x = 17$, we get a negative value. So $x = 16\tfrac{2}{3}$ gives the *maximum* value for the function $100x^2 - 4x^3$, or the function which represents the volume. So to send a parcel containing the largest possible volume through the post, its dimensions should be $16\tfrac{2}{3}$ in. by $16\tfrac{2}{3}$ in. by $33\tfrac{1}{3}$ in. The volume of such a parcel will be a little over 9259 cubic inches, or just over 5.3 cubic feet.

Having, it is hoped, suggested the value of even the slight knowledge of the calculus we have gained in this chapter, let us now discover an extremely easy mechanical rule whereby all the algebraic work we have so far used for finding the derivative of a function may be avoided, and the result written down at sight.

If the reader has not already discovered this rule for himself, he should differentiate the following functions and then compare each derivative with its original function.

| *Original function* $(y = \ldots)$ | *Derivative* $(y_1 = \ldots)$ |
|---|---|
| 1. $x^2$ | ? |
| 2. $x^3$ | ? |
| 3. $3x^2$ | ? |
| 4. $5x^2$ | ? |
| 5. $7x^3$ | ? |

6. $3x^2 - x^3$                  ?

7. $5x$                          ?

8. $x^4 + 3x^2 + 5x$        ?

9. $3x^2 + 9$               ?

[Compare this answer with the answer to Number 3]

10. $5x^2 + 27$            ?

[Compare with Number 4]

11. $x^3 + 64$              ?

[Compare with Number 2]

12. $3x^2 - x^3 + 19$      ?

[Compare with Number 6]

[The answers are: (1) $2x$; (2) $3x^2$; (3) $6x$; (4) $10x$; (5) $21x^2$; (6) $6x - 3x^2$; (7) $5[= 5x^0]$; (8) $4x^3 + 6x + 5$; (9) Same as (3); (10) Same as (4); (11) Same as (2); (12) Same as (6).]

Just in case anyone has not discovered the mechanical rule, here it is:

"Multiply each variable in the original function by the exponent of that variable (in all our examples, the variable was x); then reduce the exponent of the variable by 1."

Or, in general, "If $y = x^n$, then the derivative of this function of x will be $nx^{n-1}$."

In other words, "If the graph of $y = x^n$ is drawn, connecting values of y and x, then *the slope of the curve at any point* will be given by the formula $nx^{n-1}$, where x is the abscissa of the point in question."

Or, to put it in yet another way, "If $y = x^n$ is a formula for giving the value of the ordinate of a certain curve, then *the rate at which the value of an ordinate situated x units from the origin is increasing* will be given by the formula $nx^{n-1}$."

It will be seen that if the *derivative* found in any of the first eight examples above is taken as a starting point, then, by the application of Wallis' Law (page 262) the original function can be obtained. In other words, *in each of these eight cases,* the original function is a formula for giving the area under a curve obtained from the derived function, and bounded by that curve, the x-axis and an ordinate situated x units from the origin. If the graph of, say, $3x^2$ were drawn, the formula for the area under this curve between the origin and the ordinate x units from that origin would be $\frac{1}{3} 3x^3$, or the original function $x^3$ from which the derivative $3x^2$ was originally obtained. [We shall later see the connection between the value of an ordinate and the area under a curve: one of the most remarkable and interesting facts disclosed by the calculus.]

The reader may have been wondering why the last four derivatives found in Numbers 9–12 above were exactly the same as the derivatives found previously in (3), (4), (2), and (6) respectively. The explanation is simple. The derivative tells us the *slope* of the curve representing the function from which it is derived. It does not tell us the position of that curve with respect to the axes. Take the simple example of the three "curves" (here straight lines) shown in Figure 67 (page 213). Obviously, each has the same slope, although each represents a different function, namely, the functions $2x + 3$, $2x$, and $2x - 3$. Since the derivative of each of these functions simply tells us about the *slope* of the curve representing that function (or, in other words, the rate at which the value of the function is increasing at any given point) each of these derivatives will be the same, namely, 2 (or $2x^0$). So the graph of each pair of functions in Numbers 9 and 3; 10 and 4; 11 and 2; 12 and 6, above, will have the same *slope* formula but will be differently situated with respect to the axes.

By applying Wallis' Law, we can obtain an original function from its derived function even in the case of Numbers 9–12 above, *provided we allow for the possibility of an additional term in the function so obtained*. This is done by adding some constant "c," where "c" may stand for any positive or negative number, or for zero. Thus:

| *Derived function* | *Original function* |
|---|---|
| $6x - 3x^2$ | $3x^2 - x^3 + c$ |

It is true that the derivative of $3x^2 - x^3$ is $6x - 3x^2$, but this last expression is also the derivative of innumerable other functions such as $3x^2 - x^3 + 4$, or $3x^2 - x^3 - 7$, and so on *ad infinitum*. The effect of this constant term is simply to raise or lower the graph of $3x^2 - x^3$ with respect to the x-axis. This will be seen clearly in Figure 67: the graph of the function $2x + 3$ is 3 units higher up the y-axis than is the graph of the function $2x$, while the graph of the function $2x - 3$ is 3 units lower down the y-axis than is the graph of the function $2x$.

The reader has now discovered how to work "integration," or the reverse process to "differentiation." We shall return to this topic later, when we have talked a little about Leibniz. But all this, and very much more, was worked out by Isaac Newton within four, or at most five years from the day when he read his first mathematics book. Although we have necessarily only glanced at the surface of the subject, the reader should be able to see, at least vaguely, that here Newton had developed a tool with which to tackle the complex and difficult mathematics connected with the curves traced out by moving heavenly bodies, the areas connected with those curves, and so forth. From "the beginning of the year 1664, February 19th" Newton was observing the heavens, as we saw. He found he must have some powerful mathematical tool at his disposal if he was to find an explanation for Kepler's laws, which we discussed in Chapter VI. So he developed the "calculus" which did for the "mathematics of motion and growth" what Descartes' Geometry had done for the geometry of the Greeks. Like Descartes, he built on the foundations laid by others, and produced a generalized, far-reaching branch of mathematics, whose tremendous consequences he could little have foreseen.

Because Fermat was the first mathematician to use these

methods, he has sometimes been hailed as the inventor of the calculus. This was the view of no less a mathematician than Laplace, whose opinion of Newton's *Principia* was quoted early in this chapter. It has, however, been pointed out that Fermat only applied his methods to a few particular cases; Newton drew up a system of rules that could be applied to *any* function. When Newton said that he "had stood on the shoulders of giants" he was doubtless referring to men like Descartes, Fermat, Wallis and Barrow, so far as his development of the calculus was concerned, and to scientists like Galileo and Kepler in connection with his work on gravitation.

Not until 1736 was Newton's *Method of Fluxions* made known to the general public, in a translation of his manuscripts made by J. Colson. From this book we find that Newton conceived of a line as being generated by a moving point. So he thought of a line as being a "flowing quantity," and called it the *fluent*. The velocity with which the line "flowed" was called by him its *fluxion*. [Much confusion arose during the century that followed Newton's death by another interpretation of "fluxion."] The "infinitely small length" by which a fluent increased in an "infinitely small time" was called by Newton the *moment* of the fluent. He designated the fluxion of x by the symbol $\dot{x}$, and when the fluxion $\dot{x}$ was "infinitely small," he would represent the moment of the fluent by the symbol $\dot{x}$o. Thus, if he were dealing with two fluents, x and y, which were connected by the equation $y = 3x - x^2$, he would substitute $x + \dot{x}$o for x, and $y + \dot{y}$o for y in the equation $3x - x^2 - y = 0$.

[Contrast our present methods: we do not speak of "infinitesimals" and we do not introduce the idea of a "limit" until the final stage of our work.]

This would give him

$$3x + 3\dot{x}o - x^2 - 2x(\dot{x}o) - (\dot{x}o)^2 - y - \dot{y}o = 0$$

Ignoring $(\dot{x}o)^2$ as negligible, and subtracting the original equation $3x - x^2 - y = 0$, he would get

$$3\dot{x}o - 2x(\dot{x}o) - \dot{y}o = 0$$

$$\text{So } \frac{\dot{y}o}{\dot{x}o} = 3 - 2x$$

which is the same *result* as that obtained by our modern procedure. The important point is that in this first stage in the development of the calculus, Newton made use of the essential step in Fermat's method, handed down to him by Barrow, namely, that if an ordinate increased in length by j units, the *average rate of increase in its length in thus passing from a point x units from the origin to a point $(x + h)$ units from the origin was*

$$\frac{j}{h} = \frac{\text{difference in lengths of ordinate (in terms of x)}}{h}$$

This is still the essential first step for anyone who wishes to learn the calculus properly (not merely learn to apply a few mechanical rules without understanding the meaning of a derivative, etc.). Unfortunately, most textbooks obscure the simplicity of the ideas involved by using shorthand symbolism before the student has grasped what the thing is all about. Such symbolism is essential if the calculus is to be applied and extended; it makes the work of those who understand it very much simpler, since it suggests ideas and processes in a concise and concentrated form. The fact remains, however, that for beginners, the symbolism is often a stumbling block. One of the greatest teachers of mathematics England has ever had was Professor T. P. Nunn (later Sir T. P. Nunn), Professor of Mathematics at London University some twenty-five years ago. He once said that the symbols used in the calculus "have been known to so many students only as hostile standards floating above an impregnable citadel." (*The Teaching of Algebra*, page 21.)

The beginner should realize that the symbolism is not really as awe-inspiring as it looks at first sight. Thus, let us look at the apparently terrifying equation

$$\lim_{\Delta x \to 0} \frac{\Delta y}{\Delta x} \;=\; \lim_{\Delta x \to 0} \frac{f(c + \Delta x) - f(c)}{\Delta x}.$$

All this says is that the limit which the ratio we called $\dfrac{j}{h}$ approaches is to be found by finding the limit which the ratio $\dfrac{\text{difference in lengths of ordinates in terms of } x}{h}$ approaches.

The stranger to the calculus has already met the symbols $\Delta y$ and $\Delta x$; they were purposely introduced in Chapter VI in order to accustom him to them, despite the disturbance in chronological sequence then caused by the introduction of these modern symbols. In that chapter, $\Delta y$ stood for the difference in lengths of two ordinates, while $\Delta x$ stood for the difference between their x-values. These two symbols are used with the same meanings in the calculus, only we think of them as "increments" rather than as "differences." Thus, $\Delta y$ is a symbol for "the increment, whatever it may be, in the length of an ordinate y that is brought about by an increment $\Delta x$ in the ordinate's x-value." $\Delta x$ and $\Delta y$ are both to be regarded as definite finite quantities. We can think of $\Delta x$ as "any horizontal step to the right of a point on the curve"; $\Delta y$ as "whatever step is then necessary in order to reach the curve." If the $\Delta y$ step is upward, it will be positive; if downward, negative.

Figure 99 shows that when $\Delta y$ is negative, the slope will be negative, indicating that the value of the function (or length of ordinate) is decreasing. Both possibilities indicated in Figure 99 will be included in an algebraic solution provided the length of the left-hand ordinate is always subtracted from the length of the right-hand ordinate (both expressed in terms of x).

The meaning of the shorthand "$\lim_{\Delta x \to 0}$" is obviously "the limit which [whatever follows] approaches as $\Delta x$ approaches 0."

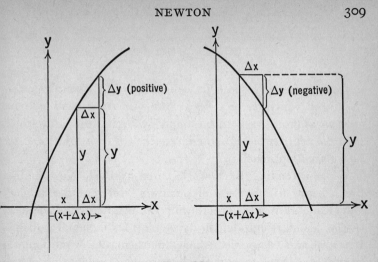

Fig. 99

Now consider the fraction, or ratio, on the right-hand side:
$$\frac{f(c + \Delta x) - f(c)}{\Delta x}$$
Here we find the symbolism for "function." We briefly
glanced at this on page 168, when we saw that the expression
$3x - x^2$, for example, being a function of x, might be indicated
briefly as "f(x)," it being understood that "f" is simply a shorthand symbol for "function," just as $\Delta$ is simply a shorthand
symbol for "increment." Further, the value of the function of x
we are considering at any moment *when x =* , *say*, 2, can be
indicated by "f(2)." Thus, if our function were $3x - x^2$,
"f(2)" would indicate $3(2) - (2)^2$, or $6 - 4$, or 2; "f(3)"
would indicate $3(3) - (3)^2$, or 0; "f(c)" would indicate
$3(c) - (c)^2$; "f(c + \Delta x)" would indicate $3(c + \Delta x) -$
$(c + \Delta x)^2$.

So the right-hand side of the equation merely indicates the
ratio $\dfrac{\text{difference between ordinates}}{\text{related increase in value of x}}$

So the equation

$$\lim_{\Delta x \to 0} \frac{\Delta y}{\Delta x} = \lim_{\Delta x \to 0} \frac{f(c + \Delta x) - f(c)}{\Delta x}$$

is really a friendly sheep in wolf's clothing. It simply means "the limit which *the ratio between the y-increment and the x-increment* approaches is to be found by taking the limit which *the ratio between the ordinate-increment (in terms of x) and the x-increment* approaches."

While attending Barrow's lectures in 1664, Newton had learned how to make use of Barrow's "differential triangle," and, while at Woolsthorpe during the plague period, he used this as his starting point in developing his fluxional calculus. Later, he was to apply this new "mathematics of motion and growth" in order to find the long-sought explanation of the laws concerning the movements of heavenly bodies that had been empirically discovered by Kepler. There is reason to believe that Newton had already in this period (1665–1666) started out on this quest, although his time was then largely occupied with studying the composition of light and with practical experiments with lenses and prisms. Not content with all these activities, he commenced to study chemistry, a subject in which he retained a keen interest all his life, and which was to prove of practical value to him when, toward the end of the century, he was appointed, first as Warden, then as Master of the Mint, and had to supervise the issue of a new type of coinage.

On October 1, 1667, he was made a Fellow of Trinity College and the following year he took the degree of Master of Arts.

In the summer of 1669 he handed Barrow a paper he had drawn up and in which he had partly explained his principle of fluxions. Barrow's admiration of this paper was so great that he described Newton to another Cambridge mathematician, John Collins, as of "unparalleled genius." Unfortunately, Newton was too modest to follow Barrow's advice and publish this paper. Had he done so, it would have prevented years of undignified squabbling between Newton's followers and those of Leibniz.

Shortly after receiving this evidence of Newton's mathematical genius, Barrow, who wished to devote his time to the study of theology, resigned his professorship of mathematics, and on his strong recommendation, Newton, then only twenty-seven years of age, was appointed to succeed him.

In those days the Lucasian Professor of Mathematics was required to lecture only once a week during term time, on some mathematical subject or on astronomy, geography, optics (the laws of light), or statics, and to give up two hours a week for consultation with students. Newton chose optics for his first lectures, in which subject he had already made far-reaching researches and discoveries. The results of his researches, however, were for some years known only to his Cambridge audiences. When, however, he was elected a Fellow of the Royal Society in 1672, he sent that body a long paper based on his lecture notes, and, in this way, his work in connection with the composition of light became known to scientists throughout Europe. Almost immediately, Newton found himself involved in the violent controversies we mentioned earlier in this chapter, especially with another Fellow of the Royal Society, Robert Hooke, an able scientist but a controversialist whose offensive style of argument distressed and disgusted Newton. Another objector to some of Newton's theories on light was Lucas, the Professor of Mathematics at Liége, whose criticisms aroused the weary complaint from Newton, mentioned earlier in the chapter.

Despite his statement to the secretary of the Royal Society that "if I get free of Mr. Lucas's business, I will resolutely bid adieu to it eternally, excepting what I do for my private satisfaction, or leave to come out after me," he nevertheless continued to publish many papers on the subject of light in the

*Philosophical Transactions*, as the official journal of the Royal Society was named. In these papers Newton put forward the theory that light was composed of tiny corpuscles, or particles, that were projected through space by luminous bodies. This theory was abandoned by scientists early in the nineteenth century in favor of Huygens' *wave-theory*, which necessitated the concept of the existence of a weightless, invisible medium called the "ether" which could not be perceived by any of our senses but which permeated space and filled the tiny gaps between molecules of air and other matter.

Until 1900, this wave theory seemed to explain all the phenomena of light, but since that date scientists have been forced to admit that it will not account for all those phenomena. Max Planck in 1900 suggested that light is transmitted in small "lumps" or *quanta*. The general reader who wishes to get an idea of the work done by Planck, Compton and Einstein in connection with the *quantum theory* will find a scholarly yet easy-to-read treatment of this branch of higher physics in Dr. D. E. Richmond's *The Dilemma of Modern Physics* (G. P. Putnam's Sons). These problems are outside the scope of the story of mathematics; we must content ourselves by noting that modern scientists cannot explain all the phenomena of light without the use of both the wave theory and the quantum theory. Thus, it may well be that Newton was on the right track when he put forward his corpuscular theory of light.

In 1673 a curious incident arose that throws light on Newton's financial circumstances, or possibly points to his possessing an unexpected appreciation of the value of money. In those days, a fellowship at Trinity College could be held only for a limited period by a man who was not in holy orders. Since Newton, though of a deeply religious mind, had no desire to be ordained, his fellowship was due to expire in the autumn of 1675. He seems to have been disturbed by this probable loss of his income, for he wrote to Oldenburg, the secretary of the Royal Society: "Sir, I desire that you will procure for me that I may be put out from being any longer Fellow of the Royal Society: for though I honour that body, yet since I see I shall neither profit them, nor (by reason of this distance) can partake of their assemblies, I desire to withdraw." Oldenburg seems to have offered to apply to the Society to excuse his payments to them, for Newton wrote to him, "For your proffer about my quarterly payments, I thank you, but I would not have you trouble yourself to get them excused." Later, "It was agreed by the council that he be dispensed with, as several others are." However, in 1675 a special exemption was made in his case, permitting him, as Lucasian Professor, to retain his fellowship without having to take holy orders. His financial affairs thus seem to have improved by 1676, for in that year he was able to subscribe £40 (equivalent to some $1,000 in modern purchasing power) toward the building of the new library for Trinity College.

During the years 1674 to 1677, the infinitesimal calculus was being developed independently in Germany by the mathematician Leibniz, though his work on this subject was not published until 1684. We shall glance at the life and work of Leibniz later in this book.

To return to Newton. Between the years 1673 and 1683 his lectures at Cambridge were on the subject of algebra, particularly with regard to the theory of equations. His lecture-notes were put into book form and printed in 1707; they deal with many important advances in this subject, especially in connection with the so-called "imaginary" roots of certain equations, a subject which we shall discuss later.

In 1684 Newton was paid a visit by his friend Edmund Halley which was to have momentous consequences. Halley, Hooke, Huygens and Wren had been engaged in trying to find an explanation for the laws empirically discovered by Kepler regarding the movements of the heavenly bodies. Halley explained that their investigations were held up by their inability to apply Kepler's laws (see page 204) in order to determine the orbit of a planet. Newton immediately told Halley that, some five years before, he had proved that the orbit was an ellipse. He was not able to put his hand on the paper in which he had made the calculation in 1679, so he promised to work it again for his friend. This promise evidently led him to return once more to the subject of universal gravitation during the summer vacation of 1684, for his lectures during the Michaelmas term of that year dealt with this subject. Halley visited him again in the middle of this term, and studied his manuscript lecture-notes. These notes, entitled *De Motu Corporum* ("Concerning the Movement of Bodies") are to be seen today in Cambridge University Library. Halley urged Newton to publish them, but had to be content with a promise that they would be sent to the Royal Society, which promise Newton kept early the following year. Thanks to the tactful pressure exerted by Halley, which we mentioned earlier in this chapter, Newton now became deeply engrossed in the whole problem of gravitation. In 1685 he was able to prove that the total attraction of a solid sphere on any mass outside that sphere could be considered as if concentrated in a single point at its center. "No sooner had Newton proved this superb theorem—and we know from his own words that he had no expectation of so beautiful a result till it emerged from his mathematical investigation—than all the mechanism of the universe at once lay spread before him. . . . In his lectures of 1684, he was unaware that the sun and earth exerted their attractions as if they were but points. How different must these propositions have seemed to Newton's eyes when he realized that these results, which he had believed to be only approximately true when applied to the solar system, were really exact! Hitherto they had been true only in so far as he could

regard the sun as a point compared to the distance of the planets, or the earth as a point compared to the distance of the
moon—a distance amounting to only about sixty times the
earth's radius—but now they were mathematically true, excepting only for the slight deviation from a perfectly spherical
form of the sun, earth, and planets. We can imagine the effect
of this sudden transition from approximation to exactitude in
stimulating Newton's mind to still greater efforts. It was now
in his power to apply mathematical analysis with absolute
precision to the actual problems of astronomy." [Dr. Glaisher's
address on the bicentenary of the publication of the *Principia*;
quoted in W. W. R. Ball's *History of Mathematics* (Macmillan).]

The efforts to which Newton's mind was now stimulated
were so immense that by April, 1686, he sent the first book of
the *Principia* to the Royal Society; the second book by the
summer of the same year; the third book he had completed in
manuscript form by 1687. The whole work was published at
Halley's expense in the summer of 1687. This was the great
work which a century later was to be pronounced by Laplace
as assured of "a pre-eminence above all other productions of
human genius."

As we have already noted, Newton made use of geometric
methods in all his proofs in the *Principia*, since he realized that
his fluxional calculus would be unknown to other mathematicians and might thus lead them to dispute results which
were themselves opposed to many of the theories prevalent at
the time, such as Descartes' theory of the universe.

Another factor that probably weighed with Newton in
reaching his decision to employ the familiar Greek geometry
was that the calculus had not been fully developed when he
wrote the *Principia*, and consequently was not then as superior
to Greek geometry as it later became. Since Newton gave his
geometric demonstrations without explanations, only out-

standing mathematicians were able to follow his concise reasoning. Nevertheless, thanks to their enthusiastic acceptance of the book, Newton's theory of the universe soon found widespread acknowledgment, except in France, where his views met with opposition for many years. In 1736, however, Voltaire, with the aid of his friend, Madame du Châtelet, a distinguished mathematician, wrote a long treatise on the Newtonian system, which led to its acceptance in France as elsewhere in Europe. So great was the demand for the *Principia* that by 1691 it was impossible to purchase a copy of the work.

In 1687 Newton took a prominent part in upholding the privileges of Cambridge University when they were threatened by King James II, and in 1689, in recognition of the firmness and determination he had displayed on this occasion, the University chose him as their member of Parliament. He does not appear to have taken any part in parliamentary debates, however, and in 1690, he gave up his seat and returned to Cambridge.

For the moment we must leave Newton, and take notice of a great contemporary of his in Germany.

Gottfried Wilhelm Leibniz was three and a half years younger than Newton, having been born on June 21, 1646, at Leipzig, where his father (who died six years later) was Professor of Moral Philosophy. Even as a child, Leibniz was an avid reader; he is said to have taught himself Latin by studying an illustrated edition of Livy's history, and to have commenced the study of Greek before he was twelve. He then turned to logic, and before he was fifteen had formed the opinion that both the ancient and medieval treatment of the subject stood in need of reform.

In the autumn of 1661—precisely the same date when Newton first went up to Trinity College, Cambridge—Leibniz entered Leipzig University, although he was only fifteen a the time. Here he studied law, a course which included the study of the works of certain thinkers of his day—men like Kepler, Galileo and Descartes—which were bringing about a revolution in scientific thought and philosophy.

In 1666—the year when Newton was busy developing his method of fluxions—Leibniz presented himself as a candidate for the degree of Doctor of Law, but found himself debarred on account of his youth. Disgusted, he left Leipzig, never to return. He then presented his dissertation for a doctor's degree at the University of Altdorf (Nürnberg) and not only obtained the degree but was also offered a professorship. Refusing the professorship, Leibniz settled in Nürnberg, where he published an essay on a new method of teaching and learning law which so impressed the Elector of Mainz that he found himself appointed to assist in drawing up a revision of the statute-book. Subsequently, he was sent on various diplomatic missions, in connection with which he wrote several essays on political matters. He took a hand in the dangerous game of power politics, seeking to divert from Germany to Turkey the aggressive threats of Louis XIV by proposing that the great powers in Europe should combine in a crusade against the Turks—and that France should increase her power by seizing Egypt from them. This Machiavellian plan came to nothing, though, strange to say, it bore good fruit indirectly. Leibniz was summoned to France to put his plan before Louis XIV, and while in Paris came into contact with Huygens. Before making this journey, Leibniz had a long list of dissertations to his credit, covering an amazing variety of subjects: law, politics, logic, natural philosophy, theology, mechanics, optics, while he had invented a calculating machine that was far superior to that of Pascal, in that multiplication, division and the extraction of roots could be performed on it, as well as addition and subtraction. Under the guidance of Huygens, Leibniz began to study mathematics seriously. In January,

1673, he had visited England on a political mission for the Elector of Mainz, and had met Oldenburg and exhibited his calculating machine to the Royal Society, of which he was elected a Fellow in April, 1673.

On his return to Germany in 1674 he wrote to Oldenburg, saying that he had discovered important theorems connected with the quadrature of a circle. Oldenburg replied that Newton had already used similar methods. In 1676, Newton sent a letter to Leibniz, through the hands of Oldenburg, dealing with his expansions of binomials, and also with infinite series and other matters. Leibniz wrote back asking for fuller explanations, and in his reply—which occupied thirty pages when printed later—Newton gave Leibniz the desired information. He then added the remark that about 1669 he had given Barrow an outline of his method of fluxions. He gave no explanation of that method to Leibniz, however, being careful to conceal its nature in the anagram "6a cc d æ 13e ff 7i 3l 9n 4o 4q rr 4s 9t 12v x." If six a's, two c's, one d, etc. are arranged in a certain order, they form the Latin sentence "Data æquatione quotcunque fluentes quantitates involvente, fluxiones invenire; et vice versa." [Given an equation involving any number of fluents, to find their fluxions; and vice versa] In this way Newton, without disclosing his method, could later, if necessary, establish a claim as its inventor. It seems strange that a mind so great as Newton's should have been capable of an unwillingness to share his invention with Leibniz; he had already made it known in Cambridge, to Barrow and Collins, in 1669. Possibly he feared he would be led into one of the controversies he detested if he allowed his method to become known to mathematicians outside his circle of friends. Finally, Newton told Leibniz that he had two methods for solving the "inverse problem of tangents" (integration). Once more, he was careful to disguise his methods in an anagram. Leibniz replied on June 21, 1677, making no attempt at concealment in explaining his method of "differences" and revealing his notation $dx$ and $dy$ for infinitely small differences in successive coördinates of a point on a curve. He also showed that he understood the principle of integration.

In 1684 Leibniz made public his methods in a scientific paper he had founded, called *Acta Eruditorum*. Thus it came about that although Newton had invented his method of fluxions many years before Leibniz had invented his method of "differences," Leibniz was the first of the two to publish his method.

At this time the two great men were on friendly and cordial terms. In the first edition of the *Principia* Newton mentioned the correspondence he had had with Leibniz and actually stated that he had concealed his method of fluxions from him in an anagram, but that Leibniz "that most distinguished man" had communicated his own method to him, which, he said, hardly differed from his own except in the expressions and symbolism used. [Later, when the third edition of the *Principia* appeared, in 1726, Newton deleted this passage.]

From 1684 until 1699 no suggestion was made that Leibniz was not the inventor of his own particular *calculus differentialis*. Then, in 1699, an obscure Swiss mathematician, who was living in England and who had been angered at having been omitted from a list of eminent mathematicians drawn up by Leibniz, insinuated in a paper read before the Royal Society that Leibniz had not invented his form of calculus but had based it on Newton's method of fluxions.

Naturally, Leibniz was annoyed, and doubtless not a little perplexed in view of Newton's emphatic assertion in the *Principia*. He replied to the attack, in the *Acta Eruditorum*, and protested to the Royal Society.

Nothing more might have been heard of the wretched business had not Leibniz in 1705 written an unfavorable review of the first account of fluxions to be published by Newton, in

1704, as an appendix to a book dealing with optics. In this review he remarked that Newton had always used fluxions instead of his own "differences."

The Savilian Professor of Astronomy at Oxford, John Keill, considered that by this remark Leibniz had accused Newton of plagiarism, and then proceeded to accuse Leibniz himself of having published Newton's method as his own, merely changing its name and notation.

Once more, Leibniz appealed to the Royal Society, of which Newton had been elected president in 1703 (he remained president until his death twenty-five years later). Liebniz requested that Keill should be induced to withdraw the imputation that he had stolen his method from Newton. A tactful remark from Newton as president (for instance, a reiteration of the assertion he had made in the *Principia*) might even now have saved the situation. Unfortunately, it was not forthcoming. It may be that Newton—always deeply sensitive to criticism—was resentful of Leibniz's unfavorable review in 1705 of his fluxions. No suggestion was made by him or the Royal Society that Keill should withdraw his imputation of fraud. Instead, a committee was appointed to report on the whole matter. In their report, issued in 1712, they stated: "The *differential method* is one and the same with the *method of fluxions*, excepting the name and mode of notation; Mr. Leibniz calling these quantities *differences* which Mr. Newton calls *moments* or *fluxions*, and marking them with the letter *d*, a mark not used by Mr. Newton. And therefore we take the proper question to be, not who invented this or that method, but who was the first inventor of the method; and we believe that those who have reputed Mr. Leibniz the first inventor knew little or nothing of his correspondence with Mr. Collins and Mr. Oldenburg long before; nor of Mr. Newton's having that method above fifteen years before Mr. Leibniz began to publish it in the *Acta Eruditorum*. For which reasons, we reckon Mr. Newton the first inventor, and are of opinion that Mr. Keill, in asserting the same, has been no ways injurious to Mr. Leibniz."

In 1715 the report was published in full in the *Transactions* of the Royal Society. In his *Life of Newton*, Brewster states that almost the whole of the manuscript of this report was in the handwriting of the president of the Royal Society, Newton.

The dispute now went from bad to worse and continued long after the death of Leibniz in 1716 and that of Newton, in 1727. In both England and Germany the rights and wrongs of the senseless controversy became submerged in questions of national pride and prestige. Today, after an interval of two centuries, the dispute seems inconsequential and fantastic. Two great minds were at work on the material provided by Kepler, Cavalieri, Fermat, Pascal, Wallis and Barrow. It is not surprising that they both reached similar conclusions.

In 1734 certain important criticisms regarding the validity of the methods employed in the infinitesimal calculus were made by Bishop Berkeley, an Irishman who spent several years in what was then the English colony of Rhode Island, and who took a great interest in what was then known as Yale College. On returning to England he was made Bishop of Cloyne, in County Cork, Ireland, though he spent much of his time in London literary circles that included writers like Swift, Steele and Addison.

Berkeley attacked the use of infinitesimally small quantities, saying that the reasoning employed was false and illogical, and that therefore the conclusions based on such reasoning were unacceptable. If correct results were obtained, this was due to one error balancing another, said Berkeley. These criticisms appeared in a book called the *Analyst*, whose primary object was to try and show that Christian doctrines were no more inconceivable than were these mathematical ideas of his day. "What are these fluxions?" he asked. "The velocities of evanescent increments. And what are these same

evanescent increments? They are neither finite quantities
nor quantities infinitely small, nor yet nothing. May we not
call them the ghosts of departed quantities?"

Berkeley's criticisms bore good fruit, for they led the Scottish mathematician Colin Maclaurin (1698–1746) to write his
*Treatise on Fluxions* (1742). In the preface he said that the
book was written in consequence of the attack on Newton's
method made by Berkeley in 1734. Maclaurin proved the
validity of Newton's conclusions by means of geometric
demonstrations. However, it was only the gradual development of a rigorous treatment of the idea of a *limit* during the
eighteenth and nineteenth centuries that finally silenced the
critics by eliminating the use of infinitely small quantities and
the baffling problems of infinity involved in them.

Meanwhile, this concept of a *limit* was being grafted on to
the differential calculus of Leibniz by mathematicians in
Switzerland, Russia (the work there being done by Swiss
mathematicians) and France. We shall return to this subject
and to a consideration of the method invented by Leibniz after
we have glanced at the concluding events in the life of the inventor of the fluxional calculus.

From the point of view of mathematics, Newton must be regarded as having wasted the last thirty years of his life in occupations unworthy of his supreme talents. While he was living
in London, as a Member of Parliament for Cambridge University, he made the acquaintance of John Locke, the great
philosopher who was also intimately connected with English
politicians, himself being for a time Secretary of the Board of
Trade. Locke and other friends of Newton felt that it was outrageous that the most eminent scientist and mathematician
of his age should be dependent on the meager salary of a college
professor and fellow. By their efforts, Newton was appointed
Warden of the Mint in 1695, an appointment worth £500 a
year (some $12,000 in modern purchasing power) but making

so few demands on his time as to allow him to retain his Cambridge professorship. In 1697 he was appointed Master of the Mint, a post worth two to three times as much as that of Warden. He then appointed a deputy to perform his work at Cambridge "with full profits of the place." In 1701 Newton resigned both his fellowship at Trinity and his Lucasian professorship. In 1703, as already noted, he was elected president of the Royal Society, and two years later he was knighted by Queen Anne. This was the period when Winston Churchill's ancestor, the Duke of Marlborough, was winning fame as a great military commander. The death of Queen Anne in 1714 brought Leibniz's master, the Elector of Hanover, to the English throne as George I. In 1714 Newton gave evidence before a committee of the House of Commons in connection with a petition that had been presented to Parliament by a group of captains in the Royal Navy and the merchant service. They petitioned that steps should be taken to discover some method whereby the longitude of a ship at sea could be determined accurately. In his evidence, Newton criticized various suggestions that had been made, and at his suggestion, large sums of money were offered as rewards for accurate methods for determining longitude at sea (see page 139).

In 1725 Newton wrote to the University of Edinburgh, offering to provide the salary for a deputy professor of mathematics. Colin Maclaurin was appointed to this post, and shortly afterwards became full professor.

During this period of his life, Newton paid much attention to theological and philosophical studies in addition to the arduous duties he undertook as Master of the Mint.

Toward the end of his long life, he was troubled with illness, though he continued to preside over the Royal Society. He died on March 20, 1727 and was buried in Westminster Abbey.

It is impossible to avoid a feeling of regret that Newton should have allowed himself to be persuaded to degrade his unrivaled talents by accepting a well-paid government post that robbed the world of his genius for a quarter of a century. Had he, like Archimedes, given up all his long life and all his talents to science and mathematics, there is no knowing what further great advances in human knowledge might have been achieved in the quiet seclusion of a Cambridge college.

As it was, in the twenty-two years between 1665 and 1687 he left for all time the stamp of his supreme genius on mathematics and physical science. It is to the author of the *Principia* and the inventor of fluxions, and not to the Master of the Mint, that the world looks back with gratitude and awe as the first mind in eighteen centuries that equalled the mind of Archimedes.

# CHAPTER VIII

# Leibniz, Gauss and Others

For more than a century after the death of Newton, English mathematicians were so involved in their senseless dispute with the followers of Leibniz that they failed to benefit from great developments in the calculus that took place on the Continent of Europe.

Leibniz, like Newton, considered that any variable quantity continually increased or decreased by momentary increments or decrements. These infinitely small changes in value were represented by Leibniz by the symbol $d$. Thus, $dx$ meant an infinitely small change, or *difference* in the value of x, $dy$ an infinitely small difference in the value of y. We have seen that Leibniz explained this in his letter to Newton of June 21, 1677 (see page 318).

Leibniz, like Newton, failed to explain the principles of his calculus with clarity or rigor. He sometimes thought of $dx$ and $dy$ as being lines of finite length, sometimes as being infinitely small quantities. He seems to have considered that any finite number is made up of an infinite number of infinitely small values, which, though so small that they cannot be measured, yet have a definite size. All the "infinitesimals" whose sum made up a number were considered to be of the same magnitude. Leibniz therefore considered that $\dfrac{dy}{dx}$ was simply the ratio of the infinitesimals of the two variables x and y, and that this ratio had a finite, measurable size. This view has long since been abandoned, though we still make use of Leibniz's notation $\dfrac{dy}{dx}$ as indicating the derivative of $y = f(x)$.

Nowadays, it is usual to introduce students to the calculus by using the symbol D for "derivative." Thus, $D_x y$ means "the derivative of y with respect to x." The small x may be omitted if there is no danger of ambiguity. Thus, $D x^2 = 2x$; $D x^3 = 3x^2$; $D(3x^2 - x^3) = 6x - 3x^2$, and so on (see page 303). In other words, to use the symbolism introduced on page 308,

$$D_x y = \lim_{\Delta x \to 0} \frac{\Delta y}{\Delta x}$$

The use of the symbol D makes it clear that the derivative is *not* a ratio between increments of two variables when such increments are infinitely small, but is *the limit which the ratio of those increments approaches as the increment of x approaches zero.*

Once the student has grasped this essential fact it is usual to revert to the notation used by Leibniz, namely, $\frac{dy}{dx}$ instead of $D_x y$. The use of this ratio $\frac{dy}{dx}$, *which must not be regarded any longer as a ratio between x and y increments* (although it was so regarded by its inventor), is one reason why many students have difficulty in understanding the calculus. However, it is now too late to eliminate this notation, since it has been established by long use. It must always be remembered that $\frac{dy}{dx}$, as representing a derivative, is misleading in appearance, since it does not represent the *ratio* between infinitely small increments of two variables, but the *limit to which that ratio approaches.*

The distinction between *dy* and an increment in the length of an ordinate can best be grasped geometrically. Figure 100 illustrates the modern view, which makes a clear distinction between $\Delta y$ (the increment in the length of an ordinate y, which corresponds to an increment $\Delta x$ in the distance of that ordinate from the origin) and *dy*.

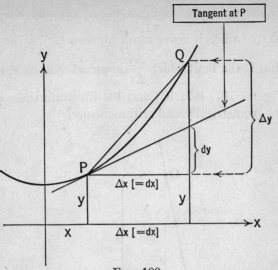

FIG. 100

We have already defined $\Delta x$ as "a horizontal step to the right from a point P on a curve," and $\Delta y$ as "the vertical step then required to reach the curve once more." We may now define $dx$ as having the same meaning, in general, as $\Delta x$, but $dy$ as having *an entirely different meaning from that of* $\Delta y$. When a step $\Delta x$ (or $dx$) has been taken to the right of P, $dy$ stands for the vertical step then required *to reach the tangent at the point P*. We have already seen (page 294) that the slope of the tangent at P is the limit which the average slope between P and Q approaches as $\Delta x$ approaches zero. In other words, the average rate of increase in the length of the ordinates between P and Q approaches the instantaneous rate at P when $\Delta x$ approaches zero.

It will be seen that except in the case of a straight line, the ratio $\dfrac{\Delta y}{\Delta x}$ (average slope between P and Q) constantly changes as the length $\Delta x$ changes, but that the value of $\dfrac{dy}{dx}$, as just defined, in general, never changes, no matter what may be the value of dx (which is never zero). Moreover, $\frac{dy}{dx}$ is never equal to $\frac{\Delta y}{\Delta x}$, but is the limit which $\frac{\Delta y}{\Delta x}$ approaches as $\Delta x$ approaches zero. Figures 101, 102, 103 and 104 illustrate these essential concepts geometrically and arithmetically.

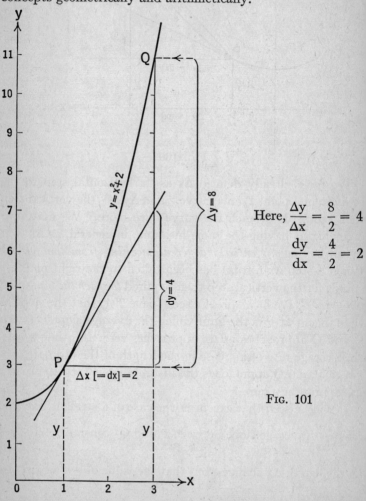

Here, $\frac{\Delta y}{\Delta x} = \frac{8}{2} = 4$

$\frac{dy}{dx} = \frac{4}{2} = 2$

Fig. 101

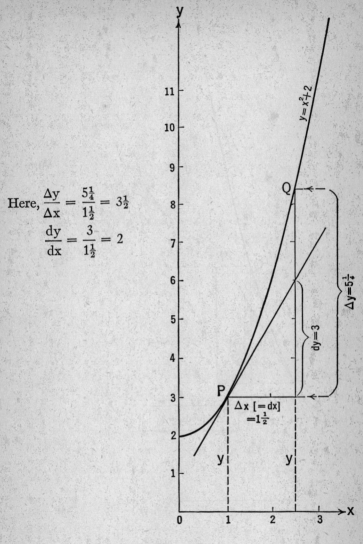

Here, $\dfrac{\Delta y}{\Delta x} = \dfrac{5\frac{1}{4}}{1\frac{1}{2}} = 3\frac{1}{2}$

$\dfrac{dy}{dx} = \dfrac{3}{1\frac{1}{2}} = 2$

FIG. 102

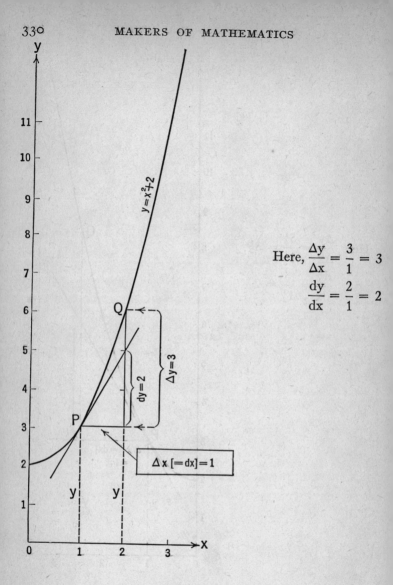

Here, $\dfrac{\Delta y}{\Delta x} = \dfrac{3}{1} = 3$

$\dfrac{dy}{dx} = \dfrac{2}{1} = 2$

FIG. 103

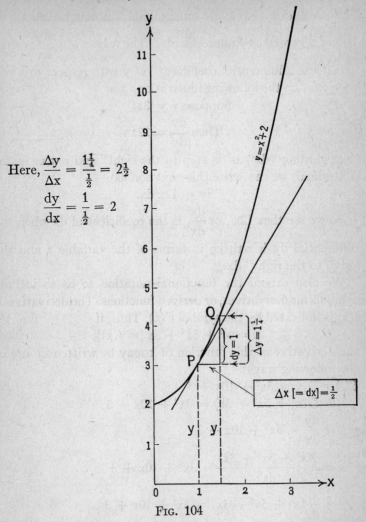

Here, $\dfrac{\Delta y}{\Delta x} = \dfrac{1\frac{1}{4}}{\frac{1}{2}} = 2\frac{1}{2}$

$\dfrac{dy}{dx} = \dfrac{1}{\frac{1}{2}} = 2$

FIG. 104

Notice that in all the above cases, $dx$ represents an arbitrary step to the right, while "the differential coefficient" $\dfrac{dy}{dx}$ is in each case equal to 2.

We still call $dy$ and $dx$ "differentials," although they are no longer regarded as "infinitesimals." The reason why $\dfrac{dy}{dx}$ is often called the "differential coefficient" of y with respect to x will be seen from the following illustration:

$$\text{Suppose } y = 3x^4$$

$$\text{Then } \frac{dy}{dx} = 12x^3$$

Regarding "dx" as "a step to the right" and not as an infinitesimal, we can write this equation as

$$dy = 12x^3 dx.$$

So we see that $12x^3$, or $\dfrac{dy}{dx}$, is the coefficient of dx when the differential dy is written in terms of the variable x and the "step to the right" dx.

We also extend the functional notation so as to include symbols for derivatives, or derived functions. The derivative of $f(x)$ is indicated by the symbol $f'(x)$. Thus, if

$$y = x^3 + 5x^2 + 3x \; [= f(x)],$$

the derivative of this function of x may be written in any of the following ways:

*Either* $D_x y = 3x^2 + 10x + 3$

   *or* $D(x^3 + 5x^2 + 3x) = 3x^2 + 10x + 3$

   *or* $\dfrac{dy}{dx} = 3x^2 + 10x + 3$

   *or* $\dfrac{d(x^3 + 5x^2 + 3x)}{dx} = 3x^2 + 10x + 3$

   *or* $\dfrac{d}{dx}(x^3 + 5x^2 + 3x) = 3x^2 + 10x + 3$

   *or* $f^1(x) = 3x^2 + 10x + 3$

Thus, if $f(x) = 8x^4$, $f'(x) = 32x^3$, and so on.

It is often possible to find *successive derivatives* of a function. Thus, the derivative of the derivative $3x^2 + 10x + 3$ will be

5x + 10. This is called the *second derivative* of x³ + 5x² + 3x, and is indicated either as

$$f''(x) = 6x + 10$$

or as

$$\frac{d^2y}{dx^2} = 6x + 10$$

The explanation of the notation $\frac{d^2y}{dx^2}$ is somewhat complicated.

$$\text{Suppose } y = x^4 \; [= f(x)]$$

$$\text{Then } \frac{dy}{dx} = 4x^3 \; [= f'(x)]$$

$$\therefore \; dy = 4x^3 dx$$

Bearing in mind that *dx* is a constant and not a function of x, we will now differentiate both sides of this equation. [Since the *dx* on the right-hand side of the equation is a constant and not a variable quantity in this case, the derivative of this side will be *dx* times the derivative of 4x³.]

$$\frac{d(dy)}{dx} = dx \left[ \frac{d(4x^3)}{dx} \right]$$

$$\therefore \; \frac{d(dy)}{dx} = dx[12x^2]$$

Divide each side by the arbitrary constant *dx*,

$$\therefore \; \frac{d(dy)}{(dx)^2} = 12x^2$$

This is abbreviated to

$$\frac{d^2y}{dx^2} = 12x^2 \text{ (read: "d 2 y over d x square")}$$

and is an alternative to the simpler notation $f''(x) = 12x^2$ [where $f(x) = x^4$; $f'(x) = 4x^3$].

Since a derivative indicates the rate at which the function from which it is derived is increasing at any given moment, it follows that if s feet = distance traveled by some object;

t seconds = time taken, and s = f(t) [that is, s is given by some expression in terms of t] then

   $distance = f(t)$

   $rate = f'(t)$

   $acceleration = f''(t)$, since acceleration equals increase in rate in unit of time.

For instance, suppose s = $15t^3 - t^4$ [= f(t)]

   Then $rate$ [= f'(t)] = $45t^2 - 4t^3$ ft. per sec.

   and $acceleration$ [= f''(t)] = $90t - 12t^2$ ft. per sec. per sec.

   Thus, if t = 2, distance = 120 − 16, or 104 ft.

                          rate = 180 − 32, or 148 ft. per sec.

                          acceleration = 180 − 48 = 132 ft. per sec. per sec.

Newton had invented precisely the same process in his method of fluxions. As we saw, he denoted a flowing quantity, or fluent, by x, and its fluxion by ẋ. He then denoted the fluxion of ẋ by ẍ, the fluxion of ẍ by ⃛x, and so on. This notation is still occasionally encountered in the works of modern writers.

[The general reader is now advised to turn back to pages 254–264, and review Wallis' Law before proceeding.]

In 1684, and again in 1686, Leibniz published articles in the *Acta Eruditorum* on what he called the *Calculus Summatorius*, since it was connected with the summation of a number of infinitely small areas, whose sum he indicated by an old-fashioned letter S, written $\int$. In 1696 he followed a suggestion made by Johann Bernoulli of Basel, Switzerland, and changed this title to *Calculus Integrali*, "The integral calculus," the idea being that some *whole* area was obtained by summation of its parts. This corresponded to Newton's "Inverse method of tangents," but was developed from the works of Cavalieri and Pascal instead of from those of Wallis. These mathematicians had shown that what we called an "area-function" in

Chapter VI could be found by summation from an "ordinate-function."

Let us compare some of the area-functions we found in Chapter VI with their ordinate functions:

| Area-function | Ordinate-function |
|---|---|
| $4x$ [or $\frac{1}{1} 4x^1$] | $4$ [or $4x^0$] |
| $2x^2$ [or $\frac{1}{2} 4x^2$] | $4x$ [or $4x^1$] |
| $\frac{1}{3} 4x^3$ | $4x^2$ |
| $x^4$ [or $\frac{1}{4} 4x^4$] | $4x^3$ |
| $\frac{1}{5} 4x^5$ | $4x^4$ |

It will be seen that *the ordinate function is the derivative of the area-function*.

Now, if the x-value of any ordinate is substituted for x in any derivative, *the rate at which the area is increasing at that point will be given*, as we saw on page 334. But this substitution will also give *the length of the ordinate* at the point having that x-value.

It follows that *the length of the ordinate at any point on a curve indicates the rate at which the area under that curve is increasing instantaneously at that point*. This fact is most curious and important. It is worth while to arrive at the same conclusion from another standpoint.

Suppose Figure 105 represents part of the graph of $y = x^2 + 4$, and that we wish to find the area bounded by MO, OP, PS and arc MS.

The greater the value taken for x, the greater will be the area involved. So the area we wish to find is a function of x.

Now take a step $\Delta x$ from P and call it PQ. QU will now be $y + \Delta y$, the vertical step necessary to take us to the curve again. By this increase $\Delta x$ in the x-value, the area has been increased by the figure PQUS. We will indicate this increase in area by the notation $\Delta$(area).

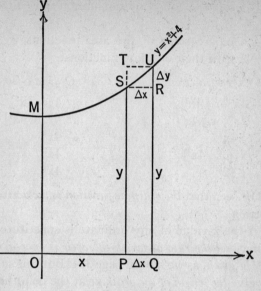

F<small>IG</small>. 105

It will be seen that in Figure 105, $\Delta$(area) lies between the areas PQRS and PQUT; that is, between $y(\Delta x)$ and $(y + \Delta y)\Delta x$. It follows that *any fraction of $\Delta$(area) must lie between that same fraction of these other two areas.* So if we divide each of these three areas by $\Delta x$ it will follow that

$$\frac{\Delta(\text{area})}{\Delta x} \text{ lies between } y \text{ and } (y + \Delta y)$$

When $\Delta x$ approaches zero, $\Delta y$ also approaches zero. In other words, when $\Delta x$ approaches zero, $\dfrac{\Delta(\text{area})}{\Delta x}$ lies between $y$ and a value approaching $y$.

So $\lim\limits_{\Delta x \to 0} \dfrac{\Delta(\text{area})}{\Delta x} = y = x^2 + 4$

In other words, the derivative of the area with respect to x is equal to y, the length of the ordinate PS. So by substituting the x-value of P, the rate at which the area is increasing at the point S can be found from this derivative.

Now let us see how the area can be found from the equation $y = x^2 + 4$. Since, in this example, the derivative of the area is $x^2 + 4$, by an application of Wallis' Law, the formula for the area will be $\frac{1}{3}x^3 + 4x + c$ (see page 305).

But in this particular example, if $x = 0$, then the area $= 0$, and consequently, $c = 0$. So we can say that for all values of $x$ measured to the right of the y-axis, the area $= \frac{1}{3}x^3 + 4x$.

It follows that by substituting any particular value of $x$ in this expression, the area up to the ordinate having that x-value can be found. Thus, if $x = 5$, the area will equal $\frac{1}{3}(5)^3 + 4(5)$, or $61\frac{2}{3}$ square units.

Now suppose we wish to find the area of the shaded portion in Figure 106, which represents the same curve as the one in Figure 105.

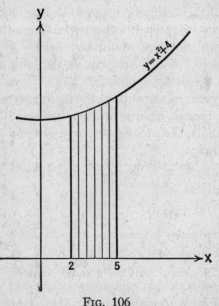

Fig. 106

We have seen that the area between the y-axis and the ordinate whose x value is 5 is $61\frac{2}{3}$ square units. If we now subtract the area between the y-axis and the ordinate whose x-value is 2, we shall have the area of the shaded portion. Thus:

$$\text{Area of shaded portion} = 61\tfrac{2}{3} - [\tfrac{1}{3}(2)^3 + 4(2)]$$
$$= 61\tfrac{2}{3} - 10\tfrac{2}{3}$$
$$= 51 \text{ square units.}$$

This process of finding an area-function from its ordinate-function is still indicated by the notation invented by Leibniz, although that notation is misleading. We have seen that Leibniz used the shorthand $dx$ to indicate an infinitely small x-increment. He expressed an area such as that of PQUS in Figure 105 *when infinitely small* as though it were the rectangle $y(dx)$. He then expressed the sum of the infinite number of such "rectangles" composing the area concerned, as $\int y(dx)$. Although this concept, together with his notion that an "infinitesimal" has a definite magnitude has long since been abandoned, we still adhere to his misleading notation. A better, and logical notation would be "Area $= \int y(\Delta x)$ as $\Delta x$ approaches zero," read "Area equals the limit to which the sum approaches as $\Delta x$ approaches zero." However, it is too late to do anything about it now; the customary notation must be accepted, though with mental reservations. Using the notation of Leibniz, the problem we have just worked would be expressed either as

$$\text{Area} = \int_{x=5}(x^2 + 4)\,dx - \int_{x=2}(x^2 + 4)\,dx$$

or more shortly as

$$\text{Area} = \int_2^5 (x^2 + 4)\,dx$$

This last expression is known as a *definite integral*, in which 5 is the "upper limit" and 2 the "lower limit."

We have seen that the process of integration is the reverse or inverse process to that of differentiation, just as division is the inverse process to multiplication. Thus, we can forget all

about "summation" and "areas" and simply apply Wallis'
Law to a derivative in order to obtain the original function.
As an illustration, consider the following problem: "A ball is
thrown vertically downward, with an initial speed of 40 ft.
per second, from a window in the Empire State Building that is
1000 ft. from the ground. How far from the ground will the
ball be after 5 seconds have elapsed?"

We saw on page 298 that *downward* speed in problems of
this nature is marked as negative. From the table on that same
page it will be seen that the acceleration of a body that rises
or falls constantly decreases (algebraically) by 32 feet per
second every second. So in our problem, both the initial speed
and the acceleration will be marked as negative.

Let the height of the ball above the ground at any moment
be s feet, and let t represent the number of seconds that have
then elapsed.

We have seen that acceleration is f″(t). So, since the acceleration of a rising or falling body is −32 ft. per sec. per sec.;

$$f''(t), \text{ or } \frac{d^2s}{dt^2}, = -32$$

$$\therefore f'(t), \text{ or } \frac{ds}{dt}, = \int (-32)dt = -32t + c$$

Since, when t = 0, the speed $\frac{ds}{dt} = -40$ ft. per sec.;

c = −40.

$$\therefore \frac{ds}{dt} = -32t - 40$$

$\therefore$ f(t), or s, = $\int (-32t - 40)dt = -16t^2 - 40t + k$

Since, when t = 0, s = 1000; k = 1000.

$$\therefore s = -16t^2 - 40t + 1000$$

$\therefore$ when t = 5, s = −400 − 200 + 1000

$$= 400 \text{ ft.}$$

Here we have a very simple example of innumerable problems that can quickly and easily be solved by means of the calculus.

Let us now turn back to the personal history of Leibniz. His invention of the differential and integral calculus was only one of his many-sided activities. Quite apart from his mathematical and scientific studies, he spent a great deal of time—wasted time, we must feel today—in diplomatic work, some of it of not too scrupulous a nature. We saw in Chapter VII how he tried to divert the aggressive ambition of Louis XIV from Germany to Turkey; his later diplomatic work was performed, not for the Elector of Mainz but for the House of Brunswick. In 1673 he entered the service of the Duke of Brunswick-Lüneburg (Hanover) and for the next forty years remained in the service of this family, serving four successive masters. His official position was that of librarian of the ducal library at Hanover, but he was frequently called on to undertake diplomatic missions. In this respect he played an important part in securing the elevation of the Duke of Hanover to the Electorate, or body of German princes who elected the Emperor of the "Holy Roman Empire," which, by the seventeenth century, had ceased to be an empire in anything but name. To support the claims of his ducal masters, Leibniz wasted much of his precious genius in compiling a history of the Brunswick-Lüneburg family, though he was able to cover only the period from 768 to 1005 A.D. The collection of the material for this history led Leibniz to make a long journey through Germany and Italy in the years 1687–1690. During this period he became deeply interested in an attempt to reunite the Protestant and Catholic churches, writing a book on the subject (which was not published until 1819, by which time all hope of reunion had vanished).

In 1700 he visited Berlin, in connection with the academy he had planned for that city. He himself was made its president in 1711. He also drew up plans for the foundation of an academy at St. Petersburg, at the request of Peter the Great. Leibniz's plans were put into effect after the death of this czar, by his widow, Catherine I. In 1712 Leibniz was made a baron of the empire, an honor he had long coveted. This was the last honor to come his way, however, for the rest of his life was clouded by neglect. In 1714, his master, the elector George Louis, became King of England as George I. Leibniz wished to join him in England, but was told to remain in Hanover and to get on with his history of the House of Brunswick. He died in 1716, a lonely and neglected man. Only his secretary, Eckhart, attended his funeral; no notice was taken of his death either in Berlin, in the academy he had founded, nor in London where his master ruled. Only at the French Academy was a eulogy devoted to his memory.

Throughout his life Leibniz possessed the power of working rapidly and for long periods at a stretch. Even while traveling, he worked out mathematical problems. He wrote very extensively on philosophical matters, basing his views partly on those of Descartes, partly on the philosophy of Spinoza, whom he met in Amsterdam in 1676. In this connection (philosophy) he published in 1666 a treatise *De Arte Combinatoria* in which he proposed a kind of mathematical treatment of logic, in which symbolism and formal rules, as in mathematics, would obviate the necessity of thinking out individual problems. This symbolism would, he suggested, be intelligible in all languages, and truth and falsehood would no longer be matters of opinion, but of correctness or error in computation.

Today, Leibniz is not remembered for his political and diplomatic astuteness, nor for his contributions to theology, philosophy and science, but for his mathematical contribution in the development of the calculus. At first, other German mathematicians paid no attention to his calculus, possibly because his statements were often obscure. In Switzerland, however, his articles attracted the attention of a great mathematician, Jakob (James) Bernoulli.

In the course of a century, this remarkable family of Bernoullis produced no fewer than eight great mathematicians, of whom Jakob (1654–1705), his brother Johann (1667–1748) and Daniel (1700–1782) the son of Johann, were the most famous.

By the time of Jakob's birth, the family had become rich and prosperous merchants. Jakob was intended for the ministry, so he studied philosophy at the University of Basel. He became intensely interested in mathematics, however, but fearing the opposition of his father, he studied the subject in secret. Later, he chose for his motto *Invito patre sidera verso* "I study the stars against my father's will." In 1682 he opened a school of mathematics and science at Basel and five years later was appointed to the chair of mathematics at the University of Basel. As a teacher, he won great renown, many of his pupils becoming well-known mathematicians. He did much to familiarize others with Leibniz's calculus, which he had mastered by himself from the difficult articles Leibniz had written on the subject for the *Acta Eruditorum*.

In 1696 he offered a reward for a solution of an *isoperimetrical* problem. The word *isoperimetrical* means "of equal perimeter." Greek mathematicians had discovered certain simple facts about the greatest and least value of a variable quantity under certain conditions. The first examples of "maximum and minimum" values were given when Euclid showed how to find the longest and shortest lines that could be drawn to a circle from a point outside the circle, and also proved that if a line is bisected, the area of the rectangle (here a square) contained by these equal segments of the line is greater than that of any other rectangle whose adjacent sides consist of any other two segments into which the line may be divided. [See Figure 107]

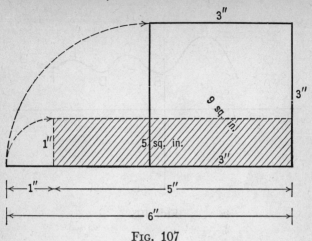

FIG. 107

After Euclid's time, other Greek mathematicians proved that a regular polygon had a greater area than an irregular polygon which had the same perimeter as the regular polygon, and that the area of a circle was greater than that of any other curve or polygon having an equal perimeter.

In course of time, the words *maxima* and *minima* came to have a wider meaning than merely "greatest" and "least." A curve, for instance, can have many maximum and minimum values, the terms indicating the greatest or least values *in a particular neighborhood* on the curve representing some function. Thus, in Figure 108, maximum values occur at the points A, C and E; minimum values at the points B, D and F.

By the aid of the calculus it is very easy to determine maximum and minimum values of a function. The arguments on pages 298–301 indicate this method. Since the derivative of a function indicates the slope of the graph of that function, it is only necessary, in general, to determine the values of x that make $\dfrac{dy}{dx} = 0$ (if y is a function of x).

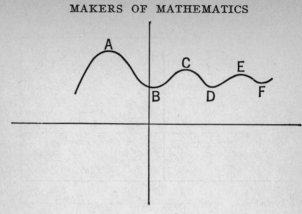

Both Jakob Bernoulli and his brother Johann were deeply interested in a new type of "isoperimetric" problem. In 1696 Jakob challenged other mathematicians, including his brother, to solve a problem in which a curve had to be found that would give a maximum or minimum area when each of its ordinates was a given function of the corresponding ordinate of another curve. Many European mathematicians attempted to find a solution, including Johann Bernoulli. When Jakob declared that his brother's attempt was incorrect, a bitter quarrel sprang up between the two brothers. Johann often displayed violent temper, although he could be loyal to his particular friends, among whom were numbered the Marquis de l'Hôpital, Leibniz and Euler, whom we shall shortly meet. After the death of Jakob, he produced a solution to the isoperimetric problem which he claimed to be his own, but which was really his brother's. This type of problem led to the development of a branch of the calculus known as the "calculus of variations."

Jakob Bernoulli was one of the first mathematicians to make general use of *polar coördinates*, as contrasted with the rectangular coördinates used by Descartes. Until Jakob Ber-

ۅoulli's time they had been used only for drawing spirals. ‪ome topics can better be investigated by polar rather than ‪ectangular coördinates. In the polar, or trigonometric system, ‪he position of a point on a plane surface is given by a *distance* *ınd a direction* instead of by two distances each at right angles ‪o a pair of axes. Thus, in Figure 109,

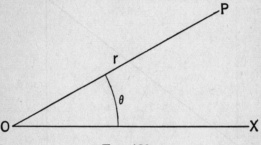

FIG. 109

‪he position of the point P may be indicated by (1) the distance ‪)P, known as the *radius vector* and marked r, from the point O, ‪ㄴnown as the *pole*, and (2) the angle $\theta$, known as the *vectorial* ‪ıngle, or angle through which OP has revolved in a counter-‪ㄴlockwise direction from a fixed line OX known as the *polar* *ıxis*. The measurements r and $\theta$ are known as the polar co-‪)rdinates of P. The connection between polar and rectangular ‪ㄴoördinates is indicated in Figure 110.

Since $\dfrac{AP}{OP} = \sin \theta$, AP = OP $\sin \theta$ = r $\sin \theta$. But in rec-

‪ㄴangular coördinates, AP = y $\therefore$ $y = r \, sin \, \theta$. Again, $\dfrac{OA}{OP} =$

‪ㄴos $\theta$, so OA = OP $\cos \theta$ = r $\cos \theta$. But in rectangular coördi-‪ıates, OA = x $\therefore$ $x = r \, cos \, \theta$. One of the curves discovered by ‪Jakob Bernoulli by means of polar coördinates was the *'emniscate*, so called from the Greek word *lemniskos*, a ribbon ‪ın which a pendant was hung (Figure 111).

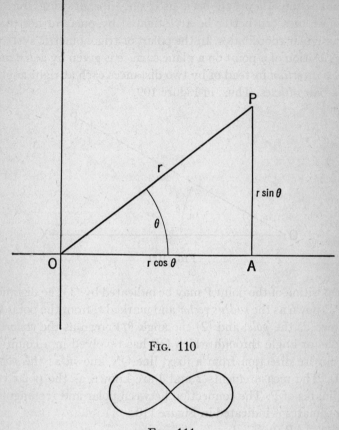

FIG. 110

FIG. 111

Like Archimedes, Jakob Bernoulli requested that a mathematical figure should be engraved on his tombstone. He chose the logarithmic spiral, presumably because it illustrates the inscription he chose to accompany it: *Eadem mutata resurgo*, "I shall arise the same, though changed." The logarithmic spiral frequently reproduces itself under many different conditions.

Eight years after his death, a work of his entitled *Ars con-ectandi* was published. Among other matters, it contained contributions to the theory of probability which played an important part in the development of the subject whose foundations, as we saw, were laid by Fermat and Pascal.

As in the case of his elder brother Jakob, Johann Bernoulli ran counter to his father's plans regarding his work in life. His father wished him to take charge of the prosperous trading interests of his family, but after a year in commerce he returned to Basel and studied philosophy and mathematics. He lived for some time in France, where he taught the principles of Leibniz's calculus, among his pupils being the Marquis de l'Hôpital, who later produced the first book to present a systematic treatment of the subject.

Johann taught mathematics for ten years at Groningen, in the Netherlands, and on the death of his brother in 1705 he succeeded him as Professor of Mathematics at Basel. There he too won great renown as a teacher. He had already become famous thoughout Europe for his problem connected with the curve known as the *brachistochrone*, mentioned on page 277, and he now played a leading part in developing the ideas and applications of Leibniz's calculus. He was frequently involved in violent quarrels and controversies and he took a leading part in the dispute with English mathematicians regarding the invention of the calculus.

He had three sons, each of whom became a professor of mathematics. Two of them, Nicolaus and Daniel, were professors at the Academy of St. Petersburg founded by Catherine I, though Nicolaus died young, and Daniel remained there only a few years, returning to Basel in 1733 on account of ill-health. Johann's youngest son, another Johann, succeeded his father as Professor of Mathematics at Basel. The more famous Daniel won no fewer than ten prizes offered by the French Academy of Sciences, sharing one of them with his father, much to the latter's resentment. He was delighted when a stranger once asked him his name, and on his replying "I am Daniel Bernoulli" to receive the incredulous and sarcastic reply "And I am Isaac Newton!"

When Daniel Bernoulli resigned his professorship at St Petersburg, he was succeeded by his friend, Leonard Euler, one of the greatest mathematicians of the eighteenth century, and one of the greatest Switzerland has ever produced.

Euler was born at Basel in 1707, the son of a Calvinistic pastor who was also a mathematician, having studied under Jakob Bernoulli. Unlike Jakob and Johann Bernoulli, Euler was encouraged and helped by his father, who eventually sent him to study mathematics under Johann Bernoulli, although he had at one time hoped that his son would follow his own example and become a Calvinistic minister. The religious atmosphere in which Euler's childhood was spent remained with him all his life. The simple, unquestioning faith he learned as a child never deserted him throughout his seventy-seven years. Maybe it was this faith that enabled him to accept blindness with quiet resignation and unfaltering courage. It also made it difficult for him to get on well with people like Frederick the Great and Voltaire, as we shall see.

In 1707, the year of Euler's birth, the stage had been set for great mathematical developments. Seventy years had elapsed since Descartes had introduced his revolutionary analytic geometry; Europe had been given Leibniz's calculus some thirty years previously; in trigonometry, all six "trigonometric functions" had been invented (though they were not so called until 1770) but were still generally regarded as lengths and not as ratios, while the whole subject was still shackled by its ancient geometric treatment. Although a mass of trigonometric knowledge existed, it was lacking co-ordination, and its many scattered formulas had not been systematically developed and co-related.

In the course of some fifty years, Euler completely freed Descartes' geometry from that of ancient Greece and made it an independent branch of mathematical analysis; he summarized everything that was known in his day about the calculus, and opened up new trains of thought which were to be more fully developed by his successors; he transformed trigonometry from a geometric to an algebraic basis, as was mentioned in Chapter IV.

Although the nineteenth and twentieth centuries have seen great developments, especially with regard to more rigorous treatment in his work, yet the foundation of practically all college algebra today can be traced back to Euler. His energy and power of application were unbounded. His output of mathematical, scientific and astronomical works was so enormous that although much of it has never been published, more than forty volumes of his work have been printed.

The mathematical world owes a debt of thanks to certain far-sighted European monarchs for making it possible for Euler to make so great a contribution to mathematics. Most of the research work done in connection with mathematics and science on the Continent of Europe during the eighteenth century was due to the encouragement offered by certain *academies*. We have seen how the word "academy" came to be applied to Plato's school of philosophy. The first society of learned men to be established for research into physical science was the "Academy of the Secrets of Nature," founded in Naples in 1560. This body, however, was short-lived, since its name suggested magic and the black arts to the ignorant world of its day.

We have seen how Pascal, when a youth, was allowed to attend meetings of mathematicians and scientists in Paris. These meetings eventually developed into the French Academy of Sciences, which not only provided salaries to enable mathematicians and scientists to spend their time on research, but also encouraged the development of mathematical and scientific knowledge by offering prizes open to all competitors. The French Academy of Sciences has been reconstituted several times and has included the most brilliant names in French science and mathematics as well as those of many brilliant foreign members, such as Benjamin Franklin, who was elected as an *Associé Étranger* in 1772.

Euler was at different times associated with two European academies, both of them formed on plans that had been drawn up by Leibniz. In 1700, the *Royal Academy of Sciences at Berlin* was founded by the Prussian king, Frederick I, though it was not opened until 1711, when Leibniz became its first president. In 1724 Peter the Great agreed to Leibniz's plans for the *Imperial Academy of Sciences at St. Petersburg*. The sudden death of this Russian monarch did not shelve the plan, however, for the academy was duly brought into being by the broad-minded empress (in more senses than one) Catherine I, the former mistress and wife, and now the widow of Peter the Great. At both Berlin and St. Petersburg, the academies provided ample salaries from state funds to enable distinguished scholars to pursue researches into mathematical and scientific subjects, and thus provided encouragement that was lacking in European universities of the eighteenth century, with the possible exception of the meager support offered to ordained Fellows at Oxford and Cambridge.

As we have seen, Euler was appointed to the Academy at St. Petersburg in 1733, and from that time onwards was able to devote himself to mathematical and scientific work. In 1735 overwork brought on a fever which resulted in the loss of sight in his right eye, but failed to slow down his enormous output of mathematical and scientific works. Three years later he won the prize offered by the French Academy of Sciences, and in 1740 he shared the prize with Maclaurin and Daniel Bernoulli.

In 1741, sickened by the political upheavals and executions

then prevalent in Russia, Euler accepted an invitation from Frederick the Great to become a member of the Berlin Academy, where he remained for twenty-five years. His character did not harmonize with the type of people—such as Voltaire—Frederick attracted to his court, and in 1766, after years of petty unpleasantness, Euler accepted an invitation by Catherine the Great to return to St. Petersburg. The Russians had always held Euler in high respect, even after he had gone to Prussia in 1741. In 1760 Prussia had been engaged in the Seven Years' War with Russia, among other enemies. While Frederick was absent with his army at Breslau in Silesia the Russians invaded Prussia and captured Berlin. In the course of this campaign a farm at Charlottenburg, some four miles from Berlin, that belonged to Euler, was pillaged by the Russian troops. On hearing the name of the owner of the farm, the Russian general saw to it that Euler was immediately paid full compensation, while the Russian Empress, Elizabeth, sent him an additional sum of four thousand crowns. In view of this warmth of Russian feeling toward him, and the contrasting coolness of Frederick the Great and his court, it is not surprising that Euler accepted an invitation of Catherine the Great in 1766 and returned to St. Petersburg Academy. Here he spent the remaining seventeen years of his life.

Very soon after his return to the capital of the czars, a cataract formed in his left eye. In spite of this calamity he remained calm and courageous and continued his work. He actually dictated a book on elementary algebra in 1770. The following year his house was destroyed by fire and the blind Euler was saved only by the devotion of a Swiss manservant who carried him from the burning building. Shortly after this exciting episode an operation on the cataract in his left eye seemed to be successful, but Euler soon lapsed back into complete blindness. Even now his courage and energy never faltered; he continued to dictate a vast store of mathematical papers to his sons. Many of these papers were published, long after his death, in the official publication of the St. Petersburg Academy.

Euler gave his approval of the use of the Greek letter $\pi$ for the number 3.14159 . . . , or the ratio between the circumference and the diameter of a circle; and of $e$ to represent the incommensurable number 2.71828 . . . , or

$$1 + \frac{1}{1} + \frac{1}{2\cdot1} + \frac{1}{3\cdot2\cdot1} + \frac{1}{4\cdot3\cdot2\cdot1} + \ldots$$

which plays an essential part in higher mathematics. He was the first to use the symbol $f(x)$ for "function of x," while, as we shall see, he invented the symbol $i$ for $\sqrt{-1}$. Again, he was the first mathematician to make a definite break away from Napier's idea of a logarithm as a connection between a term of an arithmetic progression and a term of a geometric progression. Instead, he systematically introduced the modern simple concept based on exponents. He also established the custom of using capital letters for the angles of a triangle and their corresponding small letters for the sides opposite those angles. Thus:

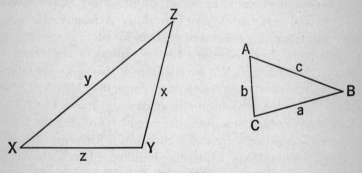

FIG. 112

In addition to many works on higher mathematics which cannot be discussed in non-technical language he wrote on the mo-

tions of the moon, the planets and comets, and also compiled a
"popular" book on mechanics, astronomy and general science
for the niece of Frederick the Great, entitled *Lettres à une
princesse d'Allemagne sur quelques sujets de Physique et de
Philosophie*. The fact that this book was written in French is
interesting; it reflects Frederick's dislike of German, which he
considered to be the language of boors. Frederick himself always wrote and spoke in French, and welcomed French
writers like Maupertuis and Voltaire at his court.

Euler's phenomenal memory stood him in good stead when
he became completely blind. He could repeat the whole of
Virgil's *Aeneid* by heart and could make amazingly complicated mathematical calculations even when blind. In 1783
while playing with his grandchildren he suffered a stroke and
suddenly died at the age of seventy-seven.

Between 1600 and 1650, Descartes, Fermat and Pascal
brought mathematical fame and glory to France; then came
England's turn with Wallis, Barrow and Newton, while Germany had her Leibniz. Switzerland then came to the fore with
the Bernoullis and Euler. From the middle of the seventeenth
century until the middle of the eighteenth, no great mathematician arose in France. Then Joseph Louis Lagrange (1736–
1813), one of the world's greatest mathematicians, brought
fresh mathematical glory to France while his fellow-country-
man Pierre Laplace (1749–1827) also won enduring fame by his
astronomical and mathematical work.

Lagrange was born at Turin in 1736, the eldest son of a well-
paid government official of French descent who had married
the daughter of a wealthy doctor but who eventually became
impoverished owing to his rash speculations. Lagrange used
to say that this loss of income led to his good fortune, since,
had he remained wealthy, he might not have studied mathematics. It is highly improbable, however, whether a mind such

as his could have avoided the insistent urge to satisfy its intellectual curiosity, no matter how hampered by wealth.

He had studied the elements of geometry while at the college of Turin, but his interest in mathematics was not aroused until he chanced to read an article by Halley, the friend of Newton, in the *Philosophical Transactions* of the Royal Society of London. In this way he became interested in the new analysis that was transforming mathematics. Within two years he had mastered it to such good effect that he was able to suggest to Euler, then at the Berlin Academy, a more general method of attacking "isoperimetrical" problems than had been developed at that time. Euler was greatly impressed, and made use of Lagrange's suggestions, though he abstained from publishing his further investigations until Lagrange had made public his improved methods, an indication of the generous nature of this great mathematician.

In 1754 he was made Professor of Geometry at the Royal School of Artillery at Turin and while holding this post he founded a society that later became the Turin Academy of Sciences. It was in the journal of this society that he published the methods he had communicated to Euler, which led to the Calculus of Variations, a title suggested by Euler in 1766. Between 1764 and 1788 Lagrange won five of the prizes offered by the French Academy of Sciences by his applications of mathematics to astronomical problems. Meanwhile, in 1766 he succeeded Euler as director of mathematics at the Berlin Academy, thanks to recommendations to Frederick the Great made by D'Alembert, the French mathematician who was anxious to avoid having to refuse the post, and Euler, who was anxious to return to St. Petersburg.

Shortly after his arrival in Berlin, Lagrange married a distant relative of his family. He told D'Alembert that he was led to take this step merely in order to have someone to look after him. Fate decreed otherwise. It was he who was called on

o look after his wife, who became seriously ill, and despite all
her husband's care and devotion, soon died.

While in Berlin, Lagrange produced his greatest work, the
*Mécanique Analytique*, in which he reduced the theory of the
mechanics of solids and fluids to general formulas by means of
which particular results could be obtained. He so completely
banished geometric ideas from the book that not one diagram
appeared in it.

In 1787, just after Frederick the Great's death, Lagrange
resigned his post at Berlin and accepted an invitation to join
the French Academy of Sciences at Paris extended to him by
Louis XVI, who had succeeded his grandfather, Louis XV,
three years previously. When Lagrange arrived in Paris he
was royally welcomed by the ill-fated Queen Marie Antoinette;
he was given a fine apartment in the Louvre, which was then a
royal palace; he was granted as large a salary as the one he had
enjoyed at Berlin.

Despite all these flattering attentions, he suddenly fell into a
deep mental depression which caused him to turn against his
beloved mathematics and science with loathing and disgust;
for two whole years he even refused to examine the first printed
copy of his own *Mécanique Analytique*. Strange to say, it was
the violent outbreak of the French Revolution that restored
the mind of this peaceable, gentle man to normal once more.
He felt deeply interested in the social upheaval, and although,
being nominally a foreigner, he could have left France, he
chose to remain and watch its progress on the spot. When the
Reign of Terror swept over Paris he bitterly regretted his decision to remain in France, his gentle soul being sickened by
the cruelty and bloodshed let loose. He repeatedly reproached
himself for staying, remarking "Tu l'as voulu," "You've
asked for it." Nevertheless, by remaining in France he found
great happiness. In 1792, the year before Louis XVI was led
to the guillotine, a young and beautiful girl, the daughter of

the astronomer Lemonnier, moved at first by compassion for the sad and lonely Lagrange, fell in love with him and insisted on marrying him. Despite a disparity of nearly forty years between their ages, the marriage proved a great success, Lagrange becoming devoted to his adoring young wife.

Fortunately for France, and for mathematics, Lagrange was not molested by any revolutionary tribunal. His salary was continued, and, in addition, he was given well-paid official appointments. In 1793 he became president of a committee that was appointed to carry on the work of a pre-Revolution commission which had begun to inquire into the need for a reform in French weights and measures. This work had been sponsored by the French Academy of Sciences, but in 1793 the Academy had been suppressed by the revolutionists. Even the new committee was later "purged" of those who were not considered "worthy of confidence because of their hatred of kings, and of their republican virtues." Among those found lacking in these qualities were Laplace, whom we shall meet shortly, and Lavoisier, one of the founders of modern chemistry, who was guillotined in 1794, his execution causing even the quiet Lagrange to exclaim in protest, "It only took a moment to cause this head to fall; maybe a hundred years will be insufficient to produce one like it."

Despite the turmoil in France, the committee on weights and measures continued its work under the guidance of Lagrange. Practically every district in France had its own weights and measures; there were more than three hundred ways of measuring area alone, for example. The original commission had decided to draw up entirely new measures, commencing with a new and standard unit of length. It was agreed to take a length equal to one ten-millionth of the distance from the North Pole to the Equator as the unit of length. Although a slight error made in calculating the length of the meridian prevented this intention from being carried out exactly, the standard was duly fixed and was given the name of *meter*. By building up a table of length, etc. based on 10, an enormous saving in time and labor was effected for all the nations that eventually adopted this *Metric System*, since 10 is also the basis of our number-scale. To learn all the essential measures, only nine fundamental expressions need be memorized. They are:

*milli-*  ("thousandth part")
*centi-*  ("hundredth part")
*deci-*  ("tenth part")
*Deka-*  ("ten")
*Hecto-*  ("hundred")
*Kilo-*  ("thousand")

> meter
> gram
> liter

[It is wise to write the last three prefixes with capital letters in order to avoid confusion when *deci-* and *Deka-* are abbreviated] Thus, the table of the measure of length is as follows:

10 millimeters (mm.) = 1 centimeter (cm.)
10 cm.          = 1 decimeter (dm.)
10 dm.          = 1 meter (m.)
10 m.           = 1 Dekameter (Dm.)
10 Dm.          = 1 Hectometer (Hm.)
10 Hm.          = 1 Kilometer (Km.)

[Approximate equivalents:

1 inch = 2.540 cm.;    1 cm.  =  .3937 inches
1 yard =  .914399 m.;  1 m.   = 1.093614 yards
1 mile = 1.609 Km.;    1 Km.  =  .6214 miles
               8 Km. = 5 miles]

For weight measures, the unit chosen was the *gram*, the weight of distilled water at 4° Centigrade (about 39° Fahrenheit) that could be contained in a cube whose internal dimensions were each 1 cm., that is, the weight of 1 cubic centimeter of such water. For the table of weight, simply substitute "gram" for "meter" in the table of length. Thus:

10 milligrams (mg.) = 1 centigram (cg.)
10 cg.          = 1 decigram (dg.)

| 10 dg. | = 1 gram (g.) |
| 10 g. | = 1 Dekagram (Dg.) |
| 10 Dg. | = 1 Hectogram (Hg.) |
| 10 Hg. | = 1 Kilogram (Kg.) |

[Approximate equivalents:

| 1 oz (Avoirdupois) = 28.35 g.; | 1 g. = .03527 oz. |
| 1 lb. = .4536 Kg.; | 1 Kg. = 2.2046 lb. |
| 1 ton = 907.2 Kg.; | 1 Kg. = .0011 tons |
| 1 long ton = 1016 Kg.; | 1 Kg. = .00098 long tons] |

For square measure, 100 sq. mm. = 1 sq. cm.; 100 sq. cm. = 1 sq. dm.; 100 sq. dm. = 1 sq. m.

If a cube is constructed with each edge 1 cm. long, its volume will be 1 cu. cm. (or 1 c.c.) and since each edge will contain 10 mm., its volume will also equal 1000 cu. mm. Therefore 1000 cu. mm. = 1 c.c.; 1000 c.c. = 1 cu. dm.; 1000 cu. dm. = 1 cu. m.

In dealing with the volume of a liquid or gas, the word "liter" is used instead of "1 cubic decimeter." So

$$1 \text{ liter} = 1 \text{ cu. dm.} = 1000 \text{ c.c.}$$

Since 1 c.c. of water weighs 1 gram, 1 liter of water weighs 1 Kg.

[Approximate equivalents

1 gallon = 3.786 liters; 1 liter = .264 gallons.

1 Imperial gallon (Canada) = 4.546 liters

1 liter = .22 Imperial gallons (Canada).]

To reduce (for example) 8 Km. 3 Hm. 7 Dm. 4 m. 8 dm. 1 cm. 2 mm. to millimeters, all that is necessary is to copy the figures

8374812 mm.

which is surely preferable to the time and labor required to reduce corresponding units in our medieval length table. Moreover, this metric length could instantly be written as

837481.2 cm.

*or* 83748.12 dm.

*or* 8374.812 m.

*or* 837.4812 Dm.

*or* 83.74812 Hm.

*or* 8.374812 Km.

All that is necessary in each case is to write a decimal point after reaching the unit in which the length is to be expressed. The only caution necessary is to look out for any unit that may have been omitted in the original expression, and to place a zero in place of such omitted unit. Thus: 5 Km. 4 m. reduced to meters would equal 5004 m. [since 5 Km. 4 m. = 5 Km. 0 Hm. 0 Dm. 4 m.].

Another tremendous advantage in the metric system is the simple connection between weight and volume. For instance: "What is the weight of a steel girder built into a house, if the volume of the girder is found to be 85,000 c.c. and the Specific weight of the steel is 7.79?" ["Specific weight" or "Specific gravity" indicates the number of times any particular volume of a substance is heavier than an equal volume of water.] Since 1 c.c. of water weighs 1 gram, the weight of the girder will be (85,000 × 7.79) g. or 85 × 7.79 Kg., or 662.15 Kg.

It was mainly due to Lagrange that more than thirty nations today enjoy the enormous advantages of a system of weights and measures *based on a decimal system*.

Another appointment held by Lagrange was that of Professor of Mathematics at the École Polytechnique, which was founded in 1794, the year after the revolutionary decree that abolished all the old French universities and colleges. Here he gained a great reputation as a teacher. Most of his students had little or no mathematical background, but this did not deter Lagrange. Unlike many distinguished mathematicians, he had the gift of seeing problems from the point of view of those who did not have his own outstanding grasp of the subject. Consequently he was able to lead them up the easy and gradual stairway that leads right through elementary mathematics and well into the calculus without their realizing that they were covering ground usually regarded as abstruse and difficult. He invented an approach to the calculus which avoided the use of infinitesimals, being purely algebraic and depending on series of algebraic functions. The books in which these methods were set out were called the *Théorie des fonctions analytiques* (1797) and *Leçons sur le calcul des fonctions* (1806). Although Lagrange's methods were soon abandoned as a means of developing the calculus, his ideas led to important developments in higher analysis. In the preface to the second edition (Volume I, 1811) of his *Mécanique Analytique*, in which book he again made use of infinitesimals, he said, "When the spirit of the infinitesimal method has been properly conceived and we are convinced of the exactness of its results [through geometric proofs] . . . we may employ infinitely small quantities as a sure and valuable means of shortening and simplifying our demonstrations."

Lagrange played a part in the development of almost every branch of pure mathematics. In addition to all his work on the calculus, and, in particular, in connection with the calculus of variations, the calculus of finite differences and the solution of differential equations, he discovered a method of finding the approximate roots of an equation by means of continued fractions, while, in the theory of numbers he solved some of Fermat's problems and discovered new ones. In addition to this work on pure mathematics, Lagrange played an important part in verifying Newton's theory of universal gravitation. It was in this connection that his contemporary Laplace made much—unacknowledged—use of his work.

While preparing the revision of the second volume of his *Mécanique Analytique* he exhausted his failing powers and died, in 1813, at the age of seventy-seven. On his deathbed he declared that death was neither painful nor disagreeable.

Pierre Laplace was born in humble circumstances in Normandy in 1749. Because of his brilliance as a schoolboy, wealthy residents near his home assisted his education. The character of this brilliant and profound thinker lacks the attractive qualities shown by Lagrange. As soon as his feet were planted on the ladder of success, he did his utmost to ignore and forget his humble birth; at one moment he would be degradingly servile to those in power, at the next he would turn against them when they could no longer advance his worldly interests. He was unpopular with other mathematicians— with the exception of the gentle, generous Lagrange—since he frequently made use of their work without acknowledgment. All the same, they were forced to admit his outstanding genius.

When eighteen years old, he had been given a letter of introduction to D'Alembert, in Paris, but this well-known mathematician paid no attention to the letter. When, however, Laplace sent him some notes on the principles of mechanics, D'Alembert at once sat up and took notice. He replied, "You have recommended yourself: my support is your due." On D'Alembert's recommendation, he was made a professor of mathematics in the École Militaire of Paris, and from this moment his future was assured. He proved himself to be a master of the analysis of his day, applying it to the verification of Newton's law of universal gravitation in connection with the movements of the heavenly bodies. His book on this subject, the *Mécanique Céleste* is regarded as second only to Newton's *Principia*. Another book of his, the *Exposition du Système du Monde* was a popular work in which analytic methods were not used. So masterly was the style of this book that in 1816 the author was chosen a member of the French Academy (not to be confused with the French Academy of Sciences, of which Laplace became a member in 1785) whose object was "the purification of the French language."

We have seen how, during the Revolution, Laplace was "purged" from the committee dealing with the reform in weights and measures. This, however, was only a temporary set-back in his career. He aspired to be a politican and had no scruples in changing his views in the ever-varying political atmosphere that surrounded the French Revolution and the rise of Napoleon Bonaparte, who showered honors on him but quickly threw him out of the post of Minister of the Interior when he showed no capacity for administration.

Certain researches made by Laplace have led to highly important developments in the study of such subjects as gravitation, electricity and hydrodynamics, the branch of science that deals with the forces exerted by liquids. He also wrote a very profound book on the theory of probability, which subject he described as common sense expressed in mathematical language.

Toward the end of his life Laplace lived in quiet retirement in a country house he owned. Here he died, loaded with honors, in 1827. His death may be considered as marking the end of the type of mathematics built up in the seventeenth and eighteenth centuries. Cavalieri, Descartes, Wallis, Newton and Leibniz, among others, had boldly pushed on into the unexplored territory whose borders had been reached by Archimedes, but into which no mathematician had ventured to enter for seventeen centuries. By their brilliance and daring, these pioneers unearthed mathematical treasure undreamed of by the Greeks. The methods they employed would have shocked those Greeks as they shocked Bishop Berkeley and shock modern mathematicians who refuse to follow the advice given by D'Alembert to his students when they found the logical difficulties of the eighteenth-century calculus to be insurmountable. "Go ahead," said D'Alembert," and faith will come to you." This single sentence summarizes the eighteenth-century attitude and is diametrically opposed to that of succeeding mathematicians.

Equipped only with imperfect tools, the seventeenth- and

eighteenth-century mathematicians nevertheless proceeded to uncover secrets of nature which until their day had been hidden from man. They realized—if they paused to think about it at all—that the methods they employed lacked the rigorous logical basis which had been the keynote—indeed, the *raison d'être*—of Greek mathematics. But during these two centuries the main object of mathematicians was the application of their imperfect tools to the solution of some of the problems of the universe, rather than the search for a rigidly logical system of reasoning. They therefore refused to be held up in their thrilling exploration by problems such as the exact meaning of the infinitely great and the infinitely small; when it served their purpose an "infinitesimal" would be regarded as a fixed quantity; at other times, as a variable quantity. They did not concern themselves with the meaning of "continuity"; they did not ask themselves whether they thought of number as being continuous in the sense that time seems to be continuous, one instant merging imperceptibly into the next. They did not allow such problems to stand in the way of their swift advance into the unknown. Descartes, for example, never paused to consider the implication of his assumption that an exact position for any number can be indicated on a curve. He took it for granted that there existed a one-to-one correspondence between points on a line and the infinite number of number values between any two points on a number-scale and thus did not concern himself with problems such as those hinted at on pages 232–239.

Before we glance at the life of Gauss, the greatest mathematician of the nineteenth century, and one who was responsible for directing the course of mathematical inquiry into its present channels, we must take a look at the origin and meaning of a mathematical concept which plays a most important part in higher mathematics. Unfortunately it still labors under an entirely misleading name given to it by a philosopher of the seventeenth century. Mathematicians have frequently been careless in the terms they have accepted or invented—witness *sine* ("bosom," "curve") for the length of half a straight line in a circle; *surd* ("deaf") for a number that cannot be expressed as a ratio; *algebra* ("the re-union") in place of the excellent, long-established and much more expressive Greek word *arithmetike* ("Science of numbers"); *calculus* ("pebble") for a branch of mathematics extremely remote from all ideas of the abacus, on which pebbles were sometimes used; *mathematical induction* for a process of reasoning that has

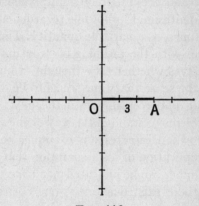

Fig. 113

no connection with its name; *plus* ("more") and *minus* ("less") as applied to *directions; inertia* ("without power of motion") for a property of matter by which it continues in either a state of rest *or of uniform motion;* and finally, *real* and *imaginary* as applied to numbers.

The terms "real" and "imaginary" numbers were invented by Descartes. In order to understand what this term "imaginary" really indicates today it is easier to depart from the chronological order in which the concept arose and consider it from a graphical point of view (which was first introduced in 1798 by a Norwegian surveyor, Caspar Wessel, whose ideas were published in the memoirs of the Royal Academy of Denmark in 1799).

First of all, we are going to invent a shorthand symbol, in order to introduce the general reader to a new mathematical concept. The symbol will be ↰, which will mean the words *"units on the number-scale that has been rotated in a counterclockwise direction through 90°."*

In Figure 113, OA represents a line $+3$ units long, measured from the origin O and lying along the x-axis and measured to the right of the origin.

Now let us represent "3↰" graphically, that is, let us draw a line equal to 3 units on the number-scale that has been rotated through 90°.

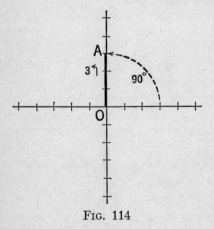

Fig. 114

We can now go a step further and say that $3$↰↰ or $3($↰$)^2$ indicates that the operation indicated in Figure 114 is to be performed twice. So $3($↰$)^2$ will be shown graphically as:

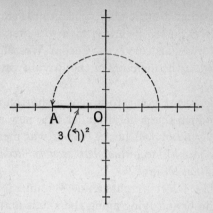

FIG. 115

Similarly, $3(↖)^3$ will indicate that the operation has to be performed three times, thus:

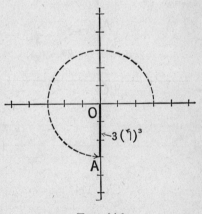

FIG. 116

Finally, $3(↖)^4$ will indicate that the operation has to be performed four times, thus:

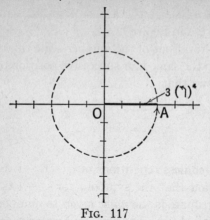

FIG. 117

Now note that the line OA in Figure 115 lies in the opposite direction (measured from the origin O) to that of the line OA in Figure 113. It follows that since the line OA in Figure 113 represents $+3$, the line OA in Figure 115 represents $-3$, as well as $3(\text{↖})^2$. So $3(\text{↖})^2$ means the same thing as $-3$

$$\therefore 1(\text{↖})^2 \text{ means the same thing as } -1$$

$$\therefore 1 \text{↖} \text{ means the same thing as } \sqrt{-1}$$

In other words, $\sqrt{-1}$ *means "1 unit on the number-scale that has been rotated in a counter-clockwise direction through $90°$."*

In 1748 Euler used the letter $i$ to stand for $\sqrt{-1}$, just as we made use of the symbol ↖. This choice of a letter to indicate an *operation* was unfortunate, as it is misleading for beginners. It must always be remembered that $i$ stands for the words "1 unit on the number-scale that has been rotated in a counter-clockwise direction through $90°$." If the line OA in each of Figures 114–117 had been made 1 unit in length instead of 3 units, it would be seen that

$i = \sqrt{-1}$ (from Figure 114)

$i^2 = -1$ (from Figure 115)

$i^3 = -i$ (since OA in Figure 116 lies in the opposite direction to OA in Figure 114)

$i^4 =$    1 (since OA in Figure 117 lies in the same position as OA in Figure 113).

Since further rotations of the number-scale through 90° would bring OA into the same four successive positions over and over again, it follows that

$$i^5 = i$$
$$i^6 = -1$$
$$i^7 = -i$$
$$i^8 = 1$$

and so on, in endless repetitions of $i$, $-1$, $-i$, 1.

We have said that the symbol $i$ for $\sqrt{-1}$ is unfortunate; equally unfortunate is the *name* given to numbers like $\sqrt{-1}$, which were called "imaginaries" by Descartes. Since it is not possible to find the square root of a negative quantity, Descartes described $\sqrt{-2}$, for example, as an *imaginary number*. But $\sqrt{-2}$ is no more imaginary than is $-2$. We saw in Chapter III that in the third century Diophantus considered that the equation $4x + 20 = 4$, whose root is $-4$, was "absurd," since in his day nobody had conceived of the possibility of such a thing as a "number" less than zero. Even Fibonacci, in the early thirteenth century, ignored negative numbers, except in an equation connected with gains and losses, when, as we saw, he interpreted the negative root as indicating a loss instead of a gain. This was the first step toward the admission of negative numbers as full members of the mathematical family. By the time of Cardan (the sixteenth century) negative roots of equations had come to be recognized, for in his *Ars Magna* of 1545 he deals with them. Thanks to the work of men like Vieta, Napier, Fermat and Descartes, the idea of negative numbers became fully accepted as indicating some measurement taken in the opposite direction to that in which a positive number was taken. Nowadays, a negative number at once suggests a *direction* to our minds; as soon as we have become familiar with $i$, or $\sqrt{-1}$, this symbol suggests the rotation of the number-scale through an angle of 90°.

It took many centuries, however, for this concept to grow in men's minds. In 1585, Simon Stevin of Bruges, whom we met in Chapter V, admitted that the subject was not mastered. About a century later Wallis almost hit on a graphical explanation of $\sqrt{-1600}$, though nothing came of it, while Leibniz showed that it was possible to perform certain algebraic operations with the numbers that Descartes had dismissed as "imaginaries." By the early eighteenth century, Euler and De Moivre (whom we shall shortly meet) were working on the subject, and applying it to trigonometry. In 1832 Gauss invented the term "complex number" for an expression that consists of a so-called "real" number and a so-called "imaginary" number, for example: $a + bi$. Ever since the time of Descartes, the terms "real" and "imaginary" numbers have been used in mathematics, despite their misleading associations. "Imaginary" numbers are no more imaginary than are "real" numbers. Any "real" number, such as 5, can be expressed as the complex number $5 + bi$, it being understood that b is here equal to zero. So all our numbers may be connected as in the following table:

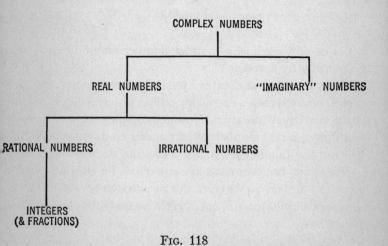

FIG. 118

Let us see how a complex number may be represented graphically. Here we meet with another mathematical concept, that of a *vector*. A vector is a straight line whose length represents some magnitude (in science, a pull, or push, or some muscular exertion, or its equivalent) and whose direction represents the direction in which such pull, etc., acts. If two forces act together upon the same point on a body, a single force can be found that could produce the same effect on the body as the two forces acting together. This single force, known as the *resultant* of the two *component* forces, may be represented by a vector which will be the diagonal of the parallelogram having the component forces as adjacent sides. Thus:

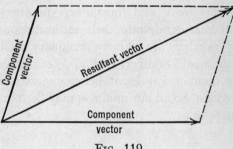

Fig. 119

Let us now see how a complex number may be represented graphically by a vector.

In Cartesian coördinates (the system invented by Descartes) we used an x-axis and a y-axis in order to determine the position of "real" numbers. Now in a complex number we have two things, a real number and a number containing *i*. We can still use the familiar x-axis for measuring values of the real-number part, but we must have a new axis for the *i* part of the complex number. So we erect this new axis at the origin of the familiar coördinate axes, *but at right angles to the plane of those axes*. Thus:

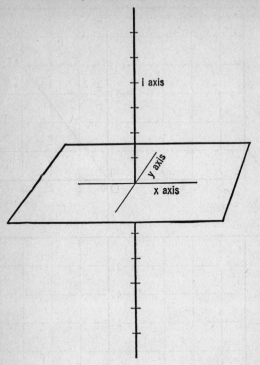

FIG. 120

We now make use of the plane that contains the old x-axis and the new $i$-axis in order to represent complex numbers graphically. Positive values of $i$ are measured on the $i$-axis upward from the origin, negative values downward from the origin. Since $i$ and $-i$ are not numbers on the "real" number-scale these $+$ and $-$ signs do not indicate "greater or less than zero." These merely indicate measurements in opposite directions.

The complex number $3 + 4i$ would be represented by the vector OP (Figure 121), which is the resultant of the components 3 and $4i$.

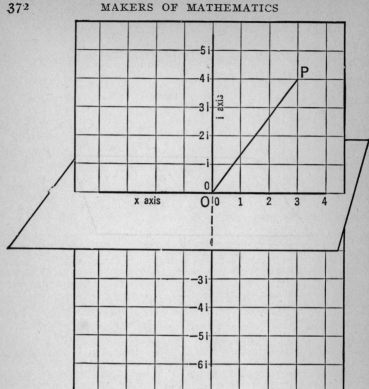

FIG. 121

[In practice it is usual to show only the plane of the x-axis and *i*-axis.]

More generally, the vector OP in Figure 122 represents the complex number a + b*i*, where a stands for the number of x-units and b for the number of *i* units involved.

Note that the complex number is not represented by the *length* of the vector OP, but by the *length and direction* of that vector. The length of the vector will be seen to be $\sqrt{a^2 + b^2}$, from the theorem of Pythagoras. This is known as the *absolute value* of the complex number, and may be written as $|a + bi| = \sqrt{a^2 + b^2}$.

It is now a simple matter to express a complex number in *polar* or *trigonometric* form (see pages 345, 346).

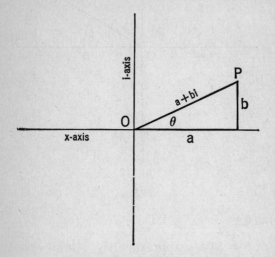

Fig. 122

The angle $\theta$ is called the *amplitude* of the complex number, OP, or r, the *modulus*. It follows that

$$a = r \cos\theta$$
$$b = r \sin\theta \; [\therefore bi = r\, i \sin\theta]$$
$$\therefore a + bi = r \cos\theta + r i \sin\theta$$
$$= r(\cos\theta + i \sin\theta)$$

which is sometimes abbreviated (Figure 123) as follows:

$$a + bi = r \operatorname{cis}\theta,$$

[the right hand side standing for $r(\cos\theta + i \sin\theta)$].

Suppose we wish to write the complex number $3 + 4i$ in polar form. Here $a = 3$, $b = 4$

$$\therefore r[= \sqrt{a^2 + b^2}] = 5$$

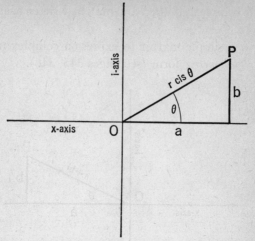

FIG. 123

Now $\tan \theta = \dfrac{b}{a} = \dfrac{4}{3} = 1.3333$

$\therefore \theta = 52°8'$ approximately (from trigonometric tables).

$\therefore 3 + 4i = 5(\cos 52°8' + i \sin 52°8')$

The advantage of the polar form lies in the ease with which multiplication, division and the extraction of roots involving complex numbers may be performed when the complex numbers are thus expressed. In this connection, every textbook on the subject today makes use of *De Moivre's Theorem* and thus reminds us of a mathematician who played an essential part in developing the study of complex numbers, though they were not so called in his day.

Abraham De Moivre was born at Vitry in France in 1667. His parents were French Protestants and were compelled to leave France on the revocation of the Edict of Nantes in 1685. The edict had been issued in 1598 by Henry IV, giving grudging freedom of worship and certain civil rights to the Huguenots or French Protestants. In 1685, Louis XIV, under the influence of Madame de Maintenon, revoked the edict and thus drove out many of the steadiest and most skillful workers in his country. In London, De Moivre gave lessons in mathematics. It is said that he secured a copy of Newton's *Principia*, tore out the pages, so as to be able to carry one or two of them in his pocket, and studied the book in spare moments. In any case, he and Newton became very friendly, and De Moivre was one of the mathematicians chosen by the Royal Society to investigate the dispute between the followers of Newton and Leibniz. De Moivre revolutionized the higher branches of trigonometry by the theorem we are about to discuss, but his greatest fame lies in his treatment of probability. He was a member of the Royal Society and also a foreign member of both the French Academy of Sciences and the Berlin Academy of Sciences. Toward the end of his long life—he lived to be eight-seven—he fell into poverty and had to support himself by solving questions on games of chance at a tavern in St. Martin's Lane. Finally, he sank into a state of lethargy, sleeping longer every night. The last time he went to bed he slept for more than twenty-four hours and then died in his sleep. Before we consider *De Moivre's Theorem*, let us see the result of multiplying two complex numbers together, both expressed in polar form.

Let $r_1(\cos \theta_1 + i \sin \theta_1)$; $r_2(\cos \theta_2 + i \sin \theta_2)$ be the numbers that are to be multiplied together.

By ordinary algebraic multiplication we get:

$$r_1 r_2(\cos \theta_1 \cos \theta_2 + i \sin \theta_1 \cos \theta_2 + i \cos \theta_1 \sin \theta_2 + i^2 \sin \theta_1 \sin \theta_2$$

Rearranging the terms, and remembering that $i^2 = -1$, we get

$$r_1 r_2[(\cos \theta_1 \cos \theta_2 - \sin \theta_1 \sin \theta_2) + i (\sin \theta_1 \cos \theta_2 + \cos \theta_1 \sin \theta_2)]$$

From the formula connected with Figure 51 (page 150), $\cos \theta_1 \cos \theta^2 - \sin \theta_1 \sin \theta_2 = \cos (\theta_1 + \theta_2)$, while by an analogous formula to the one connected with Figure 50 (page 148) $\sin \theta_1 \cos \theta_2 + \cos \theta_1 \sin \theta_2 = \sin (\theta_1 + \theta_2)$

So our product may be written as

$$r_1r_2[\cos(\theta_1 + \theta_2) + i \sin(\theta_1 + \theta_2)]$$

In other words, the result of multiplying two complex numbers (in polar form) is another complex number *whose modulus is the product of the two original moduli, and whose amplitude is the sum of the two original amplitudes*. It is therefore very simple to multiply, for example, $5(\cos 10° + i \sin 10°)$ and $7(\cos 20° + i \sin 20°)$, the product being the complex number whose modulus is 35 and whose amplitude is 30°, namely,

$$35(\cos 30° + i \sin 30°)$$

Now suppose we wished to square the complex number $r(\cos \theta + i \sin \theta)$. To square a number is equivalent to multiplying the number by itself. So the answer will be

$$r^2(\cos 2\theta + i \sin 2\theta)$$

Similarly, to cube $r(\cos \theta + i \sin \theta)$ we simply write down

$$r^3(\cos 3\theta + i \sin 3\theta)$$

De Moivre's Theorem states these last two facts in general form:

$$[r(\cos \theta + i \sin \theta)]^n = r^n(\cos n \theta + i \sin n \theta)$$

This is the theorem that lies at the root of much higher trigonometry.

It must be remembered that until the early nineteenth century, a geometrical interpretation of "imaginary" numbers had not been discovered. Consequently, mathematicians such as Euler and De Moivre had merely the knowledge that these mysterious "imaginaries," which obviously were not connected with ordinary magnitudes as were "real" numbers, were yet able to be made use of in manipulations that led to concrete results. Moreover, they began to realize that the use of "imaginaries" enabled all algebraic equations to fit in with what is now known as the "fundamental theorem" of algebra, namely that if an equation is of the $n$th. degree, it will have $n$ roots. Thus, the equation $3x - 5 = 9$ will have *one* root; the equation $x^2 + 3x + 1 = 0$ will have *two* roots; the equation

$x^3 = 1$ will have *three* roots, and so on. What will be the three roots of the equation $x^3 = 1$?

We will write 1 as the complex number $1 + 0i$ and then transform this expression into its polar form
$$1(\cos 0° + i \sin 0°).$$

Let the required cube roots be of the form $r(\cos \theta + i \sin \theta)$.

Then $1(\cos 0° + i \sin 0°) = [r(\cos \theta + i \sin \theta)]^3$
$$= r^3(\cos 3\theta + i \sin 3\theta)$$

Equating moduli, we get $r = 1$

Equating amplitudes, we get $3\theta = 0°$, or $360°$, or $720°$ etc.

$$\therefore \theta = 0°, \text{ or } 120°, \text{ or } 240°.$$

$$\therefore r(\cos \theta + i \sin \theta) = 1(\cos 0° + i \sin 0°)$$
$$= 1(1 + 0) = 1 \ldots . (1)$$

$$or \; 1(\cos 120° + i \sin 120°) = 1\left(-\frac{1}{2} + \frac{\sqrt{3}}{2}i\right) \ldots (2)$$

$$or \; 1(\cos 240° + i \sin 240°) = 1\left(-\frac{1}{2} - \frac{\sqrt{3}}{2}i\right) \ldots (3)$$

Simplifying (2) and (3), it will be seen that the cube roots of 1, or, in other words, the roots of the equation $x^3 = 1$, are 1, $\frac{1}{2}(-1 + \sqrt{3}\,i)$ and $\frac{1}{2}(-1 - \sqrt{3}\,i)$. If any one of these roots is cubed, it will be seen that the result is 1. Thus:

$$\left(-\frac{1}{2} + \frac{\sqrt{3}}{2}i\right)^2 = -\frac{1}{2} - \frac{\sqrt{3}}{2}i$$

$$\left(-\frac{1}{2} - \frac{\sqrt{3}}{2}i\right)\left(-\frac{1}{2} + \frac{\sqrt{3}}{2}i\right) = \frac{1}{4} + \frac{3}{4} = 1.$$

It is very easy to represent any root of 1 graphically. Using the symbolism "r cis $\theta$" [for $r(\cos \theta + i \sin \theta)$] we may write
$$1 = 1(\text{cis } 0°), \text{ or } 1(\text{cis } 360°), \text{ or } 1(\text{cis } 720°)$$
$$\therefore \sqrt[3]{1} = 1(\text{cis } 0°), \text{ or } 1(\text{cis } 120°), \text{ or } 1(\text{cis } 240°).$$

These three roots will be represented graphically by vectors, each of which is 1 unit in length (since $r = 1$) and having angles which successively differ by 120°. Thus:

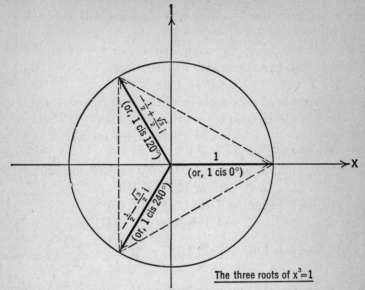

The three roots of $x^3 = 1$

Fig. 124

It will be seen that the ends of these vectors lie on a circle whose radius is 1 unit, and that if those ends were joined they would be the vertices of an equilateral triangle inscribed in the circle.

Now suppose we wish to represent the twelfth-roots of 1 graphically.

$$1 = 1(\text{cis } 0°), \text{ or } 1(\text{cis } 360°), \text{ or } 1(\text{cis } 720°), \text{ or}$$
$$1(\text{cis } 1080°), \text{ etc}$$
$$\therefore \sqrt[12]{1} = 1(\text{cis } 0°), \text{ or } 1(\text{cis } 30°), \text{ or } 1(\text{cis } 60°), \text{ or}$$
$$1(\text{cis } 90°), \text{ etc}$$

So these twelve roots will be represented by vectors, each of which is 1 unit in length, and having angles which successively differ by 30°. Thus:

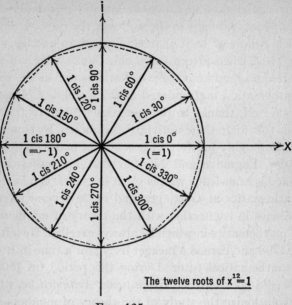

The twelve roots of $x^{12}=1$

It will be seen that the ends of these vectors lie on a circle whose radius is 1 unit, and that they are the vertices of a regular inscribed 12-sided figure.

The first mathematician who really developed the geometric concept of complex numbers—and gave them this name, as we have seen—was Gauss, the greatest of all German mathematicians.

Karl Frederick Gauss was born in 1777 at Brunswick. He came of a family which for generations had been very humble folk—gardeners, stonecutters, bricklayers. It was only by a fortunate chance that Gauss himself did not become a bricklayer. While at his first school he showed an amazing aptitude for figures, so much so that by the time he was ten his schoolmaster admitted he could teach him no more arithmetic. He

then commenced to study algebra and eventually his youthful
genius was brought to the notice of the ruling Duke of Brunswick, who saw to it that Gauss had an excellent education.
In 1792, when fifteen years old, Gauss, who had already acquired a sound knowledge of Latin as well as the rudiments of
mathematics, matriculated at the Caroline College in Brunswick, and, thanks to the generous wisdom of the Duke, was
able to remain there until he was eighteen. By that time he had
so thoroughly mastered the works of mathematicians such as
Euler, Lagrange and Newton that his professors admitted
that his knowledge was as great as theirs. Gauss then studied
mathematics at Göttingen and made several important discoveries in connection with the theory of numbers, a branch
of mathematics in which he always excelled. He left Göttingen
in 1798 and earned a meager living for a time in Brunswick as
a mathematical tutor. During this period (in 1801) he published a book entitled *Disquitiones Arithmeticae*, which was to
revolutionize the study of the theory of numbers and was to
lead to a new school of writers on this subject. Gauss began
these researches at an early age, and his book became a standard work on the subject. He always held this branch of mathematics in high esteem and affection. Although apparently
simple, yet it is actually highly abstruse and difficult. "Mathematics," he would declare, "is the queen of the sciences, and
arithmetic is the queen of mathematics." [In his day, as we
saw, "arithmetic" meant "The Science of Numbers," not the
modern simple number-reckoning.]

Gauss also made numerous astronomical discoveries and
calculations during this early period of his life. These brought
him widespread fame and resulted in two attractive offers being made to him in 1807: one, a chair of mathematics at St.
Petersburg, the other the joint post of professor of astronomy
and director of a new observatory at Göttingen. Gauss ac-

:epted the latter post, and remained at Göttingen until his
death forty-eight years later.

Although the greater part of his life was spent in astronomical work which brought about great improvements in practical
astronomy, Gauss won lasting fame for his scientific researches
into magnetism and electricity. In this connection he demonstrated the possibility of sending telegraphic signals from
Göttingen to a neighboring town, and thus played a part in
developing the ideas on which such famous scientists as Gal-
vani (1737–1798), Volta (1745–1827) and Ampère (1775–1836)
had been working.

In the midst of all this astronomical and scientific work he
yet found time to study practically every branch of pure
mathematics, proving himself a master of them all. Mention
has already been made of his work in connection with the
theory of numbers, and we have noted his interest in the treatment of "imaginaries" and his development of the study of
complex numbers. In addition to all this work on the discrete
("separate," "individual") numbers of the number-scale he
was a master of the mathematics of motion and growth that
had been developed by Newton and Leibniz, so much so that he
shares with Lagrange and Laplace a foremost place among the
founders of modern mathematical analysis.

He was one of the first to study what is known as the non-
Euclidean geometry that is now associated with the name of
Nikolas Ivanovitch Lobachevsky of the University of Kazan
(1798–1856). As a simple illustration of the difference between
Euclidean and non-Euclidean geometry, consider the case of
two lines *on a plane surface*, each of which is at an angle of 90°
with another line. Those two lines would be said to be parallel,
and they would never meet, no matter how far they were extended in either direction. Now consider two meridians of the
earth. Each meets the equator at an angle of 90°, but never-

theless, they meet at two places—the North Pole and the South Pole. Euclid's geometry is based on certain assumptions or postulates, connected with figures on a plane surface. One of these postulates has to do with parallel lines on such a surface. When dealing with points which are not all on the same plane, it is possible to conceive of different postulates which lead to conclusions that are different from those of Euclidean geometry. One such system is that of Lobachevsky; another is that of Riemann, who for a short time was a pupil of Gauss. All three systems—those of Lobachevsky, Euclid and Riemann—were shown by Felix Klein (1849–1925) to be three different aspects of a more general kind of geometry.

Gauss was the last of the great mathematicians who were able to handle every branch of mathematics. Since his day, so widely and rapidly has the subject spread that no one mind can hope to grasp the whole vast field it now covers. The nineteenth and twentieth centuries—have seen thousands of mathematicians who have limited their attention to certain highly specialized branches of pure and applied mathematics. Not only have they made possible the tremendous developments that have taken place in all branches of science, but they have polished and sharpened the magnificent mathematical tools that were created during the sixteenth and seventeenth centuries.

One of the greatest British mathematicians of the nineteenth century, Professor Arthur Cayley of Cambridge University in his inaugural address to the British Association said, "It is difficult to give an idea of the vast extent of modern mathematics . . . extent crowded with beautiful detail . . . a tract of beautiful country seen at first in the distance, but which will bear to be rambled through and studied in every detail of hillside and valley, stream, rock, wood, and flower. But, as for everything else, so for a mathematical theory, beauty can be perceived but not explained."

If it was difficult to give an idea of the vast extent of mathematics when these words were spoken (some sixty years ago), it would be impossible to do so today in a book such as this. Apart from the impossibility of explaining in non-technical language the often highly technical and abstruse developments that have occurred, the ground to be covered is so extensive that even a brief summary of the mathematical achievements since the time of Gauss would occupy hundreds of pages. Moreover, without an understanding of the vast developments that have occurred in scientific thought it would be impossible to grasp the significance of mathematical applications to the study of such subjects as electricity, light, heat, sound, elasticity, dynamics and fluid motion. In all these subjects prodigious advances have been made, thanks primarily to the pioneer work of the sixteenth- and seventeenth-century mathematicians who developed the branch of mathematics that deals with the infinite. Boldly advancing where the Greeks had feared to tread, they obtained results by methods that were often open to question. Since their days, those methods have been extended, sharpened and refined by the application of imagination coupled with rigorous logical reasoning. Deep search has been made into what may be described as the philosophy of mathematics, the closest scrutiny being paid not only to the subject matter but also to the concepts that lie behind that subject matter. Many modern developments of the subject are so abstruse and so remote from common life that it is difficult to believe they can ever have any practical application. But yet the abstraction of today has a habit of becoming the commonplace of tomorrow.

No longer is Aristotle's definition, "Mathematics the science of quantity," acceptable to mathematicians. In 1903, Bertrand Russell defined pure mathematics as consisting of deductions "by logical principles from logical principles," while on another occasion he emphasized the abstract notions on which much of modern mathematics is based by the—at first glance—startling statement that "Mathematics is the subject in which we never know what we are talking about nor whether what we are saying is true."

The average man, however, is not concerned with or interested in these abstruse abstractions. In due course, some of them will doubtless play their part in directing the future course of mathematics, but the average man has neither the time nor the requisite technical knowledge for their study. He can, however, without studying these abstract matters, grasp the vital part that mathematics has played in the development of twentieth-century civilization, and constantly plays in maintaining that civilization.

He can see the age-long story of mankind reflected in the fluctuating growth of mathematical development: great mathematical achievements coinciding with the four centuries when Greek civilization was at its height, and again when the Renaissance ushered in the tremendous outburst of intellectual activity and independent thought that has characterized the past five centuries. On the other hand, the mental stagnation and paralysis of initiative in intellectual matters that marked the Dark and Middle Ages will be found to be reflected in the great mathematical depression that set in soon after the death of Archimedes and continued until the sixteenth century. Just as the sales-chart of an established and well-conducted business reflects the varying economic and social conditions of the community, so too, the fluctuations in mankind's intellectual activities are reflected with unequalled clarity in the rise and fall of mathematical development.

It requires no mathematical skill or background to follow the story of the growth of basic mathematical concepts from ideas that were essentially simple and commonplace, and to grasp the close co-ordination that exists between the various branches of the subject.

Not only does mathematics open the door of the treasure house of modern science, with all its fabulous material riches and power; it offers us a key to a better understanding of the laws that govern the mysterious universe in which we find ourselves. Even more than all these things, it offers to all thoughtful men and women—not merely to those endowed with great mathematical aptitude, but to all of average intelligence—a share in the serenity of mind that Wordsworth associated with the subject

> ". . . that held acquaintance with the stars
> And wedded soul to soul in purest bond
> Of reason, undisturbed by space or time."

It is hoped that the story of mathematics that has been told in this book will encourage non-mathematical readers to share the fascination of the subject as unfolded in more extensive and more technical works. For the benefit of those who wish to dip more deeply into the story of mathematics, a list of books is appended, from which a selection may be made according to the topics that appeal to the reader.

# BOOKS FOR FURTHER READING

T. E. Peet: *The Rhind Mathematical Papyrus* (University Press of Liverpool. Ltd.)

Sir Thomas Heath: *Euclid* (Cambridge University Press)
*The Copernicus of Antiquity* (*Aristarchus of Samos*) (S.P.C.K., London)
*Archimedes* (S.P.C.K., London)
*Diophantus of Alexandria* (Cambridge University Press)

D. E. Smith: *Mathematics* (in the series "Our Debt to Greece and Rome": Marshall Jones Co., Boston, Mass.)

T. Dantzig: *Number, the Language of Science* (Macmillan)

L. C. Karpinski: *Robert of Chester's Latin Translation of al-Khowarizmi* (English Translation: Macmillan Co.)

Salvador de Madariaga: *Christopher Columbus* (Macmillan)

C. G. Knott: *Napier Memorial Volume* (Longmans, Green & Co.)

H. Macpherson: *Makers of Astronomy* (Oxford; Clarendon Press)

E. S. Haldane: *Descartes* (J. Murray, London)

D. E. Smith & M. L. Latham: *Descartes* (English translation: Open Court Publishing Co.)

J. M. Child: *Geometrical Lectures of Isaac Barrow* (Open Court Publishing Co.)

Sir David Brewster: *Memoirs of the Life, Writings and Discoveries of Sir Isaac Newton* (T. Constable & Co.)

A. De Morgan: *Essays on the Life and Work of Newton* (edited by P. E. B. Jourdain, Open Court Publishing Co.)

S. Brodetsky: *Sir Isaac Newton* (Methuen & Co.)

J. M. Child: *The Early Mathematical Manuscripts of Leibni*
(Open Court Publishing Co.)

A. N. Whitehead: *An Introduction to Mathematics* (Holt & Co.)

J. W. A. Young: *Monographs on Modern Mathematics* (Long
mans, Green & Co.)
*Fundamental Concepts of Algebra and Geometry*
(Macmillan)

G. Cantor: *Contributions to the Foundations of the Theory (*
*Transfinite Numbers* (English translation: Open Court Publishing Co

J. W. R. Dedekind: *Essays on the Theory of Numbers* (Englis
Translation: Open Court Publishing Co.)

B. Russell: *Principles of Mathematics* (Cambridge University Press

B. Russell & A. N. Whitehead: *Principia Mathematica* (Cam
bridge University Press)

G. H. Hardy: *Pure Mathematics* (Cambridge University Press)

E. T. Bell: *Men of Mathematics* (Stories of great mathematicians from
1600 to 1900: Simon & Schuster)


REFERENCE BOOKS ON THE HISTORY OF MATHEMATICS:

Sir Thomas Heath: *History of Greek Mathematics*, 2 Vols
(Oxford: Clarendon Press)
F. C. Cajori: *A History of Mathematics* (Macmillan)
D. E. Smith: *History of Mathematics*, 2 Vols. (Ginn & Co.)
W. W. R. Ball: *A Short Account of the History of Mathematic*
(Macmillan)


MATHEMATICAL BOOKS IN ENGLISH TO BE FOUND IN THE RARE
BOOK DEPARTMENT OF MANY LARGE PUBLIC LIBRARIES

Recorde: Grounde of Artes ("Ground of Arts" in 1646 edition)
Baker: *Rule of falsehoode or false position* (1580)
Wright: *A description of the Admirable Table of logarithm*
(1616)
Coulson: *Method of Fluxions and Infinite Series* (1736)

# INDEX

# Index A (Historical)

[For mathematical references see Index B, p. 395]

# Index B (Mathematical)

# VINTAGE WORKS OF SCIENCE
## AND PSYCHOLOGY

# VINTAGE FICTION, POETRY, AND PLAYS

| V-713 | Tolstoy, Leo | THE KREUTZER SONATA |
| V-154 | Tracy, Honor | STRAIGHT AND NARROW PATH |
| V-202 | Turgenev, Ivan | TORRENTS OF SPRING |
| V-711 | Turgenev, Ivan | THE VINTAGE TURGENEV |
| | | Volume I: SMOKE, FATHERS AND SONS, FIRST LOVE |
| V-712 | Turgenev, Ivan | Volume II: ON THE EVE, RUDIN, A QUIET SPOT, DIARY OF A SUPERFLUOUS MAN |
| V-152 | Waugh, Evelyn | THE LOVED ONE |

## VINTAGE BELLES-LETTRES

| V-708 | Aksakov, Sergey | YEARS OF CHILDHOOD |
| V-22 | Barzun, Jacques | THE ENERGIES OF ART |
| V-191 | Beer, Thomas | THE MAUVE DECADE |
| V-80 | Beerbohm, Max | SEVEN MEN and Two Others |
| V-75 | Camus, Albert | THE MYTH OF SISYPHUS and Other Essays |
| V-30 | Camus, Albert | THE REBEL |
| V-216 | Chamberlain, N. (ed.) | A VINTAGE FOOD SAMPLER |
| V-64 | Evans, Bergan | THE NATURAL HISTORY OF NONSENSE |
| V-112 | Gide, André | JOURNALS, Volume I: 1889-1924 |
| V-113 | Gide, André | JOURNALS, Volume II: 1924-1949 |
| V-104 | Huxley, Aldous | BEYOND THE MEXIQUE BAY |
| V-41 | James, Henry | THE FUTURE OF THE NOVEL |
| V-228 | Kaplan, Abraham | THE NEW WORLD OF PHILOSOPHY |
| V-167 | La Rochefoucauld | MAXIMS |
| V-230 | Leedom, William | THE VINTAGE WINE BOOK |
| V-193 | Malraux, André | TEMPTATION OF THE WEST |
| V-55 | Mann, Thomas | ESSAYS |
| V-232 | Mencken, H. L. | TREATISE ON THE GODS |
| V-34 | Montaigne, Michel de | AUTOBIOGRAPHY |
| V-197 | Morgan, F. (ed.) | HUDSON REVIEW ANTHOLOGY |
| V-54 | Nicolson, Harold | SOME PEOPLE |
| V-24 | Ransom, John Crowe | POEMS AND ESSAYS |
| V-85 | Stevens, Wallace | POEMS |
| V-53 | Synge, J. M. | THE ARAN ISLANDS and Other Writings |
| V-194 | Valéry, Paul | THE ART OF POETRY |